HOUSES

a novel by

Cynthia Rogers Parks

Leigh Walker Books

Published by arrangement with
Leigh Walker Books
Atlanta, Georgia

10 9 8 7 6 5 4 3 2 1

ISBN 978-0-615-32893-5

To my own chickadees:
Angela, Brian, and Amy

HOUSES

PREFACE

I measure my life in houses. That has always been the way I divide the befores and the afters, the success and losses, the endings and beginnings. There are other, perhaps better, ways of remembering. You will hear people say, *I was still married to Robert then*, or *I know, because it was the year that Clinton was elected. It was before Deidre was born*, or *when we were still driving the green Escort.*

Each of us, I think, uses our own favored system for marking sign posts on the long road stretching behind us. Usually it will indicate what has mattered to us most—what we have really valued. The good parent will remember his yesterdays in terms of his children. The births, difficult or easy. The first words. First steps. First dance. The school days, the ball games, the little griefs and triumphs. *Jamie wasn't walking then. Eric was still in diapers. The summer that Leslie broke her arm.*

I've heard travelers and soldiers and soldier's wives mark it with the towns, the countries, the continents where they sojourned. *It was after our first time in Italy. We were stationed in Germany. He had just received orders for Iraq.*

I expect that the ambitious and successful will see it as a series of business or commercial ventures. In terms of promotions or acquisitions. Transfers of raises. Bonuses. Even bankruptcies. *After the dot com bubble burst. The year I made Vice President.*

For lovers I guess it might be a string of romances or sexual conquests. And for the lonely and jilted, heartbreaks. Death, I suppose, is the best marker. For some it is the only one—a single Damoclean slice, splitting Before and After cleanly and forever.

Me, I measure in houses. The chapters of my life are held in the houses—the physical structures where I have lived, and where *we* have lived, and I can't tell my story any other way. If you want to know the way it was, my chickadees, you will have to know the houses. You will have to hear about moving ins and moving outs, about windows and ceilings and walls and floors. About yards and gardens and neighbors, furniture and fixtures. Because that's the way I remember.

I have been house proud, house poor, and homeless. I have lived in large, spacious houses as dead and suffocating as a crypt. And in tiny, cramped places as wide and hopeful as a new green world. Each was a vessel I poured my life into, the particular life of that particular time, and in filling each one I took away something of its shape, and left some residue of my old self behind.

You will even have to hear about houses I never lived in. The ones I sold to other people or ones I envied. Houses I wanted, but couldn't have. Houses I had, but didn't want. I can't tell it any other way. I measure my life in houses.

CHAPTER I

The very first houses I remember weren't really houses at all. They were my grandmother's apartments, a series of them actually, but all enough alike that they have merged in my memory to a single, solitary dwelling—"Grandmother's House"—like the one we lived in during the time that our Daddy was shopping for a new mother for Sophie and me and only Jesus knew what was to become of us.

Inside, Grandmother's House was always a dark, high-ceilinged place with wide mahogany moldings and ornate plaster ceiling medallions. There were hardwood floors, black almost, from decades of stains and waxing, solid six-panel doors fitted with cut glass doorknobs above Alice-in-Wonderland keyholes to which the skeleton keys had long been lost. The kitchens were cramped but functional with linoleum-clad counters and floors, ceiling fans with schoolhouse lighting, snug little white-enameled pantries. The antiquated bathrooms—one to a unit—had cast iron sinks and claw-footed bathtubs with brass fittings grown green with age. At six, of course, I could not even have described these interesting architectural details and I certainly didn't appreciate them. The radiators hissed and clunked and the plumbing could screech and scream like it was auditioning for a slasher movie. You really can't appreciate the advances that have come about in plumbing technology unless you lived in

Grandmother's House.

These apartments were alike because of my grandmother's strict rental requirements. All of them had to be in midtown, within a small radius of those neighborhoods, now become chic but then only decaying, where big square quadriplexes built in the '30s or '40s, mixed in with old single-family Victorians erected at the turn of the century. Many of those older residences were still intact, still inhabited perhaps by descendants of the original owners. But even some of these graceful old dames had themselves been chunked into apartments.

My grandmother's neighborhoods had been created before the enactment of the Euclidean kind of zoning laws that would, depending upon your point of view, reform, or destroy, most of America's great cities. Then, in my grandmother's neighborhoods, you still found what would today be called "vintage" homes standing cheek to jowl with multi-family dwellings. There was yet no Home Owner's Association to say that a hat check girl or a night shift nurse had no business living on the same street as the spent heiress to one of the city's better names—even, if truth be told, that selfsame heiress was supplementing her waning income by renting her carriage house to a bargeman. They were a mix, the denizens of Grandmother's street, but a quiet and respectful mix, with no big desire to cross-pollinate the social divides.

In the daylight there was still a seedy charm to those neighborhoods, with their enormous ivy-laden trees, shade-speckled lawns and crumbling sidewalks, but all of the ground floor windows on the buildings were fitted with wrought iron window guards and no one went walking at night. The fortifications were mostly against mashers and petty thieves.

It was only the mid-fifties then. Still a little early for drive-by shootings and gangbangers.

Behind these buildings and their small weedy back yards ran a gravel service alley—a fascinating netherworld path traveled only by stray, languid cats. Or so I thought until the day I met a thin, gray-whiskered old man there by the garbage cans. He had helpfully taken my trash pail for me and slowly begun transferring its contents into the big can, piece by soggy piece, stopping now and then in his curious examination of bits of food and coffee-ground-speckled Sunday School pamphlets to turn small wet eyes on my face, and to ask me questions. *Aren't you a pretty little thing*, he asked me, and *How old are* you*? Is that one there your building? Do your Momma and Poppa live there too?* In the rubbish he found one of my grandmother's old nylons. He chuckled and pressed it hard to his nose before stuffing it, along with some dangling pieces of eggshell, into the pocket of his long, rumpled coat. I answered his questions politely, as I had been taught to address adults, but I knew this old scavenger was nothing like the other men I knew. He was certainly not like my Daddy or his sharp-dressing salesman friends. Not like Mr. Geizelman who lived upstairs, or even Johnny Conway, the janitor at Grandmother's church who smelled like furniture polish and talked to himself.

It wasn't his grizzled dirty looks or even his odd curiosity about the garbage. It was the fact that his shoes didn't match. One was a black, high-topped basketball shoe with a bright scarlet shoestring. The other was a brown loafer, almost new, and several sizes smaller. I was fascinated by this paradox and could only account for it with the disturbing thought that maybe the old man had no toes on the loafered foot. I had seen a toeless baby once, sitting on its mother's lap on the

13

curb on Main Street. We were there for the 4th of July parade and in the crowd pressed together along the street was a woman with a boy about my age and a baby. The baby was thin and dust-colored, naked except for yellowed rubber pants, and it leaned listless in the heat against its mother, looking at me instead of the parade. One foot was perfect, five small toes in perfect descending rank, but the other one simply stopped—a fist instead of a foot, finished off with a tight ridged seam of pink and white scar.

It was my wariness over the shoes, I think, and the image of that poor scarred baby foot, which sounded some alarm in my seven-year-old brain. There's the chance, I suppose, that in snatching back my trash pail and running full tilt through the hedge break, across the yard and up the wooden staircase to my grandmother's back door, I may have escaped some tragedy too horrible for imagining. There's an equally good chance that the grimy old forager meant me no harm at all. That as an efficient and well-adapted member of that vast embarrassing sect we call the Homeless, he was merely going about the business of the day. Looking for breakfast. Looking for another shoe.

If he did pose a danger to me it was the only one I was to encounter in the time we lived in Grandmother's House but it had the effect of putting me on a very short leash. Because I had told Thelma, our maid, Thelma had told Grandmother. Grandmother had thanked the Good Lord, repeatedly, and then told Daddy, who started making his first noises about "getting them out of the city." I never finished exploring the alleys and sheds and relics of gardens that beckoned behind the houses. I've always been jealous of cats.

If these neighborhoods were not ideal for the rearing of young children, there was not much probably that my grandmother could have done about it. The places were spacious, by today's standards, and they suited her mélange of carved and animal-footed Victorian furniture and her heavy, velvet and befringed, mind-your-own-business draperies. There were always good locks on the doors and a well-lit bus stop nearby and mainly, they were what she could afford. She could not—in her late fifties then, as I think about it—have expected to be rearing children again.   If the neighbors were sullen and secretive with no time for a boisterous, inquisitive child, they were nonetheless good, honest, hard-working people who minded their own business and "kept the noise down"—a high-ranking virtue in real estate valuation for Grandmother, and one, alas, I've come to appreciate myself.

If the crumbling sidewalks were no good for skating there was usually a wide stoop where a child could sit with her dolls and tin tea set. With patience, on a long summer morning, she might coax a squirrel into accepting a bit of cookie from the bottom step.

There were no children at all in my time, but occasionally I would find some relic from the children who had once lived on those streets. In the small, cloistered back yards one might see a rusted old swing set or a broken teeter-totter rising out of the weeds like a bleached piece of driftwood. And in another decade or two, when these same old midtown neighborhoods cycled around to gentrification and young professional couples began to reface and remodel, on the porches and in the drives there would be baby strollers and bicycles and bright plastic toys to testify that the children had come back. In another twenty years these streets would completely transmogrify. I would drive down the shady boulevards and see new sidewalks and restored gardens, new roofs, and brightly painted front doors, and the wide porches dripping with ferns. In another twenty years there would be quite a renaissance on Grandmother's street and a person with a poor head for math could get dizzy with trying to calculate eighty-odd years of appreciation.

But in my time the children were gone and if you troubled at all to skate on the pebbley sidewalks, you skated by yourself. Your tea party guests were only dolls and teddies and the imaginary friends whose names and personalities shifted with your moods. You knew nothing, yet, of tag or Red Rover, and even Hide and Seek was pointless if it had to be played in four indoor rooms with a colored maid and a baby.

The reason that Grandmother's House had to be near a bus stop, or the "car line" as she called it, was because her job, or "position," as she called it, as manager of the millinery department of Silverstein's Department Store, required not only that she be punctual but that she set an example of professionalism and dedication for the young sales clerks under her care. My grandmother, as she would tell you, had certain "responsibilities."

That most of her young charges were merely biding their time until marriage and maternity—or that after forty-five years her own dedication would be rewarded with no more than a five-day notice and a fruit basket—would probably, could she have foreseen it, not have made much difference. My grandmother had responsibilities. And she took them very seriously.

For a few years there Sophie and I were her responsibility. Our daddy worked for Ideal Chemical Company–strange that I remember *that*—and during the week he was always on the road selling something. Chemicals, maybe. On the weekends he mostly "shopped in the wrong stores" as Grandmother put

16

it, for a new mother for Sophie and me. Sophie was too young to know or to care but I puzzled constantly over Daddy's behavior. Since Silverstein's, the city's oldest and finest department store, where my grandmother sold hats and knew absolutely everyone from Charlie, who ran the elevator, to Mr. Ezra Silverstein, the owner, was clearly the *right* store to shop in, I could not imagine how my daddy could be so dumb. I'd figure it out later, of course. Our father was going to keep on shopping long after he'd found us a new mother. He still shopped for someone, or something, well into his seventies.

But for the most part Daddy was not around. When he did drop in on us it might be to take us all three to the supermarket or for a drive into the country where Grandmother's sisters—my Aunts Esther and Sarah—and a slew of rowdy cousins lived. Sometimes he picked up only Sophie and me and then usually a lady came along too. Once, in particular, we went to the zoo and a blonde lady named Margaret went with us. She smelled very pretty and wore an astounding amount of glittery jewelry, but beyond that, until Miss Maureen came along and changed absolutely everything, our Daddy's lady friends were as homogenous as Grandmother's houses.

While Grandmother sold hats and Daddy shopped women, it was Thelma who tended my sister and me, dressing and washing us, making our meals, playing what games we could in the dark old building. Thelma had come from Eads, Tennessee, where Grandmother herself had been born and where her sisters still lived, and on that basis alone I expect that Grandmother thought Thelma had the requisite honesty, reliability, and humility to be trusted with our care. I don't know about the humility part. I know that I saw facets of Thelma's personality that my grandmother could never have imagined. But Grandmother was certainly right about everything else. Neither rain nor sleet nor a sudden snow storm that kept the No. 2 Fairgrounds from showing up at her transfer point and made her slog two miles to our place in lousy shoes, could keep Thelma from being there for "her babies." She came to us sick, and probably always tired, but unfailingly tidy in a clean white maid's uniform and if she harbored any bitterness about her lot in life she never took it out on Sophie or on me.

Thelma must have been a fairly young woman back then. Late thirties, maybe. Early forties. Her husband, Nolan, was a sanitation worker for the City of Memphis and they had five children of their own, none of whom I actually ever met, but all of whom I came to know through Thelma's fumings about their mischief. The one I liked best was Carlton, the eight-year-old. He was the one in the middle and the one who seemed to get into the most trouble. To this day I have a crystal clear, albeit entirely imaginary, picture of Carlton stored in my head. And he still has my undying sympathy.

"I don know *what's* wrong with that chile," Thelma would grouse to Grandmother. "Seem like he just *craves* a whippin'." Seem like dat boy rather be on da outs wid ya than ta be in da good Lawd's grace. You put a biskit on his plate and he gon say he don wan it. Gon say he don wan it and he ain' gon eat it. But jes you try an give dat biskit to his lil' brother Jesse! Dat Carlton gon stuff dat biskit down his gullet like it was da last morsel left on dis earth."

I had one sibling, not four. But I thought I knew what Carlton's problem was. Sophie was not much more than a baby then and obviously she demanded the bulk of Thelma's time and attention. But in my mind she was also Thelma's clear favorite and I lived in a constant state of competitive agony, trying to get Thelma to play *my* game first, buckle *my* shoes first, make the lime Jell-O that *I* preferred instead of the cherry that was Sophie's favorite.

"Which one do you like best?" I would press her, demanding that she choose between our little vinyl rocking chairs, baby dolls, or hair brushes—the pairs, always, identical in every respect except color.

"Which one belong to you?" Thelma would ask, because she was shrewd and wicked and knew how to make me suffer.

If I answered the green one, Thelma would allow that she was partial to yellow, reversing herself the next week if I claimed that the yellow was actually mine. She was a witch, that Thelma, but I loved her fiercely.

Little Sophie loved her, too, and I know I should have been ashamed to be jealous of my motherless little sister. At least I had a few hazy and confused memories of our mother. Sophie would never be able to dredge up any. Her image of "mother" would always be Janus-like. The white face of Grandmother and the black one of Thelma.

I *was* jealous of Sophie, though. I would be a bit jealous until we were both grown women and it had begun to seem that the good cards, the really good cards, had all been dealt to me, not Sophie. But if you look at the old pictures of Sophie and me you'll see why I had to be jealous. The contrasts between us are pretty obvious, even in the black and white photography of the 1950s. Had the pictures been in color you'd see more of what I mean.

I had brown eyes like Daddy and Grandmother. Even Thelma had brown eyes. Brown, it seemed, was the standard issue color for ordinary eyes. But Sophie's eyes were green. Under a ridiculous fringe of inky lashes. My own hair was brown, thin, straight as a poker. Sophie's head was an absolute mass of tight, golden curls. Grandmother called my skin, "olive." Olive? I had never seen, or even heard of the small Mediterranean fruit that bears the name. Olives back then weren't exactly staples of the Southern diet. Had I known about olives I expect I'd have been pretty confused. I do know for sure that, sometime before second grade, I sounded out the name of a yellowish-green crayon in the big box of 48 and was completely bewildered. I didn't know who was playing the trick, but no way was my skin that color!

I knew that I didn't sunburn like Sophie did. I could get a tan, probably, if I lived in an underground cave. But a tan in those days was not quite the attribute it would become later on. And especially not to Grandmother, who made us wear hats if we were only going to the curb, and who herself walked to the bus stop under an umbrella on the clearest of summer days. Sometimes in the summer she would even put on gauzy little gloves with ruffles at the wrist. Imagine that, chickadees! *Gloves. In summer.*

Sophie's skin, of course, was porcelain. As pale, almost, as the Dresden angels in Grandmother's curio case. Except when Sophie cried or fussed or, later, when she blushed. Dear little Sophie. She could never hide a thing. If you hurt her, you knew it immediately, whether or not she said a word. If something made her mad, or she had an unladylike thought, you would see it instantly on her face. If she spoke the name of a boy she had a crush on, that alabaster skin would flush with pink and you knew you had her.

Everywhere we went in those days Sophie caused a commotion. If Thelma took us downtown to Silverstein's because Grandmother needed us to try on shoes or get our picture taken, the entire expedition would become a Sophie Spectacular.

In the front of the city bus there was always a ripple of admiration as we passed through the white people. "Look at that baby!" they would say right out loud. "Isn't she adorable?" By the colored people, though, in the back of the bus, Sophie was received with something like reverence. No matter how crowded the seats were a magical compression would take place and space would appear for the three of us. Pairs of arms would reach out to help Thelma with Sophie. They could not keep their hands off the soft mass of Sophie's curls and any little gewgaw they might have in pockets or purses was always produced to entertain her.

The only real advantage I had over Sophie back then was that, when September came, I could go to school. For three years on school mornings Thelma brushed my hair and tied my sashes and readied me for the great adventure of learning. I had a red plaid book satchel, a wide-lined tablet and fat pencils, and the booklet of lunch tickets that Grandmother bought at the first of every month. Sophie was bundled into her stroller and every weekday morning the three of us walked the four short blocks to Maury Elementary School. It was a square, ugly, three-story red brick building adorned only by its wide center flight of concrete steps and the metal fire escapes attached like ugly vestigial wings to each of its solid sides. It exuded all the charm of a maximum security prison but I thought it was beautiful and couldn't wait to get inside. Some mornings Sophie would cry and point to the school's big doors when I leaned down to leave my business-like kiss on her fat little cheek. Sophie, too, seemed to want to join the stream of children swimming up the steps. But Thelma always seemed nervous, a little too eager to turn the stroller towards home as soon as I was dispatched. It wasn't a Nanny kind of neighborhood. A colored woman drew stares.

On one of those spring days in 1954, while Thelma was escorting me to school or back, or keeping Sophie clean, fed, and entertained at home, the United States Supreme Court was dismantling the legal basis for segregation in schools and other public places. *Brown vs. Board* was going to be historic. It would be the catalyst for the modern civil rights movement. It was going to make a big difference to Thelma's grandchildren, and to you, chickadees, and to hordes of immigrants still to come.

But to Thelma and to Carlton, to Grandmother, to Sophie and to me, it would be a long time before it mattered a whit. The children who attended Maury Elementary School and all my classmates for more than another whole decade were still all going to be white. In my junior year, in 1964, fearing that President Johnson might really mean business this time, the faculty and parents of my suburban high school chose to eliminate the tradition of the senior prom. We would miss that hallmark, the excitement and pageantry of that eagerly-anticipated ritual. But at least we wouldn't have to dance with Negroes.

There was nothing approximating cultural diversity inside Maury Elementary but there was, at least, a lot of white children, and there was also my beautiful young teacher, Mrs. Stryker, and the Bluebird Reading Group—the one place on earth where I could really, really shine. What made me such a precocious reader is a mystery. Another mystery would make me terrible at math and, when the time came, give Sophie a very hard time with both. From the very beginning, though, I thought words were wonderful and reading the best kind of magic.

The title of my first-grade reading book was *I Know a Secret*. I remember not just because I was the most stellar reader in Mrs. Stryker's first grade class but, because of that book, I did learn a secret. One that saddens me after all these years. A secret still heavy and hard to bear.

We were sitting, Thelma and Sophie and I, on the stoop of Grandmother's building after a light rain shower. Sophie was patting a little puddle on the bottom step with her fat little baby hands but I had my reader and was forging ahead, two or three stories past the one that my class was in. I had a reputation to maintain and I needed Mrs. Stryker's praise like a flower needs sun. There was a word, a phrase, something that I couldn't decipher, and I put my finger on it and held the page up to Thelma. She turned her head away, almost violently.

"I can't read it, child," she said. "Never learnt how."

Thelma couldn't read. She couldn't even read *I Know a Secret.*

I still don't know how she managed. How she navigated the city bus system or made a grocery list or picked the millions of other locks that words are the key to. I suspect I was less kind to Thelma after that. I was already vain about the reading and there is something in my nature that may have enjoyed exploiting my new advantage. I hope that I didn't. But I probably did.

When we finally left Grandmother's House to move to the suburbs, I had just turned nine and Sophie was almost six, finally ready for school. Our Daddy had found us a new mother and the house we were going to was new, too. I would live in apartments again, someday, but they would be nothing like Grandmother's House. This would be the last of radiator heat and claw-footed bathtubs. The last of being the only kid on the block and the last of walking to Maury Elementary. Indeed, it would be the end of walking to any school, ever, for from here on out Sophie and I would live in the great American suburbs and I would ride a big yellow bus to school.

We would visit Grandmother, of course. Sometimes we would spend the night or even a whole weekend, but our books and toys had been taken away and it was never the same again. We would bring little cardboard suitcases with us when we came and take everything away when we left.

I remember a little about the end of it. The end of the time at Grandmother's House. It is my first conscious memory of the discomfort of change. I know that I wanted the new life— the bright new house and the smooth new sidewalks and other kids to play with. I suppose I even wanted the new mother. I wanted all of that badly. But I also wanted to stay with my grandmother. I wanted to go back for the next school year to Maury Elementary and be the reading whiz of the whole fourth grade. Mostly, though, I wanted Thelma.

I don't know what happened to Thelma. I expect she found other little white babies to care for. I don't know what happened to Carlton. Whether he simply outgrew his obstinate and rebellious nature or if the realities of being black and poor in the American south of the 1950s took care of that for him, in a sadder, even a tragic way. I never knew what happened to any of them. On the day that it first occurred to me to wonder I was standing at the kitchen sink in the house in Emerald Hills. One of you chickadees had left one of those little two-handled toddler's cups beside the sink and when I picked it up there was something in its shape or heft that made me remember the old, white, double-handled mug that Grandmother kept by the kitchen sink for Thelma. The one that belonged to Thelma only and that Sophie and I weren't to touch.

I don't blame Grandmother. She was, as we all are, a product of the time. It was just that it was funny. Funny and sad. That my grandmother, who trusted Thelma with her life—with *more* than her life in entrusting her with the care of her only grandchildren—could not trust Thelma with our white people's glassware. Thelma could be trusted not to poison us with her cooking, or scald us in our baths, or to let Sophie go one needless minute with dirty hands or a dirty diaper. But she couldn't be trusted not to, even inadvertently, contaminate us with her blackness. I wondered that day in house on Templeton about all the ways we might have stunted Thelma's spirit so that Sophie and I could thrive. I wondered for the first time what Thelma's own house might have looked like and—if the three of us had been a little cramped in the four-room apartment that Grandmother's salary managed—what Thelma and Nolan had been able to afford to accommodate seven. I wondered who had made Carlton's lunch while his mama was making mine.

There is at least a possibility that Thelma is still alive somewhere, surrounded, possibly, by a brood of grandchildren and great-grandchildren, even great-great grandchildren. And if not? If she has already gone on ahead? Then I hope that she has found peace and rest. That now she knows the secret.

CHAPTER II

The pictures in the brochure for Beautiful Fairfield Estates had shown huge shade trees and beautifully manicured lawns with mature trimmed shrubs and colorful flowerbeds. The reality was a flat muddy wasteland in which the only signs of vegetation were the small, leafless saplings staked in the center of each front yard. The houses varied slightly in brick or trim color. Some of the carports were supported by ornamental ironwork while some had square lumber boxes, and others had "Colonial" turned posts. But all were L-shaped ranches with the very same rooflines and exactly the same setback from the street. None had porches to speak of, only tiny square stoops under a shallow eve that might protect you for a bit while you opened your umbrella, but that weren't much good for anything else. Everybody got a mailbox in the front and a clothesline in the back. The effect, on a city-bred child, was a relentless uniformity like nothing I had ever seen.

I had slept with the color brochure for Beautiful Fairfield Estates under my pillow for weeks. I had read every word of the copy to Sophie and Thelma and explained the color renderings of the houses representing each of the "three spacious floor plans." Our own house, Daddy had told us, was the third style and called "The Highlander" for reasons not immediately clear. It would be a while yet before I understood the hyperbole and euphemism of broker-speak—a long time before I understood that "cozy" meant under 800 square feet and "sunny" probably meant there was a hole in the roof. For me, back then, a Highlander conjured up images only of the guy on the Scotch tape dispenser but I wasn't, really, that far off. The street we were moving to was named "Lochinvar" and the next street up, "Lochlomand," and the next one over, "Lancelot." The developers and their marketers were shooting for something vaguely Scotch-English romantic. Developers, and their marketers, often still do. Americans are suckers for allusions to their old European roots. Half-acre tract houses still get branded as "estates." Grassless tenements bear monikers like "Lancaster Gardens" or "Ashbury Park." Apparently even trailer parks and nursing homes are infinitely more habitable if the entrance sign reads, "Camelot Manor."

I didn't fully understand the promotional reality gap but I could certainly see a few discrepancies between the tri-fold brochure and the real, raw thing. The long rows of low rooflines were a little disturbing to someone accustomed to apartment buildings and old Queen Anne Victorians. These streets certainly weren't going to be shade-dappled for a long time to come. And someone had forgotten to put in the sidewalks.

The sudden suburban eruption of large tracts of nearly identical houses built on nearly identical plans of absolutely identical materials was a phenomenon being repeated all over the country in those hip-hip-hooray days after the war. Veterans like our own father had come home eager to get on with life—to marry, start a family, and stake out their own share of the great American Dream. Uncle Sam, with his GI Bill of Rights, was making it easy to buy a home with little or no money down and savvy builders who could get their hands on cheap land outside the city limits were more than eager to help. From sea to shining sea the dairy farms and corn fields, the timber stands and soybean fields, the cow pastures and cotton patches of rural America were being razed, scraped, and replanted with instant communities.

The services of Sophie and me were not needed on the day of the actual move. We were picked up, hours late on a Sunday afternoon, along with the few boxes of clothes and bags of toys that Grandmother had packed and waiting. Sophie and I weren't bringing that much to our new life. But Daddy was bringing a lot. He was bringing the new mother, the new *mother's* mother—an unknown person called "Nana" who would care for us in Thelma's absence—and the new furniture that he and Miss Maureen had shopped for and had already had delivered. The services of Sophie and me had not been needed for the furniture shopping either, but I had shown Daddy the bed with the pink canopy in the Sears Roebuck catalog and promised that Sophie and I would give up our pigpen ways if only he'd get it for us.

Our adventure began inauspiciously, with Sophie falling on the curb at the car door and skinning her shin and Miss Maureen jerking her up a bit too roughly out of the street. Sophie wailed ridiculously for the first few miles and then settled down to a theatrical sniffling. In the back seat I patted her knee and waited while the splotches of pink in her face grew smaller and fainter. At length she uttered a simple declarative sentence:

"I do not love her." Sophie said.

"What?" I said, not sure I had understood her.

"*That* one," she said, pointing to the back of the seat occupied by Miss Maureen. "I do not love her."

In the front seat Daddy and Miss Maureen exchanged a quick glance and Daddy laughed nervously.

"Sophie!" he said. "Of course, you do! Maureen's your mommy now. We're a family! We're going to have a great time."

But Sophie had made up her mind and that's all there was to it.

"I do not love her," she said again, but this time softer, conspiratorially, and directed only to me.

The tension of that little episode passed. Daddy switched on the radio and we talked, maybe even laughed, for the rest of the journey. Everyone else, including Sophie, probably forgot the whole thing. But in the amber of my own memory those few awkward minutes are perfectly preserved. I hear her childish declaration as clearly as if she spoke it only a moment ago. And I still marvel at how prophetic it was. Sophie, indeed, did not, would not, *could not*, love Maureen. And for ten or more odd years, until she had grown entirely too weary of the struggle of all of us, Miss Maureen would not love Sophie right back.

For me it was a strange turning point. At that moment, that exact moment, Sophie the Fair-haired—the beautiful, irrepressible angel child who had turned every head and garnered instant adoration by virtue of her skin, her eyes, her dimpled cheeks—began the slow, inexorable descent into that dark painful place where she would become "*poor* little Sophie," "*that* Sophie," "your *crazy* sister Sophie." All the sibling energy that I had previously spent on envying Sophie, competing with her, blocking her radiance from casting me in shadow, I would gradually redirect into defending her, explaining her, protecting her from those who didn't understand that Sophie didn't love what Sophie didn't love.

When we finally pulled into the freshly paved white driveway of the house on Lochinvar, I was the nine-year-old version of a nervous wreck. Not because of Sophie or Daddy or Miss Maureen but because I was fairly vibrating with eagerness to see inside the new house and specifically our new bedroom and the pink canopy bed. I scrambled out of the car, bounded the three short steps of the little stoop and ran headlong into the soft middle of a white-haired lady in house dress and apron. This was Nana, the new mother's mother, who apparently had already taken possession of our new house and was there to welcome us as though *we* were the strangers.

"Well, I'll swan," she said, taking me by the shoulders and pushing me back a bit out of the cotton apron. "You must be Lacey!" Behind me on the bottom step she caught sight of Sophie and lit up like people always did whenever they caught sight of Sophie.

"I must be Sophie!" my sister announced delightedly. She was well over her twit by now and apparently willing to give this old woman the benefit of the doubt. In another minute Sophie had been scooped up onto the Nana's wide hip and we were all crowding through the new door into the new house.

My first sensation was of the pervading smell of fresh, lead-based paint. Lead, apparently, was the magical ingredient that once made paint deliver that scent of pristine cleanliness. Paint today smells like a chalky insecticide. It's great, of course, that they've taken out the dangerous lead and all those solvents. But something pleasant was definitely lost—an elimination, I think, not unlike the reduction of calories from food. You can live without it. Maybe better. But it's not going to be the same.

That place *was* clean, though. Clean like I'd never seen anywhere else on earth. Light danced off the varnished floors, the polished doorknobs and light fixtures, the new appliances in the kitchen. The walls were defiantly, don't you-dare white. There wasn't a single smudge on the doors or woodwork. Not a single dark corner filled with intractable dusty gunk.

In the living room there was a sofa and chairs with extremely thin flat cushions and a coffee table with stick legs. In the dining area, a matching table and simple wooden chairs. It all looked a little unsubstantial compared to Grandmother's heavy pieces. Sort of like dollhouse furniture, only bigger. But it was all very new and bright and colorful, like the modern furniture section at Silverstein's. The full bath in the hall that I stopped briefly to inspect was a wonder of glistening tile and chrome fittings. There was a mirrored medicine cabinet and a modern rectangular tub that set legless on the floor with its own shower head and plastic curtain. There wasn't a radiator in sight.

Don't get me wrong. I love old houses still. But everyone, at least once, should get to live in a brand spanking new one. A house without anyone else's dust or grime or fingerprints. Without crumbs in the cupboards, wadded left-behind socks, or shreds of Christmas tinsel in the attic. Without a single scrap inherited from the lives of strangers.

I raced down the hall, barely sticking my head into a small room on the left that held a more comfortable-looking sofa and a massive Admiral television set. I blew past a room with a chenille-covered double bed and a Bible on the nightstand. I whipped past another bedroom with ugly brown and green plaid throws on a set of maple bunk beds and took the L-shaped turn that ended in a slightly bigger room, obviously Daddy's and Maureen's. This one had a sliding door closet, a window air conditioning unit and its own little bath with a shower stall. The problem was that I had run out of house.

Slowly I re-traced my steps, trying to process what I had

seen. There *wasn't* a room with a pink canopy bed and lace curtains. There wasn't. There just *wasn't!*

The rest of them were clustered in the hall outside the door of the ugly boy-looking room with the maple bunk beds. All except Sophie, who was an idiot and sat cross-legged and giggling on the lower bunk.

"Look, Lacey!" she squealed. 'This is *my* bed!"

And that would work fine for me because who cared where you slept when your romantic image of dreaming like a princess under a cascade of powder pink ruffles had been shown up for what it was—a hopeless delusion.

I looked up at Daddy, hoping, I suppose, that my stricken face showed some of the betrayal I felt.

"We thought this would be more practical," he said, glancing at Maureen.

Maureen just smiled that sweet Doris Day smile of hers. The one that Sophie and I would become intimately familiar with but that Daddy would never figure out.

"Much more practical," she said. "Much."

And then, with her pocket book in one hand and a little red train case in the other, she clipped on down the hall in her patent leather high heels on her, admittedly, very nice legs and disappeared into "their" room from which, except to go off to work with Daddy, to hold whispered conferences with Nana, and to occasionally cast a few startled looks at Sophie and me, she would not really emerge for a decade.

"They" had formed an alliance—Daddy and Maureen—one not so much against us as one indifferent to us. Practical matters, like feeding and dressing and bathing, lining up our lunch money on top of the television, and making sure we made school on time, would be left to Nana. Special needs, like what to do about the teacher who hated you or the boy who wouldn't stop pinching you, would still be handled by Grandmother, remotely, over the telephone, in ritualized after-school conversations. Financial matters, like how do you pay for your fieldtrip or your class ring, would be Daddy's province—if he didn't forget, which he usually did.

Maureen's job, if she acknowledged one at all, would be to rain on parades. She would be the one to pronounce birthday parties and fireworks, sleepovers and egg-hunts, any messy projects or spontaneous notion as, "impractical," "silly," or just "not necessary."

She would not be the disciplinarian. In point of fact Sophie and I grew up without ever being swacked or swatted at, let alone spanked or beaten. We were managed, or one of us was, by far subtler devices. Maureen's contribution to the alliance was simply to convince our Daddy that she knew best. That everything was always under complete control. And that meant not being controlled by children.

I suspect that Daddy was easy to convince. As far as he was concerned the new alliance had emancipated him from Grandmother, provided a domestic solution for his progeny, and enabled him to focus now on his own goals and desires—more reachable now that the trailing odds and ends of that first bad start had all been finished off.

For that first evening, and for many nights after, I cuddled Sophie, in her bunk, not mine, while she cried, bitterly at first, and then with gradual exhausted resignation, over missing Grandmother, missing Thelma, missing everything that we would miss. It would probably have been the same if I had comforted her in a pink canopy bed. Probably. I was nine then and the metaphysics escaped me. But there was the clear sense that Sophie was my burden now in an entirely new way. I could already tell that Nana would care for her, in that conscientious custodial way that Thelma had always cared for her. But Thelma had also been Sophie's champion. Thelma had seen that Sophie needed protection even against a devoted but smart-aleck sister. That beauty as rare as Sophie's was a vulnerability in itself. I was just getting my first sense of what Thelma had known. That Sophie would always be a maiden in distress. She would always need a champion, a knight, of some type or another. Between the maiden and the knight there were always dragons. And dragons can take surprising forms.

We adapted, as those first few weeks grew into months and years, with the stuttering progress that accompanies any big change. There were times that it seemed unbearable. There were nights that Sophie and I commiserated over the strangeness of "them" and plotted the sensational escape or act of rebellion that would get us back to Grandmother's House. There were a gradually increasing number of nights when we collapsed into our own rightful bunks, giggling over events of a relatively happy day. Children are resilient. Our memories were short.

If we lacked something of mothering, of being hovered over, cooed over, kissed and coddled, we discovered something else in those years in Beautiful Fairfield Estates that, while never substituting, at least distracted. Our new life afforded us space, and freedom, on an unprecedented scale. That very first summer, on the very first day, after Maureen and Daddy had gone off to work in the city, Nana fed us some breakfast and turned to her work of unpacking boxes and organizing the new kitchen. Sophie and I stood around, unsure of our place in all this, lacking any sense of direction or a plan.

"Go play!" Nana finally said, shooing us toward the kitchen door with a clump of wadded newspaper.

Go play?

Sophie and I exchanged bewildered looks. The instructions were simple enough. But to children who had never ventured more than a few feet without adult supervision it was as confusing a directive as the injunctions we would get in later life to "Smile!" or "Be happy!" It wasn't that easy. We simply didn't know how. The fartherest Sophie had ever been sent away was to the next room, out of adult earshot. My own outdoor adventures had been strictly limited, curtailed completely after I had told about the old man by the trash can. Now this old woman was pointing to the screen door, through which we glimpsed a green and muddy *terra incognito,* and telling us just to *go.* To *go play!*

And so we did. Sophie and I pushed through the screen door onto the small concrete slab of a back porch and took our first look at the vast and amazingly vacant stretch of suburban backyards. All of the houses were very new, some not even sold or occupied yet, so no one had gotten around to erecting the chain link fences that would start to enclose the back yards and obstruct the now unbroken passage from one end of the streets to the other. The backyards of the street behind us backed up to ours also so that the effect was of a fairly wide and enormously long highway of dirt and clipped weeds with an elevated center lane of clothesline posts. We had never seen so much space. And we certainly had never been given permission to explore so much.

Sophie and I set out westerly with the morning sun at our backs and began to walk our newfound highway. We hadn't passed behind more than five houses before our new neighborhood yielded its second startling surprise of the day. The door of a red brick model—the *Fairburn*, if memory serves me—suddenly flew open discharging a matched set, five in all, of red-headed children, freckled from head to toe and whooping like Indians. They swarmed Sophie and me, asking questions without waiting for answers, shouting out their own names but hopping around so much that you couldn't keep the right name with the right kid, plucking at our clothes, dancing around us in an almost savage glee.

"I'm Dylan, what's your name?"

"That your sister? Where'd ja get those shoes?"

"Do you play checkers? Can she talk?"

"Girls!" said the tallest in disgust. "Didja' have to be *girls*?"

These were the Laughlins, three boys and two girls, and while I didn't sort them out perfectly that first day, or maybe even for another week or so, they ranged from Conner, the oldest, who was 11, to Maddie, the youngest, at 5. They had moved here, not from our city, but from New York City, which explains now, though it didn't then, why they all talked so funny.

Taken together the Laughlin children always assumed a kind of tribal Lord of the Flies mentality. They were fiercely protective of one another—which made it difficult to pick one Laughlin for your team without taking the whole set—and they were always overly sensitive to sibling slights. (Harland Simpson was once made to eat dirt for saying that Dylan Laughlin "sneezed like a horse.")

But individually, once separated from the pack, each Laughlin would reveal a unique personality and each would bring a distinctive offering to the life of the neighborhood.

Conner had leadership skills, a penchant for organization and for keeping track of the shifting rules of our made-up outdoor games. Sean, the 10-year-old, would be in quite a few of my classes at school. He would teach me to play checkers, and later chess, and liked books nearly as much as I did. Cora and Dylan were fraternal twins, eight-year-olds then and only slightly more similar to each other than they were to any of the rest of the clan. Cora was open and forthright, a tender heart and a willing listener to your troubles, but, like her mother, something of a gossip. We would learn not to tell secrets to Cora. Dylan would be good at stealing bases, at being the last one found in Hide and Seek, and at coming up with the best Halloween costumes. Maddie would become the truest friend that Sophie ever had.

The acquisition of the Laughlins was a good morning's work for the first day on the job of playing, but there was still a lot more to come. After the chaos of introductions and question-answering, and Sophie condescending to let each of them touch her hair just once, all five of the Laughlins joined us for the continuation of our trek. The Laughlins had moved in two weeks earlier and already knew a lot about the neighborhood. Conner and Sean pointed out gopher holes and bramble patches, the house where a real policeman lived and the only dog, so far, on our street. It was a chained, drooling beast that growled as we skirted it while the boys called it names and the girls shrieked in fear.

At the far end of the block we picked up David Kirk, a rather shy blonde boy whose house was on the corner by the bus stop, and whose mother we were told was the bus driver. I had never heard of a woman bus driver or even a bus that only kids rode on, but David seemed to know what he was talking about and the prospect of riding a bus without Thelma or Grandmother became a little less scary. With David we crossed to the other side of the street and began dissecting the neighborhood between houses, cutting across other backyard highways.

The next hour or two piled wonder on wonder. Sophie and Maddie were now holding hands so that, beyond looking over my shoulder now and then to confirm that they were still tagging along, I was free to laugh and talk with the older kids, especially David Kirk, who seemed a little less raucous than the Laughlin bunch and probably knew how to get us home.

In one carport we found a wooden crate that held a litter of new baby kittens. We picked up Janet Winston and her older sister Myra. Janet was my age, too, and very pretty. We were destined to become great pals, Janet and I, but that first day she seemed more interested in Conner than in me. Conner chased her with an empty paper-wasp's nest on the end of a stick but you could tell Janet was only pretending to be scared. Janet was going to be good with the boys. Very, very good.

There were kids everywhere in this neighborhood. They popped out of doorways, ran up to us in the street, fell in with, and dropped out of, our roving little band all morning long. Whatever I had lacked in the way of cohort companionship on Grandmother's street had now been offset with delicious abundance. We moved on, slow but purposeful. Somebody seemed to know where we were going, but it certainly wasn't me.

At last we emerged into a really large field of waist-high weeds bounded on two sides by black-top roads. These were real roads, not the tar and gravel stuff of our narrow neighborhood streets. These had yellow lines in the middle and real traffic was passing. Across the intersection, under a towering wooden sign with a big red arrow pointing to "Beautiful Fairfield Estates," there was a small country store with two rusting gas pumps. We were going to shop at Murphy's Grocery. There would be many times ahead, when Daddy and Maureen had worked all weekend in the city, that Sophie and Nana and I would have to trudge to Murphy's, pulling our milk and bread or other essentials home in a Red Flyer wagon by the much longer route of the neighborhood streets. There would be many times in the years to come when the gang would hit Murphy's for cold drinks on a hot summer's day or for popsicles when the Merry Mobile had somehow failed to come through. By high school Murphy's sold cigarettes, condoms and beer without asking too many questions and the place would have a whole different allure. Murphy's would certainly get our business. But it wouldn't get it today.

"Stop!" I shouted to Conner, just as he was about to lead the whole herd, pied-piper-like, across the busy street. Conner whirled and for a frightening split second he glared at me with that defiant "don't-you-tell-me-what-I-can't-do!" look that we would all come to recognize. Conner would have some trouble with limits. Particularly those imposed by others who hadn't challenged those limits themselves. Limits that Conner deemed stupid, illogical, or worse, patronizing. For most of his childhood it would keep him at hopeless odds with his hot-tempered Irish father—not a mean man, really, and never one to touch the others—but not one either to relinquish an insecure authority to a fresh-mouthed man-child without any concept of parental respect. Conner just couldn't back down. He would rather hide the bruises than shut his mouth. In seventh grade his problem with limits would get his collarbone broken over a stupid, adolescent dare. In high

40

school it would make him a track and field all-star, and also the kind of date that the "good girls" learned to avoid. In Vietnam, they say, it was exactly what got him killed.

But if there was a big part of "no" that Conner couldn't hear, he pretended, at least that first day, to stand down the challenge. Maybe it was because we were all so new to each other. Maybe because he knew he would live to push those limits yet another day. For whatever reason, he relinquished, shrugged his shoulders, bowed to me in an exaggerated courtly way, and moved to lead us lemmings back the way we'd come.

When we turned back, the early June sun had grown pretty hot. Sophie and Maddie were dragging and Sophie's face was splotchy and red. My tummy, and surely theirs, was pointing out that we'd probably missed lunch. We'd traveled a considerable distance—leagues and fathoms for city children—and made dozens of new friends. Fortunately the Laughlins knew how to get us home.

When Sophie and I (I had carried her for the last few hundred yards) finally re-entered the same screen door through which we had originally been encouraged to "go play," Nana had the boxes all unpacked and the new kitchen in tiptop shape. She didn't even inquire as to where we had been—a courteous, or careless, precedent that would stand for the next ten years. She dutifully prepared peanut butter and jelly sandwiches, chunks of apple, and big glasses of milk for our lunch, though I think Sophie started to nod off before she'd finished half of what had been set before her. I dropped her, smelling sweetly of sun and grass and little-girl sweat, onto the bottom bunk of the ugly maple boy-bed.

I meant to lie down beside her for only just a minute. I was only going to rest a bit from the adventures of the day. Truly I had never felt so awake, so nearly electric with the newly discovered possibilities of childhood, alive in a way I had never felt before. But I drifted off. I dreamed that I had been tricked by a dream. That everything that had transpired on that long, sunny morning had taken only a millisecond. That all my impressions of open space and boundless potential had been only a pink canopy-bed illusion. That Sophie and I had grown older and world-weary, as sadly wise as Grandmother, as distant as Daddy, as perfunctorily functional as Nana. And when I finally woke, with dusk signaling through the ugly plaid café curtains of our bedroom window, I didn't know what had been dream and what had been real.

CHAPTER III

I have come to see that first summer, and to only slightly diminishing degrees, all the summers of our time in Beautiful Fairfield Estates, as the greatest gift I have ever received. Our childhood was certainly not what you would call "idyllic." There would be times that both of us, but especially Sophie, would feel genuinely lonely. Times when we ached unreasonably with a hunger that we couldn't name and that nothing seemed to satisfy. Troubles came and went. Problems erupted and then receded, the way they do, I suppose, in every household. Nana and I had our clashes. Sophie had her little fits.

We didn't see Grandmother so much anymore and tensions between her and Maureen had begun to surface early, leaving Sophie and me in the odd uncomfortable place of not knowing what to tell to whom. We opted, increasingly, for not telling anybody anything, a tact that ultimately served only to make us lonelier, slightly hungrier for that unnamed food. Daddy, who might have been our ally, even our referee, was after the first months as conspicuously absent as he'd always been. He and Maureen had begun a new business together in the city and they worked long hours, sometimes not even coming home on weekends. Now and then Maureen even came home alone. When she did, Sophie and knew to keep out of her way.

Our indoor life was not so perfect. Indoors, it felt, Sophie and I were always something like houseguests. Politely treated for the most part, but never quite comfortable, never quite at home. There was the sense always that we were imposing. That we were always in danger of overstaying our welcome and that at any moment, if we weren't careful, the visit might come to an end. Our indoor life was problematic in a way that after all these long years I'm at a loss to explain and almost ashamed to complain about. On the long continuum of genuine human suffering, our own distress was negligible, happening only in that small segment that separates civil tolerance from genuine love. Our indoor life was problematic. But our outdoor life almost made up for it.

I would not want to advocate for laissez-faire parenting—to suggest that the best way to raise children might be to turn them out of the house in the morning, encourage them not to return until dinner, and not trouble yourself with anything that might happen in between. The world is a much more dangerous place now. For all of us, but especially for children. An approach like the one applied to Sophie and to me, to the Laughlins, the Winston girls, David and the rest of us—to pretty much all the young hordes roving the newly manufactured suburbs of the '50s and early '60s, would not work so well today. But it worked wonderfully then. Wonderfully.

We made up our own games and our own rules, and when the rules proved unworkable, too hard, or no fun, we changed them to accommodate slow runners, taller shooters, kids with the most chores, kids who wore glasses. We were fiercely competitive but fixed on fairness and we learned that the only really fair game was the one in which everyone got to play. We learned to suit talent to task, letting the math whizzes be scorekeepers, the artists make signs or costumes, the smallest ones hold something vitally important. We didn't suffer crybabies. At least not for very long. And bullies, too, soon got over themselves when the sweaty majority simply ignored them.

Nobody was "allergic" to anything. It was a concept we'd never heard of. We ate dirt, drank creek water, kissed dogs in the mouth, and washed our hands only before eating. Sometimes. A wart was a badge of honor, not a reason to see a physician. Our household medicine cabinets contained Vicks Salve for colds, Calamine lotion for sunburn, mosquito bites and poison ivy, and band-aids and mercurochrome for pretty much everything else. The nearest hospital was 25 miles away and the family cars were usually with the dads in the city anyway. Getting sick or really hurt was a luxury rarely indulged in.

A few of us, a very few, had moved to our suburb from more rural settings—from the small Mississippi towns just over the state line a few miles away, or from similar little outposts just over the bridge in Arkansas. But most of us, like Sophie and me, had moved out from the dense, crowded city and for that majority the suburbs opened a door to a natural world that we could never have imagined. We ran in the open spaces like wild things, rode our bikes together in packs, played kickball and Cowboys and Indians in the fields and a grand-scale version of Hide and Seek that took in whole blocks. When we bored of any of this, or got too hot, we had a secret place to escape to.

"The Woods" as we called it was really nothing more than a couple of densely brambled acres with a few mature trees that the developers had spared where our last street, Lochlomand, dead-ended. If you went all the way through the Woods, you came pretty quickly to another blacktop road. But we never wanted to go that far. For a long time shade was at a premium in Fairfield Estates and this green little copse was a cool wonderland in summer. We caught tadpoles in shallow pools, swung on vines, built dozens of variations of clubhouses or forts over the years and left no telling how many hammers lost in the deep brush. We learned to know which flying things stung you and which didn't, where the same birds nested year after year.

We collected things—terrapin shells, cottony cocoons, the perfect cast-off skeletons of cicadas—and absorbed lessons from nature that no book could explain. Not every lesson was gentle. Once a few of us squatted in a field in a quiet huddle for half an hour to watch a snake devour a still-twitching field mouse. Once we found an injured female possum in a gully by the road. In her death throes she pushed out five hairless pups, which we gingerly transferred to a shoebox and hid in the little storage room at the back of Chuck Wiley's carport. We did our best, but of course the pups died, and when they did we gave them a solemn funeral attended by no one over twelve.

In the evenings after supper, when our play had to be closer to home, we played in the front yards. Our parallel driveways made perfect boundaries or end zones for freeze tag, monster in the pit, and run-the-gauntlet. The girls liked to do acrobatic tricks, twirl our batons or hoola-hoop in the grass. The boys found any excuse to wrestle. We caught fireflies by the hundreds and attached June bugs to strings to fly them over our heads in buzzing circles. Sometimes we broke into smaller groups. One huddle might sit Indian style in the grass telling jokes or ghost stories. Two or three might head down to a house with a basketball goal. Sophie and Maddie's crew were crazy about dressing cats in doll clothes.

46

And Sean and I played a lot of chess—a lot of chess—on the front steps under the porch lights.

Not everything we did together was accomplished in a smooth, harmonious stream. We often bickered over what to do and how to do it. We could pout and punish, and briefly but cruelly ostracize someone who had become problematic. We teased and tantrumed. We were capable, as all children are, of being petty, selfish, rude, and sometimes really mean to each other. Feelings got hurt. A few noses got bloodied. But the parents rarely knew. And because we left them out of it we always found our own way through.

After spectacular disagreements, those few times when we sensed that we had come dangerously close to disintegration, we always did something large, something involving everybody, in symbolic celebration, I suppose, of the survival of our little crew. Once we staged a variety show in Janet's driveway, complete with bed sheet curtains to cover the "backstage" carport, lawn chairs for the parent audience, and acts that ranged from Conner's (pretty good) vocal rendition of "Danny Boy" to Sheila Claxton's (really terrible) French horn solo.

Another evening, after a particularly bad day when most of us felt a little sheepish and ashamed for the way we had treated Dylan, we all sat around on the lawn picking at the grass. By way of apologizing for all of us maybe, David reached over and handed Dylan a little length of clover chain to add, I guess, to the one Dylan was unconsciously making. That did it. Just like that. In another few minutes we were all laughing and talking again, good as new, and cooperating to make what may have been the world's longest clover chain. By the time they called us in, grass stained and itchy, nearly every kid in the neighborhood had pitched in, our whole block practically had been weeded, and our fragile symbol of peace and understanding stretched at least a hundred feet long.

We were our own social science laboratory, an ongoing, ever-changing experiment in communal living, executive functioning, management skills, the challenges of interpersonal relationships. There wasn't anybody there to take lab notes, of course. At least no adults. That was the beauty of it. No grown-ups looking over our shoulders, monitoring or censoring. We may have been the last generation to have been given the privilege, the gift as I see it, of just getting to be kids.

But the thing about summers is that they morph into falls. The signals would start to show themselves, first in shorter days, then in shorter tempers and shorter attention spans, in the generalized ennui and malaise that began to infect our play, in the waning enthusiasm for old ideas and a creative vacuum for new ones. The signals were received by the adult world too, but contrarily they manifested themselves in revitalization, in suddenly renewed energies for sorting through our clothes, engaging us in conversations about our "plans," and in cutting out newspaper ads headlining "Back to School Specials." With summer's end the rhythms of life would change for them too. But we were winding down; they were gearing up.

In truth we would be much more trouble to them now. We were never going to be a terribly time and energy-intensive bunch. We were barely the beginning, only the cusp, of the "teach me, show me, take me, fix me" waves that would be coming behind us. But some of us, a few of us, were starting to require "lessons," to become involved with "extra-curricular" activities and to need transporting, sponsoring, chaperoning, and supporting. A few of us were going to be a good bit more trouble. And all of us, to some degree, would now need adults looking over our shoulders. Our papers and report cards would have to be signed, our packed lunches subject to public scrutiny. There would be open houses, PTA meetings, mimeographed requests for room mothers and clinic volunteers, permission slips for vaccines, hearing or eye tests, requests to opt in or out on behalf of your child and your family for this, that and the other. It was never clear to us why the start of the school year would get them so turned on.

But the thing about summer is that it morphs into fall, and morph we did. Grandmother always managed a weekend clothes-shopping spree at Silverstein's. From somewhere we got the notebooks and pencils, the scissors and rulers, crayons, protractors, compasses, folders and dividers that equipped us to tackle each new September.

Sophie, a rising first grader, would be attending for the first time a brand new school only a few blocks away. Only wealthy children attended kindergarten then. The pre-school concept had not taken hold. She would have Maddie and a couple of others to walk with, but I would be riding the bus— the bus that David's mother drove and that picked us up, conveniently, just at the edge of his house. Every school day morning at about 7:30 we would start to assemble at the corner of our street, still a little sleep-groggy, some of us, but always open to gossip, intra-gender teasing, collaborating on just-remembered homework assignments.

On a good day, in early fall, before winter cold germs had begun to decimate our ranks, there might be as many as twelve or fifteen for David's mom to collect at our stop. Not everyone in our neighborhood who attended our school would be there. There were always a few over-zealous mothers and a few Dads who dropped their children off at the beginning of the suburban commute. But these kids weren't part of "our" crowd, anyway. We knew their names and maybe which houses they lived in, but there was something odd or esoteric about them—handicaps, a religion that required private schooling, some household dysfunction that made them too secretive, or worse, much worse, a family philosophy already manifesting in over-protectiveness or the conviction that a kid's time should somehow be "managed." The gang that assembled itself every morning at our bus stop, our gang, was not that type.

I've wondered over the years if some strange sort of time-lapse photography could have been set up at our bus stop in 1955—and allowed to run for a decade—how interesting its record, with some editing, might actually be. I envision that in the first footage you see a few of us girls in sweet little puff-sleeved cotton dresses with Peter Pan collars and sashes still to be tied in the back. Pretty quickly you'd see us evolving toward demure little jumpers or dirndl skirts. There are the younger boys in short trimmed hair, Leave-It-To-Beaver plaid shirts, high-waisted trousers, and sturdy oxfords on their feet.

In the early footage three or four of us will show up dressed in Brownie or Cub Scout uniforms and a little later one or two in the uniforms of Girl or Boy Scouts with all the fashion paraphernalia—the sashes, ties, pins, and badges—that membership entailed. Sean hangs in longest, though he took a good bit of needling over it. By the time he is thirteen, though, in our neighborhood at least, the Scouts have become extinct.

I expect that I'd look OK in most of the segments, always neat and clean, pretty well put together by virtue of Grandmother's employee-discounted charge account at Silverstein's. But until high school, when I finally caught up to permanent waves, brush rollers, and the assistance of peers and professionals, my hair was always drippy straight and drab brown, with one very bad year—eighth grade—of wearing a gross over-large curl over my right eye. I don't know what I was doing but I'm lucky not to have lost my sight.

The Laughlins, who didn't have to worry so much in dealing with their curly red heads, had a hand-me-down couture system that would enable the shirt and cardigan or jacket that Conner is wearing in 1956 to reappear on Sean in 1958 and maybe later again, not so much the worse for wear, on Dylan in 1960. Janet Winston had great, moderately wavy blonde hair that was easily adapted to the current trends. You'd be able to see her first in a short little-girl bob, giving way to a simple pony-tail, then by seventh grade a neat, luxuriantly swinging page-boy, followed by an elegant French twist in freshman year, and then changing, by graduation, to straight and silky with a center part. Janet and her two older sisters, Myra and Barbara, were all about the same size which gave Janet access to a larger, and enviably more sophisticated, wardrobe. For the one year that all three of the Winston girls were in high school together they charted their school clothes in a three-way matrix to ensure that no Winston outfit went to school two days in a row. Janet wore shirt waist dresses with wide belts before any of the rest of us, and she was the first to give them up for pleated skirts, loafers and crew socks.

It will not be so easy to date the record from Janet's clothes, but you'll notice a burgeoning precociousness in her social skills and her tendency, way before high school, to hang with the boys far more than the girls. In fact, you'll probably observe a distinct evolution in all of our behaviors as the neighborhood alliances began to weaken against the pressures of school communality.

Conner is among the oldest of us and will drive himself to school in a battered 1959 Chevy for a year or two before most of us have stopped catching the bus. Sometimes he'll just pass our stop, honking arrogantly as he scratches off from the corner. At other times, perhaps in a mellower, more nostalgic mood, he'll actually stop at our corner and beneficently open the door, inviting us all to pile in, granting us the sublime privilege of arriving at school by way station of the high school parking lot.

By the early '60s you'll notice that Sean is wearing eyeglasses, at first the dark, thick Buddy Holly type and nearer to graduation the wire-rimmed John Lennon type. By then he's quit working so vigorously on fitting in anymore and he and I, while we still feel a special connection, are not the buds we once were. I was the first girl, you see, to break Sean's heart, and though I never meant to, and didn't then understand why he chose to react so strangely—pulling away from all of us, retreating into his books and his thoughts and his odd little idiosyncrasies, I understand a lot better now.

By Junior year some of our original gang has started to disappear, being replaced by younger siblings or later editions to the neighborhood. David has no choice, but Janet won't be riding the bus much anymore at all. She'll be riding to school either with an older sister, or more likely, the current boyfriend. I will disappear too for a time—the fall before Jeremy graduated when he was crazy enough to travel every morning from his house, not more than a mile from the school, to pick me up every day. I'll still ride the bus most afternoons. Jeremy has football practice.

Toward the end you'll probably still see Sean, sitting on the little bank of grass by David's driveway, reading a weird book on chess openings or studying for the Latin Tournament. His interest in Latin did not impress most of us, but it would garner him considerable academic distinction and set him on the road to a really fine scholarship. He won't know yet that I've spared him. That particular epiphany will take longer than what our reel can hold. But somehow, even now, in the set of his jaw, in the way that something he is reading causes him to lift his head, squint his eyes, and peer off into a future that none of the rest of us can see, you can sense his quiet conviction that someone, if not me, will someday really love him. That chess is a fit and relevant preparation for life. And that Latin, should one become a pediatric oncologist at St. Jude's Children's Research Hospital, might actually come in handy.

There would be more in the time-lapse record of our bus-stop history, if only it existed. If only someone had captured it. But it wasn't that important. It was only, really, our launching pad for school. School was where it happened.

The school that we all attended was a venerable twelve-year institution on State Highway 51, about 17 miles southwest of downtown Memphis in an area, named for the school, or vice versa, but nevertheless called *Whitehaven*. The name, I would learn in civics class, came from an early settler and property owner, Colonel Francis White, and was never, as I assumed for years, a descriptive for the total absence of colored people.

There weren't any there, of course. Not in our classrooms, our scout troops, even on the teams from other schools that played ours on Friday night. They weren't even there to shop at Southland, one of the first enclosed malls in the country. The grown-ups worried about them. There was always an undertow of fear in their talk. In December that first year we followed the Montgomery bus boycott closely on the news. A woman named Rosa Parks had started it all by refusing to give up her seat to a white person. The strike ended by Christmas and while we really weren't ever going to get the opportunity again, Sophie and I concluded that the next time we rode downtown on the No. 2 Fairgrounds with Thelma, we'd all be able to sit anywhere we wanted.

The first few weeks of school, always a little crazy, were made considerably more chaotic for us by the sheer fact of our numbers. That first year, and for many more years after that, there were always more of us than had been planned for, more of us than could be accommodated in this size classroom or that size laboratory. We grew to expect that our lunch and study hall periods would keep being shortened to allow for more shifts. That double, even triple, assemblies would be scheduled to see that everyone got assembled. We learned to accept the predictable wait for workbooks or extra desks and the predictable looks on the faces of our teachers as they surveyed us, wriggling sardines in a too-tight tin.

We were the boomer generation. Members of the great post-war herd. For most of our lives we would be part of what seemed an ever-enlarging mass. Like a pig passing through a python, our fate was to be constantly squeezed by "not enough." For us, and the millions like us, there were not enough teachers in not enough classrooms in not enough schools, with not enough buses to get us there. There were not enough writers for not enough textbooks and not enough lockers to put them in. The trend would extend into college, where we would go in unprecedented masses, and where there would not be enough volunteers to help with registration, not enough rooms in our dorms, not enough seats in our stadiums, and not enough spots for our cars. By the time the almighty law of supply and demand eventually caught up with us, there was too much, in some cases, of what we had competed for. We no longer felt the lack but we had changed every institution we passed through.

Our press isn't so good these days. Now we're characterized as vain, obsessed with appearances, unwilling to grow up or to grow old. Some see our political histories and social activism as overblown and oversold. On the internet there is even a Boomer "Death Counter" to show the rate at which we're leaving the stage and reducing the threat to "their" Social Security inheritance. "They" forget, I think, how much, as the glut of us was stretching their country's systems and institutions, that we were also expanding their own individual freedoms. In our own largess we made their world larger. Larger for black people, gay people, women, the handicapped. By thinking with the same mind, speaking with the same voice, showing up together en masse at inopportune times and inappropriate places, we managed to accomplish a lot together. I enter into evidence the end of a bloody and pointless war. I enter into evidence a clover chain at least a hundred feet long.

CHAPTER IV

I was always pretty good in school. Not a stellar student, but adequate. My propensity to be better at words than numbers continued and became exaggerated by high school when I was allowed to participate in the first Advanced Placement English classes but only got through Algebra I and Geometry by the very sheerest skin of my teeth. I loved English and every one of my English teachers. I loved writing poems and stories but other than making the newspaper staff I did nothing to distinguish myself. In sixth grade, true, there had been a brief fifteen minutes of fame in representing our elementary school in the county spelling bee. I went down on "motley" (spelled with an *e* in case you didn't know), but seeing Mrs. Carlyle's face fall ended my competitive aspirations. Daddy and Maureen didn't come to see me anyway. It was hardly worth the trouble.

Sophie didn't fare so well. From the very beginning there were problems. Poor report cards and notes from school suggesting that Sophie had trouble "following directions" or "participating in class." That she was "inadequately prepared" or (God forbid for a six-year-old) simply "careless." From time to time the school sent home requests for special conferences about Sophie's problems, but being late for work, or having to come back to the suburbs in the middle of a busy day, was the kind of inconvenience that Daddy and Maureen

57

could barely abide. In the beginning they went to a few of them with the result that our household was enshrouded in a miserable black miasma for several days but pretty soon they started ignoring the appeals altogether. Eventually the requests stopped coming. Someone at Sophie's school, in guidance or administration, probably noted her permanent record: *Parents do not give happy damn.* And that was that.

That is the flip side, you see, to laissez-faire parenting. It succeeds or not, throughout the animal kingdom as it does with humans, in direct relationship to the strength of the offspring. Some of us don't need very much. Some of us need a lot.

I tried, in the beginning, to give Sophie some of what she needed. I lectured her, read to her, helped her with homework as much as she'd let me.

"Now you put down the 5 and carry the 2," I'd tell her.

"Carry it where?" she'd demand. "Why do I have to carry it?"

I lived in a world of metaphor and simile, poetic figures and tropes that spoke more clearly to me than any simple language could. Sophie was as literal-minded as they come. She could no more understand how someone could be "like a rose" than she could follow why you had to carry a number. She was also constitutionally incapable of deceit. Or hate. She was genetically, or psychologically, or neuro-chemically—or whatever the current theory is—unable to comprehend the complexities of human behavior that cause us to act, time and again, against our own self interest. To put it in her own words, Sophie could never understand why we had to be "mean" to each other.

In second grade when Sophie saw on the news that hundreds of soldiers (with guns!) in our neighboring state of

Arkansas had walled off a high school to keep only nine teenagers from going in, she was not only mystified but heartbroken. When she saw those teenagers cursed and spit on, an angry mob hitting black people with bricks and dragging them by their feet, she was inconsolable. What made only a little sense to me couldn't possibly be explained to Sophie. Our grandmother, Daddy, Nana and I answered her questions with the same lie that always masks, to the innocent, the undeniable truth of our human capacity for evil. "It's complicated," we'd tell her. "You'll understand when you're older."

To her credit Sophie failed, continually, to understand the incomprehensible. She was "passed over" as they said back then, for promotion to third grade, and again to fifth. Daddy took it personally. A reflection, somehow, on his own intellectual prowess. Nana was still good to her. Maybe even, as time wore on, more inclined, as Thelma had been, to favor Sophie with special foods and extra attention. Grandmother, from her long distance perspective, definitely sensed trouble brewing. But her way, the only way she knew, was to ask for "special" prayers from her church congregation for a "special" burden that lay heavy on her heart. Maureen, if she didn't actually gloat, seemed to take all of Sophie's failings in perfect stride with a supercilious "I told you so" attitude that confirmed that spoiled children would always disappoint.

Me? I gave up. I became dismayed with Sophie's infuriatingly literal thinking and her slow progress toward sophistication. More importantly I became distracted and redirected by my own junior high, and then high school, diversions. In the beginning I had done what I could to help Sophie make sense of the world. But the beginning didn't last very long. By the ninth grade I was my own planet and Sophie

59

and I were orbiting different suns. She had Maddie's friendship. And Grandmother to talk to after school. Sophie, I knew, would be just fine.

There are theories I've heard that suggest that many of us live our entire adult lives in an attempt to replicate, or correct, our high school years. I'm not sure about all that. I concede that high school can be pretty important. For me, a lot of it was really great. I was never the most popular girl, or the prettiest. But I moved on the fringes of a popular crowd and felt most of the time more "in" than "out." Most of my teachers seemed to like me. I didn't find study too onerous because, except for English classes and newspaper staff, I did only enough to get by. We went to sporting events, danced at parties, got completely swept away by Beetle mania. School was part of my authentic outdoor life and that made a lot of it pretty good. A little of it, though, I would not want to ever experience again.

In November of junior year the door to Mrs. Romero's Spanish II class opened abruptly and our assistant principal, Mr. Walker, with ashen face and trembling voice informed us that the president, *our* president, the President of the United States of America, had been shot. It was one of those moments, for those of us who lived through it, when time became a frozen chrysalis, permanently fixing every thought, every movement, all the sensory input of which we are capable. I can still see the look on Mrs. Romero's face. I hear the startled little gasps of shock, the shifting of bodies in desks, the first sobs of girls starting to cry. I clearly remember looking out of the window, seeing the blood red leaves of a maple tree and wondering where Sophie was and who might be with her.

By then she should have been there with me, or across the

street at least, in a nearby seventh grade classroom of Whitehaven Elementary. But the two failures to be promoted had made her tenure at the neighborhood school overlong. I was leaving her behind and I didn't know if she'd ever be able to catch up.

It was ironically a consequence of the president's death and the days of national mourning and school closure that I came to meet Jeremy. I already knew who he was, of course. Everybody did. He was a senior football jock and until very recently had been the handsome property of Charlotte Brooks. Charlotte was a cheerleader, naturally, and about as good-looking as any 17-year-old girl had a moral right to be. Nobody knew exactly what had broken them up. It was rumored that Charlotte was dating a college boy. But it didn't matter much to me one way or the other because I thought Jeremy Greer way too cool and way too stuck on himself to even make a charity appearance in my dreams.

Except he wasn't. Stuck on himself that is. He was actually quiet, modest, and very sensitive. All this I learned on that very sad Monday at Marsha Swift's house while we watched the young president being laid to rest.

We had all been glued to the television at home with our families for three solid days. We'd seen the cortege take the president to the capitol and the endless lines waiting in the cold to pay their last respects. Intermingled with the funeral preparations the details of the story unfolded. Over and over again we had watched the scenes of the Dallas motorcade. Incredibly we had watched live as the assassin himself was murdered. Television, and to a great degree all of us, were coming of age in the space of four day's time.

At about 9:00 that Monday morning David Kirk pulled into my drive. He already had Janet and a couple of others. A bunch of us was going to watch the funeral in Marsha Swift's rec room.

Most of my friends were already there when we arrived, as well as a few of the senior class, friends of Marsha's brother, Ed. We sat around on the floor, all very quiet, and Cronkite, too, was soft-spoken and reserved. Between his comments he left spaces to hear the sounds—sounds that would be etched as indelibly as the images. We heard the slow muffled cadence of the drums, the mournful bagpipes, the clop of the horses' hooves on the paved street as they pulled the caisson with the flag-draped coffin. We heard the bells of St. Matthews when the mass ended. The three volleys of the seven guns over the Arlington graves. The bugle playing Taps, the last note going sour.

Somewhere in all this I noticed that Jeremy Greer was sitting next to me, leaning against the legs of someone who sat in a corner chair. For the second time the cameras showed little John-John stepping forward to salute his daddy's coffin and beside me Jeremy Greer emitted a huge convulsive sob.

"It's his birthday," Jeremy said. "He's three years old today."

I hadn't known. Somehow in the avalanche of news coverage I had missed that little detail. Jeremy and I hugged. We cried a little more together. When it came time to go home I let Jeremy give me a ride.

One of the things I liked best about Jeremy was that he looked you right in the eyes when you talked to him. I was not accustomed to having my opinions so dignified by the male of the species and I liked that a lot. I also liked his natural, old-fashioned manners. He pulled out chairs and opened car doors and helped you with your coat. He had a way of making me feel protected and cherished. He was certainly the best kisser who ever lived.

For the ten months before Jeremy went off to college, and any time during the next year that he was able to get home for the weekend, we were inseparable. I went to his prom, we had an amazing summer, and during the next school year we wrote letters and shared a few long-distance phone calls, but otherwise suffered the agony of separation. Given the social climate of 1965, it was an agony that couldn't easily be relieved.

I don't know what was going on then out in California. But the army of the sexual revolution had not yet even sent any advance scouts down to the Mississippi Delta. "Good girls" in the South, just didn't "do it." If they did, they didn't even share the experience with their closest friends. A girl's reputation was still pretty much the same valuable commodity that it had been in Jane Austen's time. The "pill" had only been available for a very few years and teenagers, unless they had an understanding—and extraordinarily progressive—family doctor, were not part of its market. Eight states still prohibited its use and the Thalidomide tragedies in Europe and news of serious side effects from the birth control pill had combined to make it a shaky option, even if you had access to it.

The best bet was condoms, "rubbers" as we called them back then. The older boys, whether they knew what to do with one or not, were inclined to carry one in the side of their wallets, and they deliberately worked at the leather so that the telltale ring showed through when they took out their billfolds to buy movie or game tickets. If a girl should ever be caught with a rubber, her life was effectively over.

Jeremy and I knew what was at stake. We indulged in marathon rounds of French-kissing, rubbed and touched and worked ourselves into aching frenzies, but we always managed to pull back, promising ourselves that in five more years, when we'd both finished college and had a big, beautiful wedding, we would build a love-nest like the world had never seen.

We probably would have made it, too, if the new drive-in theater hadn't opened on Highway 51.

We didn't have a lot of options. There were places in Mississippi, we'd heard, where a girl could get a coat-hanger abortion on someone's kitchen table but we never considered it. *Roe v. Wade* was still eight years away. I was scared to death but lucky, too, I knew, in more ways than one. My timing at the very end of senior year meant that I would be able to graduate. Pregnant girls back then were not allowed to complete their public school educations. The thinking, I suppose, was that it set a bad example. How a fat co-ed, waddling down the corridors in maternity clothes with a stack of schoolbooks on her hip could serve as an incentive for getting knocked up strikes me now, as it did then, as completely incredible. But that's the way it was.

I was lucky, too, because Jeremy wanted to marry me. He didn't *have* to, I told him repeatedly, although I didn't mean a word of it. He *wanted* to. He was actually stupidly delighted at the idea of becoming a daddy and he devised an immediate plan for withdrawing from college, getting a job, finding us a place where—the best part—we could have sex as much as we wanted.

We decided to tell the Greers first.

Jeremy picked me up and we went over to break the news on a Wednesday night, well past supper and almost dark. The Greer's house wasn't actually in a subdivision, but on a big lot at the back of a long gravel drive that wound through a grove of pecan trees that Mr. Greer himself had planted.

The Greers had lived in Whitehaven a long time, probably since the time it had been mostly cotton fields and country roads. Although he had never graduated, Mr. Greer had actually attended our school himself as a boy and he was still quite the booster. During the years that Jeremy had played I don't think Mr. Greer ever missed a game and even during last fall's season, while Jeremy was away at college, Mr. Greer had still come to most of the games. He always sat, alone, in the section just to the right of the band and though he never actually yelled or cheered, he never took his eyes off the field and you knew he was still a tiger fan, through and through.

He was a simple, quiet, country man, Mr. Greer, but I liked him. Actually I liked both of them, although I got the feeling sometimes that Mrs. Greer wasn't exactly mad about me. Apparently she had been pretty close to Charlotte Brooks, and to Charlotte's mother, and you know how that goes. I can't deny that some part of my black little heart was looking forward to finally, once and for all, squelching Mrs. Greer's hopes of Jeremy and Charlotte getting back together, but that's about all I was looking forward to. Frankly, I would have cut off my arm at the elbow to be anywhere else on earth. But the good tidings had to be carried. And if Jeremy was willing to back me up when I had to tell my family, then I was going to be there for him.

We pulled up the long drive and parked in the gravel turnaround. I tried to catch Jeremy's eyes but he wouldn't look at me. My throat filled with an unswallowable aching lump. We got out of the car and started walking around to the back of the house. He still didn't look at me and neither of us spoke, but on the last few steps Jeremy took my hand and I felt the lump melt a little. I could face anything with Jeremy beside me. Anything.

Mr. Greer was in the kitchen drinking coffee and eating what looked like some type of cobbler at the kitchen table. It was a big round Early American table with turned spindle legs, big enough to seat six easily. I'd always admired that table, and the nice little milkglass creamer and sugar bowl that Mrs. Greer kept in the center. It wasn't my taste, actually. Early American is kind of, well, *early*. But it gave that big kitchen such a nice homey feel.

Mr. Greer rose, smiling, when he saw us.

"Well, hey there, Miss Lacey," he said. "Y'all come on in here!"

Mrs. Greer appeared in the doorway, dressed up more than usual, in a pink sheath skirt and white blouse. She'd probably been to prayer meeting. I thought again what I always thought. That Mrs. Greer had a pretty face but wore way too much pressed powder.

The Greers were older than most of our parents. Jeremy's brother, Michael, had been married a long time and had two pretty big kids of his own. Jeremy himself had been what my grandmother called a "change of life" baby, as though, now that I think about it, there could really *be* any other kind.

"Mom. Dad." Jeremy said. "We need to talk to you. Can we all sit down?" He headed toward the door of the family room and Mrs. Greer moved aside to let him pass. Her eyes went wide and she cast a quick glance at her husband who was still smiling sweetly. Mr. Greer dropped his spoon into the cobbler dish and we all followed Jeremy into the family room.

When we had all sat down Jeremy took a deep breath and then simply stated the facts. That we were going to have a baby and had decided to get married.

They took it pretty well.

Mr. Greer, like he was just waking from a long nap, stood up from his chair, slowly stretched his arms high over his head, and yawned. He then picked up his pipe, knocked it a couple of times in the stand-up ashtray by his chair and then walked right out of the room, right through the kitchen and out into the back yard.

Mrs. Greer watched her husband go and then turned to look at me. She blinked once, twice, three times and then dropped her head into her hands and began to bawl.

Jeremy stood up and moved to sit on the sofa next to his mother. He shot me a pleading glance but I certainly didn't know what to do. It was probably better to leave them alone. I got up and took the same path of retreat that Mr. Greer had taken.

Mr. Greer stood in the center of the large brick patio lighting his pipe. His kept his back turned to me and I figured that either he didn't know I was there or didn't want to look me in the face. I was turning to go back inside when he spoke.

"Well," he said softly. "You've gone and done it now."

"Yes, sir," I said.

With his pipe lit now he walked over to the swing glider at the back of the patio and slowly sat down. He was facing me now and I was pretty surprised to see that, while he wasn't exactly smiling anymore, he didn't look really angry either. I was surprised again when he patted the space in the glider beside him, inviting me to join. I went over to sit with him and for a long time we were both quiet, Mr. Greer gently pushing the glider with his foot in an easy swing, back and forth, back and forth, back and forth.

"You love my boy?" he asked at length.

"I do!" I said and my mind set off on a frantic search through every book, every poem I'd ever read. I wanted something strong, something profound and beautiful to impress upon Mr. Greer the depth of my love for Jeremy. What I came up with was hardly worthy of the illiterate, let alone of someone with my supposed expressive skills.

"I do," I said. "I love him to pieces."

Mr. Greer nodded and for quite a few minutes more we both sat quietly gliding.

"She'll be all right," he said, motioning with his pipe toward the house. "It's just what we done."

"Sorry?" I said. I had no idea what he was talking about.

"It happened just like you done," he said. "She got in the way with Michael."

Still it took me another minute. But when I finally realized what he was telling me I felt a flood of cleansing relief wash through every fiber of my being.

"You mean . . ." I stammered. "You and Mrs. Greer? And you got *married*? And you've been together all these *years*?"

"Yep," he said. "Been hell."

That was not at all what I'd been expecting next. The cleansing flood turned to solid ice. I had absolutely no idea how to proceed. In another second I believe I would have simply taken flight, stood up and begun running, hard, down the long gravel drive. I guess he knew that, too, because he laid his hand on top of mine and the glider's motion abruptly stopped.

"But it don't have to be," he said. "Don't have to be at all."

I relaxed a little.

"And you love my boy?" he asked again. And again I waxed eloquent.

"I *do*," I said. "I love him more than anything."

"Then just remember it," he said, and started the motion of the glider again. "It ain't any harder than that. Unless you make it hard."

CHAPTER V

If Jeremy's father's response to our new life plan was better than we could have hoped for, my own father's reaction was worse than anybody could have predicted. Mrs. Greer, as her husband had known she would, eventually dried her tears and stifled her disappointment and got on the telephone with Grandmother to start making arrangements for a precipitate wedding. Grandmother, who had never really had any grander plans for my future than that I get a good job, say, as a telephone operator or a file clerk for the government, didn't seem to think an eighteen-year-old was too young to marry. She had always felt that colleges were merely dens of iniquity anyway and she viewed my literary ambitions as mildly amusing, on the same order as Sophie playing the guitar or collecting movie star pictures. Grandmother didn't seem interested in discussing the real reason behind the nuptials. Frankly she behaved as though she had missed that information. But she liked Jeremy and was delighted to know that Mrs. Greer was such a good Christian woman. They formed an immediate bond in the Lord.

Daddy, on the other hand, went through the proverbial roof. I had been forced to tell him without Jeremy beside me because it was so hard to know when he and Maureen might be around. Home these days just seemed to be the place where he picked up fresh clothes, lingering just long enough to share an occasional family meal, which he made miserable for all of us by fussing at me, railing about some aspect of how the way the household was being run, or mocking whatever subject Sophie was foolish enough to want to talk about.

Our father, you see, was narcissistic in the clinical sense. I didn't know the term for it then but I know it now, absolutely, because I looked it up, two weeks after he died, in the *Diagnostic and Statistical Manual of Mental Disorders, Fourth Edition.* The DSM-IV should have had his picture pasted right there in the description of the Cluster B Personality Disorders.

The book said that narcissists believe that they are "special" and can only be understood by other special people. *Special.* I'll say! Daddy's typical response to anything that didn't suit him was to fly into a blind rage, usually accompanied by a lot of yelling and hand waving (if he were standing up) or yelling and fist banging (if he were sitting down). He could throw things sometimes, but usually nothing heavy or valuable and nothing aimed to injure or maim. He never hit us. His violence was almost completely verbal.

"You're *what*?" he bellowed when I was finally able to break the news. I had followed him out to the car because he was about to leave again and another opportunity was going to be missed.

"Can we go inside?" I asked meekly.

"Hell, no, we can't go inside! Have you lost your mind?"

He was really, really loud. Mr. Palmer across the street had stopped watering his marigolds and was looking our way.

"Daddy," I tried again. "It's going to be OK. Jeremy and I are getting married and . . ."

"Who the hell is *Jeremy*?" he yelled. He had put a couple of hangered shirts into the back seat of the car and now used both hands to slam the door. The noise echoed down the street like a booming canon.

"Jeremy!" I said. "Jeremy Greer. You know Jeremy, Daddy. We've been going steady more than a year."

He was moving around to the front of the car now and I followed after, not sure if I could talk fast enough to get it all said.

"Grandmother and Jeremy's mom are going to give us a little wedding, Daddy. I want you to give me away."

"Listen!" he said, spinning around to face me. "You've given *yourself* away!" His voice lowered and he looked me square in the face but he spoke through gritted teeth. He was trying now to maintain composure.

"Don't you *see* that?" he said. "You little . . . you . . . *you little . . .*"

"What?" I said. "Little *what*?" I wanted him to finish his sentence. I wanted to know what he thought, no matter how bad it was. But he got into the car, slamming the driver's door, too. He started the engine and I just stood, expecting that he'd drive away. He did back out a few feet but he slammed on the brakes and then worked furiously to roll down the window. He looked up at me and spoke, his voice lower but filled with barely controlled rage.

"I thought it would be Sophie," he said. "Not you!"

"But you're just alike," he continued. "You're all exactly the same!" And then he did drive off, leaving Maureen, whether he'd meant to or not, to suffer through another weekend with just us.

I didn't feel so good. I hadn't yet absorbed, beyond his anger, the sense of my father's words. I certainly didn't feel like dealing with Maureen who stood in the open door on the porch and who apparently had heard some, or all, of what had just transpired.

I tried to push past her. I didn't want to, although I was willing if need be, to shove her or hurt her or say something I might regret. But people will surprise you. Just when you think you've got them all figured out, pigeon-holed in their neat little boxes, they'll throw you for a loop.

"Your Daddy's a jerk," she said, and she put her arm around my shoulders and gave a little squeeze.

The rule on weddings, I now know all too well, is that if you have five years to plan one, the preparations will take five years. If you have, as we did, only a little over fourteen days, you'll find that you fill that too, but you arrive at exactly the same end. We were pretty busy. Invitations were extended by telephone. The church, minister, a soloist and a cake were secured, and Grandmother found me a wedding dress. It was a party dress, actually, a passed-over prom dress, heavily discounted because it was much too plain and a little too old-fashioned to have sold in this year's fashion offering. I liked it though. It was simple and elegant, made more so when Janet's mom replaced a couple of tulle pom-pomish things with simple satin bows. Sophie would stand up with me, Bobbie Belcher with Jeremy. A few special friends like Janet and David, Sean and Maddie were given the assignments of ushering, covering the guest book, presiding over our punchbowl. A lot of us would be graduating on Friday night. I felt pretty good about the fact that, deprived of our prom, some of our friends would still have festive plans for Saturday.

The gentlest way to describe my Grandmother's

congregation is to say that it was pretty "geriatric." In the years that Sophie and I had attended with Grandmother, we had frequently been the youngest, and second youngest, in attendance— if you discounted, that is, the babies brought by visiting children, or children's children, or even maybe the children's children's children.

The small sanctuary, with its long wooden pews and desperately faded center aisle and altar carpeting still had its exceptionally distinctive fragrance—an aroma combining the smell of decaying flesh with O'Cedar. (Imagine a nursing home that someone polishes every day.) It was still Johnny Conway's job to care for the little church and since Johnny had now gotten much older, and had never been the brightest bulb on the porch anyway, no one in Grandmother's church had yet had the heart to tell him that a little O'Cedar can go a very long way. Mrs. Greer had arranged for someone to arrive early to wipe down the excessive residue from the pews and to see also that the surfeit of Garden of Gethsemane hand fans were tastefully distributed.

The basement where Sunday School classes were held, and where we were to hold the reception, exuded the damp, much less complicated smell of simple mildew. But the electric water fountain at the bottom of the stairs rendered, to this day, the coldest, cleanest, purest-tasting water I have ever experienced. Grandmother and Mrs. Greer and some of the ladies of the church had set up a crepe-paper festooned punch bowl table and made some pretty little finger sandwiches. Mr. Chisholm, who had chronicled the church's history since the end of the Great Depression, had agreed to be our wedding photographer. By Thursday afternoon we were pretty much set.

I don't remember too much about graduation. We had a

speaker, I think, who was a State Assemblyman, and he went on, I think, about how important this milestone was and how what we did next was going to make us or break us. Sean, as Valedictorian of our class, made a strangely cryptic speech rhetorically questioning who we really owed our allegiance to, with some anti-establishment undertones delicately suggesting that actually grown-ups might not know Jack. His speech drew only polite applause, a little surprising in light of the fact that there were more than five hundred in our graduating class and ordinarily at least half of them would have cheered for the Apocalypse.

Daddy didn't make the ceremonies. I figured he was still pretty mad at me or that, best case, he'd just forgotten, but Jeremy had picked up Maureen and Nana and Sophie and afterwards we met the Greers at Leonard's, the hands down best barbecue place the Southeast would ever produce. We all ate pork sandwiches and those decadent, quarter-pound onion rings and laughed and talked like one big family. I remember being pretty happy that night. But the next night I would be blissful.

We got through the wedding fine. Just before the ceremony, at the very last minute, Daddy showed up and at the end of the aisle in the little church vestibule he took my arm and leaned over to plant a light little kiss on my cheek. I hadn't gotten over my hurt. In truth I wasn't entirely pleased to see him. I had been fully prepared to walk the aisle all by myself and after that to never lay eyes on him again. But blood is thicker, as they say. And having him there presented a much more united front to the Greers, my friends, the congregation. He was almost movie-star handsome in a dark suit and soft, silver-gray tie. I would be glad to have him there for the pictures at least.

We said our vows, the old traditional kind where I promised to love, honor and obey and to understand fully that the husband was head of the house. Jeremy, who had never had any fear of plowing into four two-hundred pound linemen, shook like an aspen leaf. Grandmother's little congregation coughed and hacked so much you could barely hear a thing. But we got through it fine and after our little lime sherbet and Ginger Ale punch reception, we departed under a hail of rice, as Mr. and Mrs. Jeremy Wade Greer.

Childhood was over. I would never spend another night with Sophie in the top bunk of the ugly bedroom decorated like a hunting lodge. I would never play another game of chess with Sean or roam the streets with our energetic little band. For a long time there I relied on nothing but memory to recall our years in Beautiful Fairfield Estates. But a decade or so after our wedding, in the chaos of preparation for yet another move, I found a box of forgotten pictures.

The earliest ones are grainy things, taken amateurishly with the Kodak Brownie that I got for my tenth birthday. But they show the flatness of the land, the monotony of the houses, the sickly young saplings and grassy open fields that bespoke the assembly line qualities of those first post-war subdivisions—the very qualities of landscape and architecture that had so surprised me in coming from Grandmother's House. There are a few transitional shots. In a picture meant to capture Sophie and Maddie with their dressed-up cats you can see in the background that the chain link fences had started to go up. In another you notice that the clothesline posts are coming down.

The last pictures in the box, though, were astonishing in comparison to the first ones—a lesson, I think, in the grace that Time sculpts with. The last photos show the obligatory

FHA trees grown mature and beautiful, so large in some places that they form an arch over the streets, exactly like they did on Grandmother's Street when I was a child. The lawns are lush and tidily edged and there are perennial beds fit, really, for actual estates. Some of the houses have been added to. Here you see a second-story addition; there another room extends an L deep into the back yard. There are even carports completely enclosed to make space for an in-law or a game room. The chain link fences have been superseded by a variety of fencing and enclosures. There are pickets and stockades, even brick walls with pretty gates that hint of a real backyard garden. In short, the cookie cutter houses of Fairfield Estates have become individuals, differentiating themselves from each other in the same ways that we, Sophie and me, David, Janet, Conner, Sean—that all of us—had become individuals. On the outside we had changed. On the inside, more. We were no longer the cookie cutter, baby boom children born into the herd.

And yet, for a few of us, there has surely been a kind of stasis. After finding the box I made a search of the property records and found a surprising number of the original owners still there. I couldn't be sure of some of the names. A Smith or a Jones or a Thomas could be just about anybody. But some of the names were undeniable. The Reggieros, for example, who supplied my first babysitting job, are still there. Or at least one of them is. The Gustafsons and the Snowdens still show up on the registry. And David Kirk's parents still live in the corner house by the bus stop.

How much I envy them. The idea that David Kirk still goes home, to the corner lot on Lochinvar Drive in Beautiful Fairfield Estates to eat his Thanksgiving dinner or open his family Christmas presents makes me achingly jealous. The thought that year after year, decade after decade, David can walk out onto the very stoop of the home he grew up in, to light a cigarette or escape the household patter, and gaze down "our" streets, walk casually out onto the actual lawn where we once turned cartwheels, played Cowboys and Indians, planned assaults on imaginary enemies, fills me with melancholy envy.

To someone for whom continuity is the most esoteric of life experiences, the notion of biological parents, who still live together, in the same house, in the same neighborhood in which you grew up, is nearly incomprehensible, the philosophical extensions profound. They suggest that home is not, as Frost said, just the place where they've got to take you in, but rather an overarching constant—a literal, physical place whose molecules have so merged with yours that you are essentially inseparable. As in *I am this place* and *this place is me*. If that is the case, I may never be home. And neither will you, my chickadees.

I don't know where my place is. I would have liked it to be tied to the earth. To the geography of a town or a mountain, a vineyard or a valley. But for me, for most of us, it's much too late for that. We've become transients, hobos, all of us. We go where the wind blows, where the company sends us, where the prospect of bigger or better or warmer or cheaper tugs harder than any root can withstand. Home is not connected in any way to any specific spot on the smaller and smaller planet we inhabit. Home is where we get our mail. This month. This week. In an increasingly digital age, we may even lose that grounding.

The pictures made me wonder if David sees our ghosts. Maybe he sees us standing, in a conspiratorial little huddle at the bus stop. Maybe he sees us roaming the open spaces behind the houses, forming our hierarchical bands, playing our crazy games. Or maybe—a smaller focus—he sees us in twos or threes, teaching ourselves to play chess on the backdoor steps, or pairing off to whisper the first forbidden words of love and sex in The Woods.

And then it occurred to me that maybe, despite all those years of constancy, David never gives us a thought. Maybe, when David goes out on that tiny little stoop to smoke or get some air, his thoughts are consumed with something else entirely. With the chances of his next promotion. With the state of his mutual funds. With wondering whether, really, his wife could be having an affair. Maybe the whole, redundant annual holiday trek to his parents' house has left him numb and bored. Perhaps he even resents exactly what I envy. Maybe he secretly hates his parents because they never moved on from Beautiful Fairfield Estates. That would be ironic. But not really surprising. It would just be, as Connor used to say, "the way the cookie crumbles."

CHAPTER VI

The distinctive features of the Schimler's house were the steep pitched roof and prominent cross gables, the plastered sections of the exterior with decorative half-timbering, (OK, fake half-timbering, but it looked like the real thing, at least from a distance, and certainly if all you'd ever seen of the real thing was in magazines). There were the tall narrow windows with small window panes, and the big chimneys topped with chimney pots. (Again, fake chimney pots, but reasonable facsimiles.) That these are the classic structural elements of traditional English Tudor architecture is not something I could have told you that evening in 1965. Nor that this particular example was a good and tastefully understated American interpretation of that style, given its size, sighting on the lot, and the considerations of local materials and current building codes. All that I would conclude, dare I say confirm, later— goodness, maybe thirty years later—on the several drive-by pilgrimages I would make to look at and photograph this self-same house. By then I knew a great deal about houses. Had seen far grander, more painstakingly authentic, and couldn't be easily taken in. By that time I had become something of an expert on houses. But I still found this one special.

About the only thing I could have actually told you that first night was that the Schimler's had a beautiful home. A *really* beautiful home in a beautiful neighborhood in a world in which Jeremy and I didn't belong. At least not yet. We were coming, we hoped, to sign a lease on a two-bedroom duplex that Dr. Schimler, a retired dentist, owned in another part of town. We were just beginning. But at least we were beginning.

I had enough sense to know that these weren't rich people. Not really rich. At least not rich in the rock star, Beverly Hills, Elvis Presley kind of way. Not necessarily rich in the other way, either. Grandmother had long ago fortified me with all those camel-through-the-eye-of-needle-lectures and I, as the Great Reader of Books, had even had a few "value" experiences that even she wasn't privy to. I wasn't completely slain by the opulence of it all. It was just that the Schimler's house was *so* beautiful. The hand-painted house number sign hanging below the period-perfect gas street lamp. The small, sweet, carefully tended front lawn and the flowerbeds. The ceramic English spaniel sitting beside the door. The slightly tarnished brass doorknocker shaped like a fleur de lis. *My God, I fell in love with that house.* There was just—and here's the ticket—just enough of everything, not too much of anything. Nothing that appeared either random or contrived. Neither comfy kitschy nor stage-set House Beautiful. Some houses just have *harmony*.

Maybe I exaggerate. But I can't see that it matters. The main thing here is the impression. And the impression I got of the Schimler's house that soft, warm June evening made a big impression on me. It impressed the life I had with Jeremy and it impressed you, too, chickadees, whether you know it or not. For all we know the rug you bought last month in New York is an indirect result of something I took away from the Schimler's house. That little iron dog I have on the patio? The one that made you think of me and inspired you to get the stone Greyhound for your entry hall? Well, how do you know its antecedent is not the Schimler's ceramic spaniel? Our houses, really, are montages all. Made from the scraps of our history, half-remembered images from a magazine or movie, forgotten influences of neighbors or friends—styles and schemes cobbled together as unconsciously from our dreams as they are deliberately from our plans. Maybe I exaggerate a little. But I noticed a lot that night at the Schimler's.

I can't know what Jeremy noticed. I'm guessing he was also impressed. But I expect Jeremy was concentrating pretty hard on affecting his grown-up persona. On wondering whether these people would think him mature enough, responsible enough, to sign a legal contract and be entrusted with their property.

He's got a lot on his mind, poor Jeremy. In less than ten weeks he's gone from being a free-wheeling college freshman with no heavier responsibilities than passing the Econ finals and getting a good coat of wax on his car, to being an expectant father, a bona fide member of the working rat race, and the source of bitter heartbreak and disappointment to his parents. The football scholarship is defunct. But he's got a bank account now, with real checks, and a balance of $237.14. He's wondering if, after the first month's rent ($79.50), and the damage deposit ($25.00), the utility deposits for gas and electric ($7.00 each), there will be anything left until the next paycheck comes for maybe installing a telephone or that new Dylan album he's been wanting. Jeremy is very mature for 19 and probably has a perfect handle on it, but still I can tell he's nervous.

Me? I'm in better shape, psychologically speaking. I'm puking my guts out now every morning for the last ten days but the hormones are doing their other job, too. Delivering that evolutionary advantage of shortsightedness which protects the young and dumb and pregnant. I've got no long-distance vision at all. I can't see one step farther than the front stoop of that cute little duplex on Ellison Street—which Jeremy will carry me over, because that's the way it's done. I can see us having sweet little candle-lit dinners in our own snug little kitchen but I can't see where the groceries are going to come from or even, for that matter, a table and chairs. I can see the cherubic face of a perfect smiling infant (Jeremy's nose, my mouth, Sophie's eyes) but I can't see the pain and gore of labor and delivery or the hospital and pediatrician's bills or any infant-like activities beyond the placid smile. I can see a few things very clearly on the long smooth road of our future. The rest is obscured by a rosy pink fog.

"How do I look?" Jeremy asks me, his voice a little funny as he pushes the Schimler's doorbell. It's a cunning ivory oval set in a brass pineapple. I make a mental note on the importance of small details in creating a sense of welcome and pat the head of the ceramic spaniel.

"You're gorgeous," I tell him, leaning over to plant a quick kiss on a downy smooth cheek, lightly scented with Brut cologne. It doesn't seem right to be so eager and excited when Jeremy's so clearly scared, but I can't help myself. Our future is about to start.

And Jeremy *is* gorgeous. He's wearing his blue Oxford cloth shirt and Windsor tie. There are crisp creases in his khakis and his Penny loafers gleam with burnished polish. Ever the Preppie, that Jeremy, even if most of our peers were already converting to tie-dye and earth shoes and stonewashed jeans. I wear my own version of the uniform: Bass Weejun loafers, pleated skirt, round-collared Oxford blouse, obligatory circle pin.

We have an appointment, of course, but I believe Mrs. Schimler is still a little startled at the two green kids who stand in the open door. To her credit, after a quick scan to assure herself that we aren't merely selling cookies or band candy, she welcomes us in cordially and ushers us through the foyer, past an enormous, exquisitely furnished dining room into a wonderful high-ceilinged study with paneled oak walls and an arched gothic fireplace. Dr. Schimler, a stout, balding, smallish man in his fifties or sixties, rises from his reading chair to shake hands with Jeremy. Mrs. Schimler encourages us to sit down and asks if we would like a cup of tea. Jeremy says no, but I accept. You had to figure the Schimlers for tea-drinkers.

My immediate feeling is that Dr. Schimler is going to be a hard case. He is looking at us with a kind of bemused, glassy-eyed tenderness. It's the look you use to watch puppies frolic or baby birds pecking through the shell. It's not at all the look for a serious business transaction. I can't see Jeremy's face from where I'm sitting but I feel my own face grow warm and I use my eyes to roam the room. While Dr. Schimler begins his gentle inquisition of Jeremy, I absorb the leather-bound volumes in the bookcases, the lacquered Chinese cigarette box, the hunting tapestry over the fireplace. It's all so beautiful and so impossibly out of reach. Like Alice, I feel myself shrinking smaller and smaller.

When Mrs. Schimler returns with the tea we make our own little small talk for a bit and then suddenly, brightly, like it was the very first time it had ever occurred to any member of our gender, she says, "Well! Would you care to see the rest of the house?"

And so I get my first home tour. The first of hundreds,

perhaps thousands, to come.

I don't remember every detail. Even on the drive home I won't be able to account to Jeremy for every gorgeously furnished room or even begin to explain the orderly profusion of the real English-style gardens out back. But I remember a whole lot more than you might think. And tabula rasa that I was back then, it all got written somewhere. Mrs. Schimler, like the best tour guides do, tells amusing little stories about this piece or that. She educates me about antique and period furnishings without being the least bit preachy or authoritarian. She seems genuinely delighted if I compliment anything particular, as though I, of all people, have enough powers of discernment to confirm her good taste. I had loved her house instantly but in the half an hour or so that we wander, I also come to admire Mrs. Schimler herself and something of her grace and wisdom gets through to me.

Clearly, we *are* too young. We have no credit history whatsoever. Jeremy has been in his job only weeks and I don't have one at all yet. The rental ad had specifically said, "No children," and if the fateful question arises, Jeremy will never be able to lie. I am sad, but resigned.

I am also wrong. Whatever had transpired, whatever man-to-man assurances Jeremy had been made to give Dr. Schimler, it had worked to get us our lease. When Mrs. Schimler and I return from touring her beautiful Tudor Revival, Jeremy is writing out check 101.

On June 21, 1965, while twenty or thirty thousand of our contemporaries were otherwise occupied in holding a history-making anti-war demonstration in Berkley, California, Jeremy and I were moving into our very first home. We were a little worried about the war, too, but only a little worried. Now that he'd dropped out of college Jeremy's deferment status had changed. But a baby on the way would set it right again. And we had a lot of other things to think about.

The Ellison Street duplex was in a small residential section at the edge of an industrial complex bounded by a railroad track in a not-so-great part of town. It was certainly not an area that Grandmother approved of, but this particular little street was rather nice, actually. There were little clapboard houses, built in the '30s most of them, in pretty good repair and a few of them really charming, with tiny green lawns and flowerboxes on the porches. Our own place was newer, a replacement for a single family home that had been demolished a few years back when Dr. Schimler had foreseen the low maintenance and double rental possibilities of a shotgun style brick duplex.

You opened the front door directly upon the living room. Behind this was the kitchen, replete with sink, stove, diminutive refrigerator and exactly three cabinets. From the kitchen a narrow offset hall led past the only bath and the closet-sized spare room where I planned the nursery, and ended in "the Master" where Jeremy and I, at long last, were going to make love in real privacy, in something without wheels underneath it. Granted, at some times, and in some cultures, this might be enough space for six to eight people. But taken from another perspective, the whole place was not much bigger than the Schimler's dining room.

Against all logic, we filled it up immediately. Our move was managed by Benny Belcher and his Ford pickup. He and David had loaded at Jeremy's house early that morning and then swung by my house where Sophie and Janet had helped to load my stuff and then followed Benny in Janet's car. After the guys had brought in the folding card table and chairs that Grandmother had provided for our candle-lit dinners, the mattress and box springs that I had bought with graduation present money, and a dilapidated Naugahyde sofa and small chest of drawers that Jeremy's Mom had donated, everybody started bringing in boxes. Everybody but me, that is. Any attempt I made to lift something heavier than two pounds met with shrieks of resistance. All I could do was watch as the mounds of boxes completely filled our tiny living room.

When everything was in, Jeremy cracked the first six-pack of Budweisers and we all stood around surveying the cardboard mountain.

"What the hell *is* all this stuff, anyway?" Benny finally asked. Janet had started to investigate, too, working the tucked flaps of one of the boxes.

"Yeah," said David, pulling at another box. "What *is* all this crap?"

"It's not crap!" I said. But it was too late. The vultures were already circling.

"Whoa!" said Janet, dragging out a huge set of Jeremy's football shoulder pads. "You wearing these things to bed, Bubba?"

Sophie rolled her eyes and looked despairingly at me.

"Boys," she said. "Silly, silly boys. Maybe you can make a coffee table out of them?"

"Oh, yeah?" said Benny. "And what do you suppose a preggo is going to do with these?" In one hand Benny hoisted one of my white leather roller skates and in the other a red skating skirt, ten inches long from waistband to hem. Everybody hooted and in ten more seconds they were all over those boxes, tossing things into the air, cracking themselves

88

up with particular finds. The guys roared over my Ginny doll and the cache of stuffed animals. The girls bent double with laughter over Jeremy's Roy Rogers holster and matching cap pistols. Each treasure they uncovered seemed funnier than the last.

We'd brought a lot of crap.

There was an entire box (mine) of back editions of the school newspaper, *The Tiger Rag*, for which I had been associate editor, and another whole box (Jeremy's) of back issues of *Playboy*. I had brought two boxes of novels and textbooks and Jeremy had brought an entire carton of Little League baseball trophies. We had pep rally pom-poms and miniature megaphones, baseball pennants and baseball cards, autograph hounds and letter jackets, hula girls, fur dice, and a completely mysterious, but apparently *really* funny, hood ornament for a 1963 Lincoln Continental. Jeremy had a nice, but unacceptable, collection of pictures his mother had framed of him in white jackets with old girlfriends in dance dresses. I had a stash of my own memorabilia—ticket stubs, play programs, pressed flowers, folded notes from Study Hall, a terrific 8 x10 glossy of Troy Donahue.

When our so-called friends had finished pilfering, and mocking, the contents of all of our boxes, they collapsed, one by one, still giggling but exhausted, onto any open floor space they could find. There wasn't much of it. The living room looked like a trash dump. Jeremy and I had retreated sheepishly to slide down a wall some time back. Now we all surveyed the disaster.

"Yep," said Jeremy softly. "That's a lot of crap."

There was one more explosion of laughter and then a few more tasteless jokes while Benny retrieved the second six-pack from the fridge and a Tab for me. We all sat around on the floor, sipping our drinks, and after a while growing quiet and thoughtful.

I don't know what the rest of them were thinking. For Janet and David, still fresh from our high school commencement speeches, there was probably some renewed reflection on that "Crossing the Bridge to Adulthood" business. Benny was probably thinking that, in future, he'd damn well better remember the rubbers. Sophie, I imagine, was feeling pretty sad. She and I wouldn't live in the same house anymore. We wouldn't share the same bedroom, wrangle over clothes or closet space, or ever again be united, in exactly the same sisterly way, against the dark forces of evil and adult stupidity. I can't even speculate on Jeremy's thoughts. I guess I'd rather not.

They were good sports about the mess. Everybody pitched in to address the trash pile with almost the same energy they had expended in creating it. When we had culled through everything again, re-sorted and re-packed the boxes that would go back to our parents, and loaded them back on Benny's truck, there wasn't much left. I kept my books and a few old pictures and—by arguing that it would go in the nursery—the one plush teddy bear that Jeremy had given me for Valentine's. Jeremy got to keep his 45s and LPs, though we had nothing to play them on, and I relented on his letter jacket and one box of miscellaneous sports equipment. None of the boxes had produced extra sheets or towels, pots or pans, or even a brush for the bathroom bowl.

At twilight, when we said our last goodbyes and finally closed the door, our place was only a little less empty than it had begun. But it was full, as the song says, of really good vibrations. We had spent our first day in friendship and laughter and that, I somehow already knew, would always be harder to come by than crockery or furniture.

Jeremy puttered with stowing a few things away while I made us our first home-cooked meal. Ham and mustard sandwiches and Campbell's pork 'n' beans. After we'd cleared the card table and washed our two plates and glasses, Jeremy gave me a devilish look, one eyebrow raised and a quizzical half-smile on that drop-dead handsome face. It was still early yet, but we couldn't watch television. We didn't have a TV.

CHAPTER VII

Imagine, if you can, the reaction of our nomadic fore-parents: Finally, after nine long millennia, the company announces that it has decided to establish a permanent headquarters in the Fertile Crescent.

He's thinking: *Gee, no more road trips. I can get out of this animal pelt and tie. Lay back on the hunting and gathering. Domesticate a goat. Maybe put in a garden.*

She's thinking: *Cool! Now I can invent decorating!*

Well, maybe it didn't happen exactly like that. They say our brains back then were a few grams lighter and maybe she wasn't so quick on the uptake. I'm betting, though, that it didn't take long. I'll wager that no sooner had she positioned the perfect rock in that drab empty corner than she was out foraging for the perfect accessory. Decorating requires staying put. It demands some stability. It demands something of substance and permanence. It demands something, well, like a *house.*

With the transition from hunting and gathering to farming and herding, the advance of civilization could really get in high gear. Gone were the frustrating days of trying to hang pictures on the walls of tents. Over, the anguish of having to keep eating the centerpiece so you didn't have to pack it. *Fini* to the dreary boredom of a color palette limited strictly, and literally, to earth tones.

Now the possibilities were limitless. The way had been paved for the decorative pillow. For gimcracks, knickknacks, brick-a-brac and whatnots. For wall-to-wall carpeting, lava lamps and feng shui. For women everywhere (and a few good men) an important evolutionary corner had been turned and the future of Pottery Barn was finally secure.

That's pretty much how I imagine it. And that's pretty much the way it happened to me. Like all my life I had been waiting, tensely poised, ready to spring on the first paint chip that passed my way. All I needed, fundamentally, was my own place. But my initiation into the world of decorating was escalated by the fact that I did, pretty quickly, get a paying job. I was hired, based certainly on my charm and congeniality, but bolstered by fair typing skills and the fact that I had also taken one semester of short-hand, as a receptionist for the real estate firm of Mitchner and Hogan. My official duties were to answer the phone, welcome clients, make coffee, keep up the filing, make more coffee, and juggle the appointment books of two brokers and four agents.

It was not exactly the kind of first job I had originally planned for myself. I'd had in mind something more along the lines of cub reporter for the city newspaper or assistant curator of the city museum. But niggling details like qualifications aside, Jeremy and I needed money and we needed it now. This was my first offer and I took it, thereby setting myself off on a path that I would rarely stray from the rest of my whole life long. There's a lesson here, chickadees. Maybe two or three. But the one that's easiest to explain is this: Be careful when you pick your first job. Life has a way of making that first one really stick. The world is full of salesmen who meant to be bankers, bankers who planned to become chefs, school administrators who only wanted to teach, accountants who only meant to earn enough to start a poultry farm. And of course there's an entire underworld continent of writers and artists, poets and dancers, who daily sell us our shoes and cut our hair, clean our teeth or manage the corner Starbucks.

I'm not suggesting, mind you, that all of these paths were the wrong ones and the journeys weren't worthwhile. That taking an unplanned or expedient path will necessarily leave you unsuccessful or "unfulfilled," whatever that may mean. Only that paths tend to become ruts, ruts deepen into ditches, and one day you can easily look up to find yourself in a walled canyon with your first Social Security check in your hand.

I was not thinking of any of that, of course. Not when I had absolutely forever to get back on track, go to college, become an English professor, head librarian for the Library of Congress, or at the very least, a real journalist. There was time for all that. Right now I had this pretty good job, on the same route that Jeremy took to his work, with only a forty-five minute time differential while I waited for him to pick me up—time which I could spend, profitably, looking at pictures of houses.

Boy, there were a lot of houses to look at! For one thing we subscribed to every decorating, home and garden, and architecture magazine that was published in those years. They were stacked ten inches deep on the coffee table and end tables of our reception area. Mr. Mitchner believed, and he was probably right, that a client kept waiting long enough to peruse the pages of a few editions of *House Beautiful* would net him hundreds of dollars in extra commission. Beyond the magazines, which I adored, and which I got to take home outdated issues of, there were our own listing books, huge binders with color photos of homes of every imaginable size and style, age and condition. I learned how to interpret the truncated descriptions: that a 3/2 Brk Bung, blt Brkf br, E-Rng, Cdrcl, Atfn, for example, was really a three bedroom, two-bath brick bungalow with a built-in breakfast bar, electric range, cedar closet and attic fan. I also came to pick up on which parts of town added, or subtracted, that intangible "location" value, although $15,000 for a three-bedroom ranch, in any part of town, made me laugh out loud.

Thanks again to us boomers, it was still a booming time for real estate. Many of our parents were moving up to their second or third homes. Tardy vets could still take advantage of Uncle Sam's real deal and a few of their more precocious offspring, like Jeremy and me, were starting to need their own lodging. Existing homes were being passed around like hot potatoes and new ones couldn't be thrown up fast enough.

Our firm specialized in managing new subdivisions, many of them similar to Fairfield Estates, though the newest big developments tended more to split-levels now. I especially liked the pictures of the furnished models and could see from all of my research that it was the accessories, really, that knocked a place out.

"What are you *doing*?" Jeremy asked me, on one of those nights that I had spent too much time in the magazines, working my decorating impulse into a need for action.

"Nothing," I said. "Just arranging."

"But you've moved that ashtray three times already. And I can't see over that plant!"

We had acquired a 21-inch black and white television on time from Western Auto and Jeremy had already begun to fall into husband mode, collapsing after work and again after dinner to watch the endless stream of westerns and variety shows that were TV fare back then. I didn't really mind. I had so much myself to do and most of it he couldn't help with anyway.

In under a month I'd made pillows for the Naugahyde sofa, arranged our books artfully on cinderblock bookshelves, hung scavenged curtains over our blinds, and found a little gingham tablecloth and matching napkins to disguise our kitchen card table. We'd fessed up to the Schimlers and been given permission to paint the nursery a soft butter yellow. We'd gone back open-handed to Grandmother and the Greers, resulting in a few more kitchen essentials, the desk and chair from Jeremy's old bedroom and a lamp and pretty good rocker from Grandmother. A few more wedding presents had trickled in—glasses, a set of Melmac dinnerware, towels and a toaster. We'd bought, for cash, a Danish modern coffee table. The place was looking pretty good. All it really needed now was accessories.

"Greenery is important," I told him, pushing the plant a few inches over. "It gives life and freshness to a room."

"You're crazy," Jeremy said, pulling me down to sit on his lap. But I knew he liked my newly discovered domestic self. My cooking was coming along. About every third try I managed to make something almost edible and a couple of times we had even "entertained," having a few of our friends over for pot roast, which I was getting pretty good at, or meat loaf, which had a sharper learning curve. It had come as something of a surprise to Jeremy, I think, to learn that girls weren't issued cooking skills along with their breasts and vaginas but he was being pretty patient with me and I was getting used to checking for the toilet seat up.

The notion that Jeremy, who actually spent one and a half fewer hours per day than I did trapped in the workaday world, might actually bear some responsibility himself for cooking, or that knowing how to change a tire or check the oil might properly belong in my own skill set, really never seriously occurred to either of us. The Feminist Movement was definitely gaining momentum. The '64 Civil Rights Act had been amended to include women, of all things, and the Equal Opportunity Commission had been created to guarantee us equal wages. Hemlines were going *way* up, even in Tennessee, and out in California brassieres were coming off. The Virginia Slims commercials were telling us that "we'd come a long way, baby," but in truth most of us were in pretty much the same place that our parents were. Girls cooked and cleaned, worked briefly for significantly lower wages, and then settled down to bearing and rearing children, running the house, and keeping domestic detritus from cluttering *his* career path.

Some of my friends, especially the college-bound ones, were talking a lot of politics these days. Janet's sister Myra, particularly, seemed mad about pretty much everything and her influence was starting to show up in a lot of Janet's ideas. Janet was going to follow her sister Myra to the University of Tennessee in Knoxville in September and then she wanted to go to law school.

I had received the news of Sean's full scholarship to Harvard with unalloyed pride and happiness but I was oddly uncomfortable when I listened to Janet's plans—none of which apparently included a husband or a family. Sometimes I tried to examine my own hypocrisy, but I never got very far. If ignorance is bliss, then the corollary must be true. I was just too happy to deal with it. On the radio the Rolling Stones hit "I can't get no satisfaction" was clearly resonating with some of us, but it didn't connect with me. I had never been more satisfied. I thought everything about our lives was absolutely wonderful.

At the end of that June I was barely straining my waistbands, undecided as yet on whether I wanted to stay newly-wed thin and sexy as long as possible or to jump quickly into maternity skirts and over-blouses, confidently broadcasting to the world at large that I was a woman now, a wife, and pretty soon, a mother. Wardrobe decisions aside, the prospect of becoming parents was never very far from our talk.

In bed at night Jeremy and I played a hilarious version of Name the Baby, laughing sometimes until we nearly choked at the ideas we came up with.

"Ezra Nehemiah Esther Job Greer," I'd offer, if Jeremy had suggested our baby's name might be something Biblical.

"Melville Wadsworth," he'd counter, if I thought it should be literary. "We can call him *Waddy* for short."

We reviewed the names of our favorite movie or rock stars and put them together in weird combinations. (Herman Hermit Greer, Martha Vandella Greer). We tried place names, astrological signs, and abstract values like Liberty, Equality and Fraternity. We tested names from nature—eliminating Earth, Wind, and Fire a full decade before *they* ever thought of it— and nixed virtues like Prudence, Patience and Chastity when one of them, at least, was still just a gleam in Sonny Bono's eye. For a couple of nights we seriously considered the names of musical instruments or musical references but abandoned that line of thinking when we tried to imagine a teacher calling out "Banjo!" or "Timpani!" or "Crescendo Lynn!" When everything was said and done we had pretty much narrowed it down to *Natalie* for a girl (Jeremy was crazy for Natalie Wood) and *Wesley* for a boy. We would get to the middle names later. I still had months to go.

That night, on the streets of Dodge City, Sheriff Matt Dillon magnanimously chose to only wound the bad guy in the shoulder. You could tell the villain was reformed and would shortly mend his evil ways. The episode of *Gunsmoke* ended and the nightly news came on. The big networks had just gone to a 30-minute news format and Jeremy never missed either NBC's or CBS's take on the day. The newscaster was talking about how Australia had entered the war in Vietnam. That 800 or something of their soldiers had joined up with thousands of our troops to lead a jungle assault northeast of Saigon. There was war news almost every night lately and in other ways, too, the war was getting uncomfortably close to home. Tad Litton, who had been in Jeremy's class, had come home with a hand missing and Jeremy and Benny had gone to visit him in the Memphis VA. Neither of them would talk about it much but I got the idea that Tad, who'd been an all-state basketball guard, was having a pretty hard time.

There were hints, too, that President Johnson was going to increase the draft. Some said he might even double it. The lottery system had not been invoked yet, although there were rumblings, but the dynamics of how the Selective Service System was actually operating were pretty confusing then. Kids still enrolled in school were getting changed from II-S to I-A for no apparent reason. Others, prime for the taking, lingered at I-A for so long that their nerves, or their parents, sent them to enlist in something other than the army and in the hope of a shorter stint.

The newscaster droned on, intoning about how the operation had been called off after three days when it failed to make major contact with the enemy. Then, without explaining how the hell that could be, he noted that one American had been killed and nine others wounded. I remember being just about to ask Jeremy, sarcastically, how many dead soldiers it took to qualify for "major contact" when Jeremy himself brought the war home to me.

"Lacey, I've been thinking about enlisting," he said.

I popped up off that Naughahyde sofa like a tight-springed jack-in-the-box.

"What!" I said. "Are you crazy?" I had an immediate vision of Jeremy holding our baby in his arms but with one of his hands missing.

"No," he laughed, trying to pull me back down. "Not in the army! In the reserves. It's the best way to stay out. I can join the Guard or the Army reserve. There are bases just over the bridge in Arkansas. I don't know about the Navy. But there's a base in Millington, even closer. I'll have to do some weekend drills, but it won't be bad. It even brings in a little money."

I didn't really believe him. Something told me that this plan of his had something to do with his stewing over Tadd Litton, or with the macho talk I'd overhear sometimes between him and Benny about 'choppers and M16s and killing "gooks." And he'd left out the part about Boot Camp. I wouldn't get that piece of the picture for several weeks.

Jeremy managed to calm me down that night, convincing me, almost, by bedtime that joining a reserve unit was the pro-active approach. I could have Sophie or Janet stay with me on his duty weekends. It wouldn't be nearly as bad as the separations we had endured while he had still been in college. It would hardly disrupt our lives at all. And absence, he joked, makes the hard grow harder.

It may have been a pretty good plan but we weren't the

only ones it had occurred to. There was a waiting list for all reserve units. Jeremy got himself signed up for both the National Guard and the Army Reserves but eighteen days before my regularly scheduled obstetrical appointment Jeremy received notice to appear for a pre-induction physical. He was being drafted. It was up to me to stop it.

The first thing I did was to call Dr. Grave's office and to relay the situation in near-hysterical terms to his receptionist, Alice Crocker. She was sympathetic but couldn't be made to understand my urgency. She insisted that I still needed to see the doctor but that everything would be fine. She did concede to move my appointment up a couple of days.

Jeremy reported for his physical and, needless to say, passed with flying colors. He could have taken with him the x-rays of the ankle he'd broken playing football sophomore year. But he didn't. He could have told them that he was a Quaker or a Buddhist. But he wouldn't. The idea of hinting to the doctors that he had homosexual leanings—while it probably would have worked at that early stage of the war—was totally out of the question.

When I finally got to talk to Dr. Graves he told me that Alice would write us a letter saying that we were expecting a baby, that Jeremy would have to take it to his draft board where he would fill out an Economic Hardship form and then apply for re-classification to III-A. Economic hardship was exactly what would happen to us without Jeremy's salary, but I wasn't thinking much about the money. Dr. Graves wasn't positive that simply being a father-to-be instead of a bona fide father would do the trick immediately but the medical letter would already be on file and we had less than five more months to go.

True to her word, Alice did write a letter on our behalf. But before it arrived Jeremy got another one, a "Greeting," from the President of the United States. He had forty-eight hours to report to Local Draft Board 86 for induction into the United States Armed Forces.

CHAPTER VIII

For the next few months it would be hard to even imagine what Jeremy's world might be like. I received only one postcard from him the entire time he was in basic training—it had obviously been written at least two weeks before it was mailed—and only two or three letters while he went through AIT. He sounded fine. Upbeat, full of funny anecdotes about his new Army buddies. He closed his letters by saying how much he loved and missed me but the descriptions of his emotional state sounded weak and anemic compared to my own. I had slowly progressed, by painful stages, from abject misery, to deep depression, to simple self-pitying sadness. It was the first time in my life that I had ever really been alone, that there was no one to kiss or say good night to when I crawled into bed. I had been sleeping with the plush bear that Jeremy had given me for Valentine's and its face was getting just awful from my bedtime tears and snot.

But some good things had happened, too. I had finally learned to drive Jeremy's stick shift and didn't have to arrive at work over-early or stay so late anymore. I was getting a little behind on the house listings now and on the decorating magazines, too, because I only spent real time now in the outdated issues that Mr. Mitchner let me take home. But when you're eighteen, broke, and live in a shotgun style duplex, last month's issue of *House Beautiful* will still serve you pretty well.

I had made a few more improvements to our place. I had found a real bookcase at Salvation Army and lugged it home in the car by myself. (The decorating magazines were starting to demand their own real estate.) I'd moved the cinder-block arrangement with my schoolbooks and novels to the bedroom (I'd had a little help with that) because I had the idea that pretty soon I'd start studying again, brushing up on my Spanish or prepping for the ACT. I'd rearranged the living room a couple of times, and I'd framed a little picture grouping of pen and ink drawings over the TV. One of the pictures was of an old house, an English Tudor cottage. A cozy smoke was coming out of its clay chimney and a light snow spotted the hay fields in the background. It reminded me terribly of the Schimler's house and made me, like the big photo I kept of Jeremy on my bedroom nightstand, sometimes happy, sometimes sad.

At work I had received a sort of promotion—if by promotion you mean that I was now allowed to type pre-closing documents on my IBM Selectric, five copies each, with carbon paper and only a gritty pink eraser and its little green whisk to clear the endless rubbery crumbs. There were days that I started over a half-dozen times, filling the wastebasket with legal paper before I could produce a set that was error-free enough to actually use. Chickadees, the next time you pass a laser printer, give it a big fat kiss.

Another really good thing had happened in the friendship I had recently developed with our first neighbors, the Tillotsons, who as it turned out, shared the other side of our little brick duplex. Jeremy had not been disappeared more than a week when I encountered *her* first—Merrilee Tillotson—near the street at our twin mailboxes on Ellison.

"Well, hello, hello!" she said as soon as she saw there was

another, any other, human life form within earshot.

"Hello yourself," I said colloquially, trying immediately to affect the easy spontaneous style that was ever Merrilee.

"Ya'll live next door!" she said, "Grady and I seen you moving in! We woulda' helped, you know, but we could see you had a houseful. Grady said you wuz college, but I said I didn't think so. It's a long drive to Memphis State from here, and I seen you both leaving the same time in the mornings. He's a cutie, that hubby of yours, if you don't mind me saying so, but Grady's got eyes too and we been crazy to meet you. Y'all ain't college, are you?"

"Oh no, we're not college," I said, as though I wanted to disassociate myself from that darkest of dark cults. "We just got married in June. This is our first place."

Merrilee, as I think about it now, was aptly, perfectly, named. She was one of that rare and lucky inveterately optimistic breed who simply finds it easier to be happy than not, to find the good in others more self-evident than the bad, to naturally see the glass half full rather than half empty—or worse, and like I'm prone to perceive it, missing entirely from the shelf. I could go on and on about Merilee, but I think you get the idea. She was my polar opposite, my antithesis, my radical contrary. She was a delight and a wonder and, in that dry and lonely time, exactly what I needed.

The best thing about Merrilee, or at least the second best thing, was the fact that she was also pregnant—a month farther along than I was but light years more knowledgeable about our shared biological state. Some of her notions were pretty strange and she could be comically superstitious at times. But she had good, practical information, too. She knew things about what to eat to make the baby smart, how we were going to avoid heartburn and swollen feet. And she had dangled my wedding band on a string over my tummy, establishing by its pendulum-like swing that I was carrying a boy.

Merrilee had been a cosmetology major at Memphis Vocational Tech when her "situation" had intervened and precluded her graduation. More importantly in Merrilee's case, it had precluded the certification she needed as entrance to gainful employment. She was now trying to compensate for her setback by taking classes at a commercial beauty school downtown and was only a few months away from graduation and her license.

Merrilee's husband, Grady, was a solid IV-F by virtue of a birth defect that had left him with one leg shorter than the other. Except when he tried to run, or really hurried, it was a thing you'd never notice and he was a brilliant mechanic who could fix not just cars but leaking faucets, shorted-out lamps and jammed doorbells. I don't know what I would have done without them. They had me over for dinner several nights a week. Merrilee could really cook and I was learning a lot from her. I wrote Jeremy long letters about them and couldn't wait for the fun we'd have together when he got back.

I had also grown closer to Mr. and Mrs. Greer in the last weeks. They wanted me to call them Mom and Dad. I was having a little trouble with it but figured eventually it would seem natural. Grandmother had resumed her pattern of calling to check up on me every day although now she called in the evenings. She was a little worried about Sophie who had dropped herself out of an after-school tutoring program and I had concerns, too, but there was only so much I could do. I picked Sophie up to stay with me on Friday or Saturday nights as often as she would let me, but she was starting to have her own weekend activities now and I couldn't always pin her down on exactly what they involved. I knew that Nana and Maureen and Daddy weren't paying any attention. She could actually have been into almost anything. Frankly I hadn't set the best example.

But certainly the best thing—the very best thing—that happened in those first forsaken weeks occurred one scorching night in the middle of August—a Saturday, when Sophie had condescended to stay with me and we sat together on the couch in only our underwear and old tee shirts of Jeremy's, eating TV dinners and watching in silent dismay as the Los Angeles neighborhood of Watts went up in flames.

Snipers fired from rooftops as the firemen battled the blazes. Sirens wailed in the background as the camera showed surreal scenes of burned out stores and overturned cars and armed soldiers striding down empty smoke-filled streets. From out of nowhere, without digestive or emotional encouragement, I suddenly experienced a painless but undeniably strong butterfly flutter in my abdominal region. Immediately I knew it to be what it was—the Biblical "quickening"—that first most private of signals from unborn child to unknown mother.

It was not the best moment, perhaps, to be receiving that special message. Merrilee, were I ever to share with her exactly what Sophie and I had been watching at that moment, would doubtless have frowned, scrunching her nose up as though she had just gotten a whiff of something bad on the wind. For all I know she might have made me wear garlic around my neck or put a copper penny in my shoe. She was certain that the squiggly raspberry birthmark on the back of her shoulder had been caused by her own mother killing a snake.

"Sophie," I whispered. "I felt the baby move!"

"You did?" she said excitedly, putting down her aluminum dinner tray and placing her hand on the little pooch of my tummy.

Our baby would not perform for Sophie. It wouldn't go public with its acrobatics for many weeks to come. But that once, that first night, was plenty enough for me. The abstract had become very, very real.

At the beginning of September, for nine glorious days between his basic training and deployment, Uncle Sam let me have my husband back. Jeremy came home lean and sun-tanned, still himself of course, but subtly different, too, in ways I couldn't quite get a handle on. For the first couple of days we were a little awkward with each other, strangely shy and formal. By the third day though we were well over that, back to our silly teasing ways, making love like we had in our very beginning, only with a lot more space and privacy.

Jeremy loved Merrilee and Grady, just like I had known he would. The guys spent *way* too much time, we thought, tinkering under the hoods of the cars, spoiling their clothes and their fingernails with black grease and oil. Jeremy was significantly impressed with my cooking progress, at least until the first night we ate at Merilee's. I would experience a few other twinges of jealousy, too. Merrilee was six and a half months pregnant but she looked like a supermodel who had merely swallowed a small basketball. I was scarcely "showing" as they say, but my personal approach to gestation had been to distribute a nice little fleshy padding all over the rest of my body. My upper arms were getting downright meaty and Jeremy thought it was funny to call me "chipmunk cheeks." We got through that stuff, too, after a brief but intense hormonal crying jag on my part, and a surprise and completely unaffordable bouquet of roses on his.

Those nine days went by in a flash. Jeremy spent some time catching up with his parents, visiting his old school friends, and stopping by his office to remind his co-workers, he said, that while they were lolling around in shirts and ties, pushing pencils and lifting heavy telephone receivers, he would soon be in the bloody trenches, fighting for Truth, Justice and the American Way. We dropped in on the Schimlers, who treated us like long-lost relatives. I had tea, again, with Mrs. Schimler, but the men had a whiskey, neat. It had really only been a few months since we had first rung their bell, two children quaking in our respective loafers over the momentous boon we were asking of them. Now it seemed we were almost equals, four grown-ups with shared concerns and a whole lifetime in common.

While I didn't really have it coming to me, Mr. Mitchner gave me two days vacation at the end of that week. Merrilee skipped school and Grady called in sick and the four of us took off for a day of picnicking. We drove to the reservoir at Sardis Dam, spending our day swimming, lying for a time in the sand on the little man-made beaches, staring over the rail at the dam's frightening and beautiful spillway. We ate our lunch in a leafy-green park area, falling asleep for a bit on our blankets under the freckled tent of trees and sky.

If it's really true, as they say, that in your final moments your whole life can pass before your eyes, I believe my review will pause there. That it will linger there for much longer than its actual value in physics or history should rightfully appropriate. In that last panoramic sweep of my lifetime I know that day will stand out as one of the happiest I have ever spent.

On the last night before I had to return my husband to the United States Army—who apparently needed him much more than I did—we threw a big barbecue cook-out in the tiny back lot behind the duplex. Grady manned the charcoal grill. Merrilee provided deviled eggs and the world's best potato salad. Jeremy hosted, spreading himself democratically among the guests, seeing that no hand remained beer-empty very long. Everybody was there almost. Sophie and Maddie and Janet and Myra, David, Connor and Sean, Benny Belcher and maybe a half-dozen more. Everyone was having a great time, until suddenly they weren't. Toward the end of the evening the talk turned dark. The frustrations of our generation, and what we believed to be our collective powerlessness, began to bubble up. There were references to many issues—civil rights, the draft and voting age, the women's movement, the "bomb" and missile testing—the assortment of causes that would unite, and divide, us for at least another decade. Before long Myra Winston, by then a little too much in her cups and always a little strident in expressing her liberal views, got into serious arguments with David first, and then with Benny. Janet chimed in and suddenly everyone was on their feet, all except Sophie and Maddie, shouting all at once.

"A crime is a crime!" Myra was yelling.

"You don't know what you're talking about," said David. "They're animals! Have you forgotten what they did to the Maddox? They take out whole villages! Hanoi won't stop until they get to Saigon!"

"It . . . *just* . . . seems . . . to . . . me," said Janet, nearly spitting as she enunciated each specific syllable, "that if we're really so *fucking* concerned with promoting freedom for the North Vietnamese, we'd stop *fucking* bombing them!"

Benny was in her face. I knew, or thought I knew, that Benny would never hit a girl. But I had never seen us behave

112

this way before, never known that so much anger was smoldering in people I knew so well. Our farewell party had turned ugly. It was dangerously close to leaving a memorable black stain on the end of an otherwise perfect week.

It was Jeremy himself who saved it. Who suddenly came out of the slamming screen door of our little shotgun-style duplex, wearing, on his head, the pink, broad-brimmed straw hat I had worn last Easter and to our Baccalaureate Services, on his shoulders his high school football pads, on his chest a red brassiere, over his Levis my powder blue maternity skirt, conspicuously revealing its stretch-panel construction and its dangling price-tag, and combat boots on his feet.

The effect was generalized, hysterical convulsion. All ill-feeling, indeed, all capacity for cogent thought, simply evaporated. Jeremy paraded around the little yard in his ridiculous regalia, allowing the guys, and the girls, too, to say outrageous things about his gender persuasion and what the Army may have done to it, about his fashion taste, his new "pussy-whipped" lifestyle, his chances of seducing, rather than killing, the VC.

I laughed, too. It was very funny. But it was also very confusing. It had never been like Jeremy to play the clown. It was completely uncharacteristic of him to resolve a social dispute at the expense of his own ego. But somehow he had seen what was needed. For the first time I realized the changes that had taken place in him. For the first time I saw his emotional intelligence, his nascent leadership skills, the natural capacity for intuitively knowing what kind of oil to throw on what kind of water. In that seemingly trivial half hour I completely revised the naïve profile I'd had of the man I had married. I saw that big things, bigger than anything I had previously imagined, could be his natural inheritance.

113

On Sunday night when I drove Jeremy, impeccably clad in the starched uniform of an Army PFC, to the Greyhound bus station for his transport to Ft. Benning, Georgia, I was nowhere near the emotional mess I had expected to be. I was sad, certainly, but I was not being left so nearly alone as he had left me last time. I had Merrilee and Grady now. Right next door. And now I also had the undeniable companionship of the growing child within me.

On our drive downtown Jeremy had explained to me, patiently, with the tone that adults take with children, how it was not necessarily a foregone conclusion that he would be going to Nam. There were other jobs for the Army to do, all over the world. And even the worst case didn't necessarily mean combat. Even his short work experience, he said, and his MOS training, meant a chance of being assigned to something not even remotely dangerous. I didn't believe him. He didn't expect me to.

We weren't the only ones that night at the bus station, to cling and kiss and whisper, to hold on until the absolute last moment before the buses had started their engines and the loudspeakers had warned "Now boarding . . . " for the third or fourth time.

"Be safe," I told him, "I love you."

"You bet" he said. "Take care of my boy."

And then he boarded the bus and I stood and waved, with nearly two dozen sniffling others, until the bus had turned the corner and there was nothing left to see. On the way home on the radio I heard Joan Baez sing "There But for Fortune." I wondered if Jeremy had ever listened to the lyrics.

I was going to be fine, I knew. I had promised Jeremy and now I promised myself. It was time, as you chickadees would say, to put on my big girl panties and deal with it.

114

I tried. I really did. For the most part I was pretty successful. But sometimes my moods, as another song says, "swung like a pendulum do." Some days, after someone at work had flattered me, or I had run into an old classmate who was having trouble getting the right traction for the next post-high school endeavor, I would feel positively euphoric, inflated with what seemed like the progress Jeremy and I had made. I had a good job. I had been given TWO raises by now. We had found AND FURNISHED our own first place. We were STARTING A FAMILY, and Jeremy would soon have his MILITARY OBLIGATIONS out of the way.

At other times I felt completely stalled. There would be a boring or tedious day at work and I'd come home to the empty duplex without any remotely interesting plans for the evening, the weekend, the rest of the month. For the first time in conscious memory the first of September meant nothing but . . . the first of September.

Lots of my friends were leaving town for college, others were staying here, but their talk now was of clothes and courses, "rush week" and campus activities. With the start of school most of my friends, even Sophie, had other interests. I was just idling. Waiting for them to have time for me. Waiting on the baby. Waiting on Jeremy to come home. Waiting, it seemed, on everything.

"Why, you just need a hobby!" Merrilee would tell me, showing me the plant hanger or the macramé owl she had just finished or the little quilted potholders and matching toaster cover she had made for the kitchen.

But I wouldn't listen. Someday, as you chickadees know all too well, I would come to share her appreciation for the "womanly arts." Someday I would knit and crochet, decoupage and weave rugs, quilt and sew and craft. But not

115

now. I wasn't ready. I managed to make curtains for the nursery, with Merilee's help, but then I put my petulant little foot down. I stopped wanting to even hear about any of her stupid little projects.

Eventually I saved myself, and perhaps our friendship, by starting again to read. Someday, in only a year or two maybe, I'd be able to go to night school. So, I wouldn't ever get to be the sweetheart of Sigma Chi. That was OK. Most of that stuff now seemed pretty juvenile anyway. But I really did intend to "further" my education some day and I decided to ensure that when the time came my brain would still be functional. Janet got me copies of UT's course catalog, the schedule of classes, and a few real syllabuses and I used them to plot out a serious course of study. It was a fairly scattered and unconventional one to be sure. Something like a major in English and Journalism and Psychology and Art History with a minor in Spanish and Home Economics (the decorating part) and electives in Astronomy, Philosophy and Elementary School Music. There was no math at all in my curriculum but I saw no reason not to throw in a graduate course in Modern American Architecture. I didn't know what I wanted to *be*, but I knew what I wanted to *read,* and though I couldn't afford the actual textbooks I found close approximations, stopping once or twice a week at the public library on the way home from work.

Merrilee felt about college pretty much the same way that Grandmother did but she was glad that I was over my snit. For a lot of evenings those first weeks of that still *very hot* September, Merrilee and I sat companionably side by side, sweltering together, while she knitted wool baby booties and I sweated through Dante's *Inferno*.

Merrilee was seven and half months down the road already

116

and was beginning to be plagued by insomnia, but I was reading myself to sleep every night now, waking fully rested in a bed so strewn with books that even the teddy bear had sought other quarters. One night, late in September, after I had fallen asleep reading some Greek mythology, I woke from a dark and oddly disturbing dream. I had been wading in the moonlight in a shallow black river. I wore a long white dress and behind me I trailed the silvery string from a ball of yarn that I was unraveling as I went. I sat up in bed and felt immediately a deep clinching ache in my back. I reached for the bedside light and flipped back the covers, sending books sliding off to the floor. I saw that I was sitting in a pool of bright red blood. It had soaked my nightgown and penetrated deep into the bedding.

I'm not sure why I chose not to use the telephone. Perhaps in the dark kitchen I would have misdialed Merrilee and Grady's number anyway. Instead I walked down the straight hall through the duplex, went out the front door, and felt my way to their doorbell. I leaned into the doorbell long enough to hear voices and to see a dim light flick on, and then, on my neighbors' threshold, I fainted dead away.

CHAPTER IX

For four and a half days they sat with me, a compassionate relay team composed of the people I loved, the people who loved me, in that sad and mournful time. For a while I thought that the passing of the baton was serendipitous, merely accidental. Pretty quickly I figured otherwise. Are there really any accidents? Merrilee, in the chair at the foot of my bed, would gather her knitting and stand up, say that she guessed she'd be going on now because Grady would be wanting his supper soon or that she needed to study for her last style exam tomorrow. And then, right on cue, Benny Belcher would coincidentally push through the swinging door of Room 456, with a potted plant or a bright balloon, and his, "Hey, are you decent? How the hell ya' doin'?"

I never knew who was the organizing force behind their effort to keep me from being alone, to keep me, I suppose, from grieving.

Everybody came to visit me. Grandmother had been there from the first foggy moment that I had opened my eyes in the maternity ward of Memphis Methodist Hospital. I remember her face coming in and out of focus and thought I recalled a strange surreal experience wherein a man of God, but a total stranger, had "laid hands" on me, touching the hard starched sheets over the soft and vacuous place where my baby had been, but was no more. Maybe it never happened. I didn't

119

want to ask.

Grandmother had been there, too, when Dr. Graves explained to me that my baby, my Natalie—Merrilee had been wrong—had not actually been "born." That because she had been so small, because she had never breathed, it was too late to see or to hold her. That she had been "taken care of." They'd had to sedate me again then, locking me for nearly another day in a black hallucinatory storm where I fought with no strength at all against howling white-coated fiends who were trying to steal my baby.

Janet and Myra drove back, on a football weekend, from Knoxville, still apologetic over their behavior, now nearly six weeks ago, at Jeremy's going away party. It was my job to comfort them, to minimize the significance of that now distant and insignificant little social breach. We focused on Jeremy and managed to laugh about the outrageous way he had ended the evening. Myra said she was through with drinking. Grass didn't make her hostile.

Maureen took her own turn, courageously alone. She was the only one really who broke down. She told me that she had wanted children once. That she had been told as a young girl that there wouldn't be any. She said also that she believed it was what had made her most attractive to our father—the fact that there wouldn't be more children. I'm not sure Maureen realized what she was telling me. I resolved not to share her confidences with Sophie and hoped Maureen never would either. But she had more to confide. She told me that there was trouble with the business. That Daddy was taking out too much money. She didn't know where the money was going but the creditors were getting impatient. I had no idea why Maureen had chosen this time to decide she wanted to share private, grown-up realities with me. She seemed to be expecting advice. I had none to give her.

Daddy came twice. The first time he came late, after regular visiting hours, but the hospital staff was obviously cutting me lots of slack. He talked, that first visit, of being impressed with the fact that I was studying again. He told me an interesting story. Apparently, toward the end of the Depression, when he had been not much more than a boy and there weren't even jobs for men with experience, he had been ashamed to tell Grandmother that his job searches were coming to naught. For weeks, he said, before the war had heated up enough so that a skinny kid with flat feet, color blindness, and a history of headaches, would be deemed fit enough for service, he had left home every morning, with the bus fare Grandmother provided and a tote lunch in his jacket, to go directly downtown to the main Cossitt branch of the Memphis Public Library, to spend his day lost in the world of books. He had come home then, every day, fabricating stories to Grandmother of the applications he had put in and the important contacts he had made, of great impressions and well-received interviews. His deceit, he let me know, was something that was clearly justified. Through it he had discovered that he was a born salesman. It had helped to make him who he was.

When he left me that night I spent a long time trying to make the right meaning out of what he had told me. I could see that I would fail, as I always had, to understand how my father's experiences, which had made him "who he was," could provide a usable example for me or for Sophie. He believed that he had lived a life worth emulating. I already thought that Jeremy was twice the man he would ever be.

When he came the second time he brought Sophie with him. It was really only Sophie I wanted to see but with Daddy there we couldn't really talk. Sophie held my hand while Daddy regaled us with the plans he had for expanding the business, for maybe going national sometime soon.

They came and went, a whole parade of people intent on distracting me, on getting my mind off the reason I was there. I received more than a dozen "Get Well Soon" cards, as though I had just been sick and now, with my baby dead, I would soon be all better.

I had many offers to take me home. Grandmother, who'd never owned a car, even offered to fetch me in a taxicab and take me back to her place for a few days more rest. It was the Greer's offer, though, I accepted. Neither of them had jobs or school or other obligations to make coming to pick me up a hardship. And I had something on my mind I needed to discuss with them.

On Monday, after the interminable waiting for this form, that prescription, one more doctor's signature—that sacred rite of passage, or discharge, secretly written into hospital procedure—the Greers were finally able to collect me, after two trips to the car to load flowers and gifts, for the journey back home. I insisted on going back to the duplex rather than to their house or any place else. It would be hard, I knew, to walk past the yellow nursery. It would be hard in the days ahead to pack away the baby things I had accumulated, and hardest of all to put away the plans and the hopes I'd had for all of us. But delaying wasn't going to make it easier.

They settled me in the back seat, both of them tenderly solicitous of my comfort. I remember—I will never forget—that I was wearing a long, pink, quilted satin robe and pretty matching slippers that someone had obviously made me a present of in the hospital. They were not the kinds of things I would probably ever have bought for myself. A little too prudish, even for me. But the robe and slippers were very pretty. And probably pretty expensive.

For the first part of the trip we just chatted. I clearly remember—it's odd, isn't it, what you remember, stranger still what you choose to forget—that Mr. Greer, who was never a talker, was very intent on talking about how the heat, lingering as it had well into September, was affecting his backyard garden.

"Why the summer harvest," he said, "used to be pretty much over by now. You'd get some more pole beans, and some wormy tomatoes, but that's about it. You used to be looking for winter squash coming up, that kind of thing, by now."

Mrs. Greer, *Mother* Greer—I had resolved to try to practice it—cast me an irritated little glance over her shoulder, but for a change she let him go on.

"But I got tomatoes and cucumbers, two kinds, and spring onions, too, still coming up like it was June. We'll have to bring you some," he said. "I know you ain't got room for canning in your little place, but we might as well eat what we can. They's a whole lot better that what's in the stores."

"I'd love to have some of your vegetables," I told him. "I'd like to have a garden myself some day. I don't know anything about growing things, though. You'll have to teach me."

He seemed pleased with that. So did she, actually. I think there was something healing in the idea that this tragedy didn't mean that we wouldn't go on. That Jeremy and I might not actually benefit, someday, from their vast and practical wisdom.

I took this as my opportunity point, the place to ask them what they'd heard from Jeremy lately.

"Why, nothing," Mrs. Greer said. "We haven't heard

anything since the day the troop ship docked. There was a big hoopla, you know. I know you got *that* word. When the boys all got there and there was the band and the Vietnamese girls and all!"

She seemed suddenly embarrassed, but I had received a letter from those first few days, too. I wasn't worried about the Southeast Asian welcoming committee. I was worried because Jeremy had said they would be "in country" in a couple of weeks and I hadn't heard anything since then.

"I need to ask a favor," I said. They both nodded their heads. "I need you to let me tell Jeremy. About the baby."

"Of course!" Mrs. Greer hurried to assure me. "You do whatever you think best. We wouldn't . . ." Her voice broke a little then but I still wasn't sure she understood.

"I don't want to worry him," I said, but that still wasn't my point. "In case you hear from him first. In case he should call or something. I just want to make sure that we tell him when it's an OK time. When he won't be thinking about me, or the baby, instead of what he needs to be doing."

I hadn't said *to stay alive*, but I could tell by the look they exchanged that now they understood.

"I'll write him," I said. "I'll tell him."

And truthfully I had already started writing, and already torn up, that letter in my head many times in the past three days.

"Sure you will," said Mr. Greer. "You do it the way you think."

We had an understanding. These people, still strangers really to me, and I certainly to them, had conceded to me, easily and respectfully, a superior knowledge of what was best for their son. It was a conversation I would long remember.

124

We turned onto Ellison Street, all of us I know already anticipating the sad clumsiness of restoring me, now so diminished, to the place I'd been before. We needn't have worried about that. As we approached the house we saw the long, drab-green station wagon bearing the logo and the white block lettering of The United States Army. Just at the front the door of our little duplex stood Merrilee, Grady, and two uniformed strangers. Even before we had parked, before the engine had been stopped and any of us had made a move to open the door and approach the truth, the meaning of that little quartet on our doorstep had became all too clear and Mother Greer had already begun a high-pitched keening wail.

CHAPTER X

And so it was all over. My first love, first marriage, first child, first home—more "firsts" that some people manage in a decade—had all been reduced to a footnote, at best a short essay assignment: "What I did after Graduation."

I could have become cynical.

I did. Very.

I could have railed at my country's government and the stupid paternalistic system devised by privileged old white men to make wars at the expense of the young ones they sent to die in them.

I did. Often.

I could have raised my fist to God, who I had been brought up to believe was loving and compassionate and who, in His tender devotion and all-seeing wisdom would go with us even through the shadows of the Valley of Death.

I did that too.

But it didn't happen all at once. First I had to grieve my child. The little girl, Natalie. *Natalie,* named by her Daddy but never, as they said, officially *born,* and thus never officially real or alive. I needed to remember. I needed to recall that first quickening, and after that the thumps and bumps and tumbles of her definite life within me. I needed to defy what they had told me and to work hard and painfully against the scientific explanations and religious platitudes they had handed me to

127

deny what I knew to be true. I needed to dwell on that night on the bed when I had been reading Emerson against my belly, and she, my Natalie, real and alive, had thunked the book shut as if to say, "No more of that! Read me something fun!"

Then I had to grieve my husband. The war hero. Killed, as we would learn, not from *artillery shelling*. Or *mortar, guns, small arms fire*. Not from *air loss* or even *explosive devices, other*. These were the descriptions my friends, my friends' wives, my friends' parents, could take some comfort from in the years to come.

Jeremy had not even died—I would have been grateful for it—from the sad collateral damage of friendly fire from our own American troops. Jeremy had died, one might say, poetically, "in a rainy season." Of simple suffocation. When the earth walls of his bunker had collapsed on him, burying him under a mucky ton of wet Asian mud. They had found a paper with his body. A mostly undecipherable, half-finished letter beginning "Dear Lacey."

I try, these many years later, not to think about the fact that, had Jeremy not been writing that long over-due letter, had he not stayed in the bunker that night when his buddies had decided that braving the bone-soaking rain was slightly less torturous than simply staying put and only partially drowning in the rotting bunker . . . I try. But it doesn't always work.

We laid him down, in his own native soil, two weeks after he had been really and truly gone, in his family's plot in Memphis Memorial Gardens. There was his grandmother's marker, two empty spaces for his parents, and then the spot where Jeremy would rest. The military provided a full honor guard, a bugler, the three-volley gun salute. It was a nice rounding, if you notice those things, and apparently I do. Many of the sounds of Jeremy's service were reminiscent of the Kennedy funeral—that very sad occasion which had brought us together, ironically providing the happy accident of our lives together.

At the end of the service they handed to me, not to Mother Greer, the triangularly folded flag that symbolized Jeremy's sacrifice. I was ashamed and embarrassed. As though the fitful little burst that had been Jeremy and me could weigh more than a lifetime of mothering. On the return to the black cars I surrendered it over to her. I'd had only squatter's rights. Jeremy had always been her boy.

My next order of grief was the duplex. (You can moan your disappointment here.) What is the loss of a *place,* after all, to the loss of husband and child? Nothing, I'd say. Nothing. Except that you can never separate the loss of a place from the things that went on there. From the life, the memories, the hope or frustrations once contained by the place where they happened. We are physical, earthbound creatures, surely. But even some birds, the most heaven-held of all things, come, some of them, back to the old places. The songbirds, maybe, would scoff at me. My robins come now every year to the same tree, but never to the same dirty nests. Robins, I expect, get on fairly well without estate lawyers or succession planning schemes. Maybe they don't even hold family reunions. But they aren't the only kind. Other common types, and especially the large majestic ones—eagles, hawks, ospreys—*they* get me. These return year after year, season after season, to the place they know as home. These, I suspect, even when they're well over the "nesting" phase, deep into avian menopause, still cast wistful looks back at the old nesting grounds, the place where it all happened. I know I do.

At all of the places I've nested.

The Schimlers were extraordinarily kind to me in my leaving of that first nest. They offered to give me the remaining months of our lease rent free and encouraged me to take all the time I needed in planning my next step. I didn't really have a next step, and I probably should have slowed it down a bit more, but the duplex, as much as I had loved it, felt now like a skin I would have to shed. There was Merrilee, too, next door, and while in another six or eight weeks I would be infinitely stronger, or angrier, (it didn't matter to me the order in which this might occur) and would probably be more open by then to sharing in the beautiful fruition of her perfectly normal pregnancy, I wasn't looking forward to any sharing right away. Sometimes, in life, you just get a bitch pass, and I needed to use mine now.

I packed up. Janet and Benny and Sophie and David helped me, another nice rounding if you notice such things, and we returned almost all of Jeremy's belongings to the Greers. I kept a little of his stuff—his letter jacket, some tee shirts and sweaters that still held the scent of him, a few more of the silly items that we had made so much fun of on the day that we'd moved in. I gave my baby things to Merrilee. If she thought that accepting my offerings might be dangerous, she didn't let on. I returned to Grandmother and the Greers some, but not all, of the furniture we had inherited from them because most of it I wouldn't be able to use any more.

I was moving downtown to a mid-rise apartment near the U.T. medical center. Incredibly the apartment was even smaller than the duplex and incredibly it was more expensive, by ten dollars a month. But it included all utilities, parking and trash service, so I figured I'd actually be saving. The apartment was an "efficiency" plan, meaning that you could practically scramble eggs on the kitchen stove with your left hand while you brushed your teeth at the bathroom sink with your right. I was expecting to become terribly efficient.

It was a Sunday evening. The last night before I planned to surrender the key to the duplex and—except for a few holiday greetings and the isolated remorseful phone calls through the years—what would actually be the entire gentle tether that had held us to the Schimlers. Sophie and I went back to "finish up."

It was the first time for me. But chickadees, you know what it's like. You think that you've cleaned. You know, in your heart, that you've been a pretty good housekeeper and have never been one to let things slide. For however long you've lived there you know that you have been endlessly, *ceaselessly* engaged in washing, swiping, wiping, dusting, de-griming and degreasing. But it doesn't matter. There is the evidence—the pudding-proof fact of your domestic slovenliness. There are dust bunnies blowing across the floors, a layer of sticky film anyplace you put your hand down, windows you can barely see through, mirrors that look like they must have been used in a TB ward. In the bottom of the already packed bathroom cabinet there is a glued-down bottle of fingernail polish, mucky half-squeezed samples of hand lotion and several dozen stray Q-tips. In a supposedly empty closet you will find one odd shoe, a squashed roll of Christmas wrapping paper, the thin blue belt you'd abandoned hope months ago of ever seeing again. And don't even *open* the oven door!

"Geez," Sophie said. "I thought this was going to be easy!"

"Well," I said, my heart sinking at the severe discrepancy between what the duplex actually looked like and what I ultimately wanted to return to the Schimlers, "maybe I'll keep the place another month. Or two. "

Sophie laughed and tossed her head. She was wearing her hair long now, a golden cascade of Botticelli curls. The younger girls especially were giving up their bouffants. The style had begun trending toward longer, simpler, with maybe a little contrived flip at the ends. We were verging on one of those rare short segments of the fashion continuum when I would have the right stuff. Straight and flat was going to be easy for me. But Sophie's hair was Sophie's hair, and fashion be damned, there was nothing for her but to do but deal with it, to suffer the biblical crowning glory that she'd been born with and that had made her, in our early years, everyone's special favorite. I remember that night that Sophie wore a little green headband. She had dozens of devices for keeping her hair out of her eyes. For a while there had even been Elvis Presley hound dog barrettes.

I wouldn't suggest that Sophie was completely unconscious of her physical attributes. You could never have been the kind of hands-on (other people's hands) baby and toddler that Sophie had been without developing a little vanity at least. Out of the corner of my eye I watched her as we went to work, mopping, sweeping, dusting, lifting. In her movements she was as natural and unaffected as a child.

Now, at fifteen, she was taller than I was by a smidge, still slender, but developing, with small breasts showing beneath her T-shirt and a womanly curve coming to her hips. We were a generation not yet effected by Bovine Growth Hormone or any of the other mysterious chemical incentives for early maturation that were already being planned for our food. Back then, even fluoride was a relatively new thing. "Better living, through chemistry," as the DuPont folks told us, was certainly on its way. But it had not been noticed yet in our own lives or in our growth charts. Through all of my years of grade school, junior high, high school and early adult life, I would never think of myself, at five-four, as being short. True, we were not a terribly body-conscious generation. We would leave that to you, chickadees, and the influence of a sexual revolution become ubiquitous and global. But as the years went by, and our adolescent children began to tower over us, our granddaughters entering puberty four to six years earlier than we had, my own normal shoe size becoming the one used for display purposes only and not readily available, it gradually became clear that something, or someone, was tinkering with the program. Even before we were chronologically entitled to begin to shrink, many of us we would find ourselves "short," definitely shrunken.

I digress. I want to fix what I remember about that night.

We went to work, Sophie and I, cleaning yet again, packing another half-dozen boxes from the remains of the supposedly empty duplex. I recall the eerie echo of our voices in the familiar place, the strange reverberations that our heels made in walking and the exaggerated auditory effect of even our simplest action. It was the sound of an empty house—the sound I would come to know, to especially enjoy, in showing a new home to a young couple, or to any client to whom that echoing emptiness meant space and possibility. It was a sound I would also come to associate with endings. With loss and sadness and with ghosts.

What's all this?" Sophie asked me, going through a dilapidated shoebox stuffed with papers, pictures, and little trinkets. I had thought, in picking it up and setting it down again myself over the past days that it was Jeremy's baseball card collection, overlooked in the transfer of his belongings to the Greers. Sophie sat down on the floor with the box and began to pick through its contents.

That's the thing about moving out. Stuff gets mixed up. You are likely to pack, preserve and carefully transport a box of used cat litter, but you will toss your passports and current tax records into the curbside trash. The box actually held my most prized and sentimental possessions. An award ribbon for memorizing the most Bible verses in Sunday school. Pieces of glittering micah from the Woods. A tiny gum-wrapper crown made for me by Sean, for beating him, the first time ever, at chess. There were other little treasures—all from a time that preceded this house, Natalie, even Jeremy.

"Who is this?" Sophie asked me, holding out a crackled black and white Polaroid photograph. I sat down beside her. I couldn't recall having seen that picture in eons. But now I remembered having stolen it—yes, stolen it—years and years before, from a small rubber-banded packet of papers and pictures in Grandmother's bottom bureau drawer.

"I'm not sure," I said, taking the picture from her hand.

"I think it's one of us," I said. "With our mother."

The woman's face was out of frame, but you could see her arms and a young woman's hand with manicured nails cradling a baby on her lap.

"*Which* one of us?" Sophie demanded, snatching the picture back.

"I don't know," I answered. "I used to think it was me. I guess I wanted it to be me. But it's probably you. There's just too much hair."

And it was true. The couple of professionally-taken photographs that existed of me, while I had not been quite so young as the infant in this picture, showed only a sparse veneer of straight dark hair thinly painted on my round baby head. It was unlikely that this child's hair, a pale unruly little halo, could have changed so much in a few months time.

"Yes," Sophie said softly, as though she were just now remembering the day, the occasion, even the anonymous photographer she looked to, wide-eyed. "It's me!"

She continued to peer at the picture, waiting it seemed, for more to come flooding back.

"Why don't they ever talk about her?" she said.

"I don't know," I said, but what I thought was probably more to the point. *Why did we never ask?* How do children learn, from the frown, the raised eyebrow, the sudden irritation in adult voice or manner, that some subjects are just taboo? Maybe we *had* asked. Once. But we had stopped. And Sophie and I had been left to make up our own stories, our own history, of the woman in the picture.

Sophie began putting the scraps and pieces back into the box.

"No," I said, taking the picture back out of the box and handing it to her. "You keep it. It's yours."

It was nearly two in the morning after we'd finished up and I dropped a sleepy Sophie off in the suburbs with a ready-made excuse for missing the next day's school.

It had all seemed real enough. But in the end I saw that on Ellison Street I had only been playing house. Everything that had happened there, everything that Jeremy and I had wished or hoped for, every secret shared and crazy plan we had made there now seemed make-believe, a short, bittersweet game of pretending. The house on Ellison had held only a training exercise, a practice or learning experience for whatever happened next. There would be happiness again in my future—I was too young to abandon that hope. But the innocence, as Jeremy and Natalie were, was irretrievably gone. At nineteen I had learned that plans are jokes you make for the gods. That all leases, really, are short.

CHAPTER XI

Sirens. In the middle of the night there are the wails of ambulances and police cars. The downtown apartment I have leased, my new house if you can call it that, is near a major medical center, within blocks of a half-dozen 24 hour emergency rooms. Even on the seventh floor, through my stuck-down windows, the urgent life-or-death screams of the sirens penetrate. I learn to distinguish among them. To tell the difference between the routine transport of a hired, private ambulance moving almost at the speed of normal traffic and the racing, higher-pitched wails of the city vehicles delivering the late-night emergency, perhaps of a dying child, to the ER at LeBonheur Children's Hospital.

Maybe I can. I think I can.

When the wails wake me from sleep, I lie there, imagining a hundred tragedies. When the sirens stack up in the night, too many coming too close together, I think riots, earthquakes, the first response to the first dropped bombs. A child of the cold war, I am astonished on many mornings to look out my seventh-story window to see that the city, after all, is not in rubble.

Living with the sounds of police cars and ambulances is only one of the adjustments I have had to make to life in my "urban flat." Another is coping with the fact that, seven floors up, I am impossibly far from the ground. Bringing in groceries and emptying trash—neither of which I do all that often, but even picking up the mail, which I mostly remember to collect at least once a week—requires the services of an elevator, and elevators, as it turns out, tend to be annoyingly public places. You don't just dash into one with your head enlarged by twenty-two hot pink magnetic hair rollers unless you're prepared to pay the price of stares or giggles. You cannot reliably gamble that the Indian radiology technician, with whom you've been hopelessly unable to communicate the last four times, will not try again, on the fifth, to test your skills in Hindi. If you are in a sullen mood you will find yourself riding with the talkers. I am almost always in a sullen mood. Everybody is a talker.

Incredibly there are tenants with no apparent need to go either up *or* down who will nonetheless offer to "ride with you," as though moving seven floors in a mechanical box was every bit as good as a companionable drive through the country. Others seem to think that an elevator is a confessional on pulleys. They tell me things I would rather not hear, sometimes unburdening themselves almost breathlessly as the seventh floor approaches. Mr. Libbey has been drinking too heavily since the end of the war. He has moved here to be near the VA hospital and spends almost as much time at the VA, he tells me, as he does at home these days. Laura Fielding, who lives on one of the three floors above me, admits that her bruised cheek is a gift from her boyfriend. If he hits her again, though, she's really gone this time.

Others are sincerely interested in me or, more likely, lonely themselves. Mrs. Chisholm, who lives on my own floor and, thanks to Grandmother, knows a little, but only a very little, about my sad situation always wants to know how I'm getting on. She has lots of advice for taking my mind off "it" and invites me so often for dinner or tea that sometimes I have to go. Some of the people who live in my building are very nice. I am not one of them.

I had chosen this place, economics aside, because it had seemed a radical departure from everything before it. No suburban ranches. Certainly no more sweet little duplexes. I have avoided midtown, with which I am slightly familiar, in favor of coming almost downtown, where I can barely navigate the maze of crowded one-way streets. This time, though, I have signed a shorter lease. Six months only, so that the gods would know I am onto them. But six months stretches before me, an unbearable eternity. I can't breathe up here. Or sometimes I think I can't. Only one of my windows will crack four inches and it has taken three panic attacks and two calls to the Super to get it opened that wide. Twice the Super only promised to come back with some tools, but with the aid of a table knife and a heavy Spanish-English dictionary, I'm making a little progress.

I am usually too hot or too cold. I freeze or I swelter. The building, as advertised, is centrally heated and cooled. What this means is that, if the outdoor temperature changes suddenly, the system will accommodate it, three or four days after Mother Nature has made her own correction. The freezing I can live with. I pile on sweaters, bathrobes, even my winter coat. The sweltering means I sleep on the couch, beneath my "open" window.

In my haste to take my next step I have overlooked some other telling details. The lobby furniture is seedier than I first noticed. There is often trash in the stairwells. Perhaps worst of all, except for a few elderly residents who have doubtless been here since the building was new, the tenants are mostly hospital workers. They come and go in green scrub suits, in nurse's uniforms, but especially white lab coats. I find I have developed an aversion to white coats of any type.

Work, though, is going well. I'm closer to the office than I was before but still I arrive early and stay late. I volunteer for everything and take on the work of others. They think me a regular eager beaver at Mitchner and Hogan and take me along sometimes to look at properties and let me organize the open houses. The trunk of Jeremy's car these days is filled with yard signs and sales leaflets. On the way home, sometimes quite late, I usually stop at a diner for eggs or a burger. The diners are brightly lit and a person can eat alone without attracting too much attention.

To put myself to sleep, at least until the time that a siren will wake me, I read. I have all but abandoned my systematic study plan, though. Now I read only novels. Dark ones. Tragedies. The sadder the better. The librarian near our office has decided I am perfectly daft, but each week, when I inquire, "Don't you have anything more depressing?" she always manages to come through. She had originally recommended *Madame Bovary*, which I found deeply, blackly satisfying. She'd had a good suggestion with Dreiser's *Sister Carrie* and another with Wharton's *Ethan Frome*. After Edith Wharton's tale of the doomed love affair between Ethan and Mattie Silver, I had thought I was really on to something. But I couldn't stand the rest of Wharton's hoity-toity, constipated, rich people stuff. There was too much humor in Faulkner for me. Hemingway was just too bloodless. And while I liked the Russians—Dostoevsky and Tolstoy—I had too much trouble late at night keeping up with their over-stuffed casts and the strange, Russian-sounding names. It had been really hit or miss there for a while until I discovered Thomas Hardy. Now, there was a writer. An artist who understood. In the tragedies of poor Tess, Eustacia Vye, Jude and Sue, I had found misery almost equal to mine. And fortunately Hardy was a prolific writer. I might have completed his entire opus if Janet had minded her own business.

"What the *hell* is going on here?" (Janet's initial greeting, inspired by the hasty impression made from merely peering over my shoulder into the interior of my urban flat) I had made the mistake of answering my bell on a Saturday morning to find her standing, uninvited, in the hallway.

"Janet! I wasn't expecting you. Did you call?"

"Call? You know damn well I did! I've called you twenty times!" She was inside now, standing in the little corridor made between the stacks of unpacked boxes in my studio living room. It was true. I had erased whole answering machine tapes filled with messages from Janet, and others.

"I've really been busy," I said, wrapping my bathrobe a little tighter around my flannel pajamas.

"I can see that," she said. "Too busy even to unpack. You've been here four months, Lacey! When were you thinking of settling in?"

In two minutes Janet has given herself a tour of my little place, sticking her head into the cluttered bedroom and the not-so-terribly clean bathroom, fingering the dead leaves of my African violet on the windowsill. When she opened the refrigerator I knew I was doomed.

"Holy shit! What do you eat? It looks like the Lambda Chi house, only with a little more mold. No wonder you look like a scarecrow!"

I wanted, really, to take offense at that. Especially since Janet looked so fabulous. I knew I had lost a little weight. And that I looked like a perfect slob right now. But it was

141

Saturday morning for God's sake, and I hadn't known she was coming.

"Listen, Janet. I was going to call you. I've just been . . "

"No, *you* listen!" she said. "People are worried about you. Your grandmother called me long distance at the dorm. Even Sophie doesn't know what's going on with you."

Now she took me by the shoulders and pushed me down firmly into a folding chair. I had kept Grandmother's card table and two of the chairs. I don't know what had happened to the gingham tablecloth.

"This isn't good," she continued, bending her head down to squint her really blue eyes at me. "I don't like this. This looks like clinical depression."

"Ah," I said. "You're taking Psych 101 this quarter! Can we just jump ahead to my penis envy? How I was frustrated in the anal stage of my psycho-sexual development?"

Janet stood up and slowly turned her back to me. I waited. When she turned around again there were tears welling in her really blue eyes.

"Lacey, you're in trouble here, babe," she said softly. "I only want to help."

And so I let her help. We cried and hugged and cried some more and then, for most of the morning, we cleaned and unpacked boxes. Janet made more than one joke about how she was cursed, destined, as a result of our friendship, to spend a lifetime packing and unpacking boxes. Poor Janet. She didn't know the half of it yet. There were more moves to come. One day I'd even move out of state and Janet would again be enlisted, for a really big move this time, to help me pack and unpack boxes.

She made me shower and dress. We went out to lunch—a

142

really nice place with white tablecloths and the civilized tinkle of china and cutlery. I ate a salad. Pork medallions and three kinds of vegetables. Strawberry shortcake for dessert. Some meals you just remember.

Janet dropped me off to a much cleaner and more organized apartment. But she was coming back, she told me, at 7:30, to take me to a fraternity party. Drunk on food, delirious from laughing, out of my mind from the sheer contagion of her personality, I had agreed. She'd been gone less than half an hour before true hysteria set in.

To my female chickadees, I don't need to explain. You can imagine the scene because I know you've been there. For two hours I ripped through everything in my closet, trying on garments in every possible combination, rejecting every item into the growing pile on the floor. For one thing most of my clothes were too big now. For another, they were ugly as sin, and lastly, they were out of style. I had gone from preppie, to preggo, to dowdy little office suck-up without an intervening period of shopping.

I washed my hair, set it on rollers, sat under the bonnet hairdryer until I was parched. Then I combed every bit of the curl out trying for suitable styles. I tried putting my hair up, hated that, washed and set it again.

Through all of this I tried calling Janet repeatedly. I called everyone we knew and everywhere she might have stopped. On the third try to the Winston's house Myra's lies were not halfway, not *even* halfway, convincing.

"She's not *here*," Myra sing-songed. "She said to tell you that she'd see you at *sev-en thir-tee*!"

When Janet rang the bell at 7:30, I was in my outfit of last resort. A black skirt and plain sweater from tenth grade. I had put on little pumps and had my usual, boring hairdo. Janet

143

was in a plaid miniskirt, red tights, and knee-length black patent go-go boots.

"Myra says to tell you she's sorry," Janet said. "I made her do it."

"Please," I begged. "Don't make me do this."

"I'm making you do this," she said. "Get your coat."

There was no "fraternity row" at Memphis State then. The sororities had a Panhellenic Building (I looked this up and it means *pertaining to, or involving all the Greeks*) where each sorority got a room, I suppose, in which to conduct their sorority-like activities. But the fraternities had to make do with headquartering themselves in the Craftsman style homes in the transitioning middle-class neighborhoods bordering the campus. The one we went to—the home of the *Kappa somethings;* I don't actually remember—was a good-size two-story structure with a wide front porch under a pitched roof with a center dormer upstairs. It was obvious, once inside, that walls had been knocked out and a few other alterations made to accommodate its current use. I could see immediately the nightmare that resale would be once the brothers decided to move on.

The place was wall-to-wall bodies, with males outnumbering females at least by five to one, a near-deafening chaos of talk and laughter and blaring music. Janet had promised to stick with me. And she did, for about two minutes, until an extremely tall someone, holding his drink high over the heads of the crowd, spotted Janet, shouted, "Well, hello, gorgeous!" and moved in. He threw his other arm around her waist, picked her up bodily and carried her off into the crowd. I assumed this was someone with whom Janet had at least a passing acquaintance, but I wouldn't have bet a serious nickel on it.

For a minute or two more I stood in the middle of the room, letting myself be buffeted by the backs and rumps of strangers, and then I started to make my own move, seeking out the refuge, always, of wallflowers. When I reached one, near a non-working fireplace filled with crushed beer cans and paper cups in lieu of logs, I was comfortable enough to look around.

They had used the little built-in butler's pantry to good advantage, making a trophy case of sorts from it. It held the regular assortment of silver and gold people in sports postures, but also some definitely handmade medallions and ribbons commemorating feats you would rather not know about. There was excellent, although sadly painted, beadboard wainscoting, and a couple of light fixtures that, had the Kappa Somethings the sense to know it, were probably quite valuable. I was in the process of mentally restoring this lovely old home, testing the material of the mantel with both hands to determine if I would need to replace it, when someone stuck a drink directly under my chin.

"You a building inspector?" he said, in a liquescent baritone.

I took the drink. (Always take the drink if you need some time to think.)

"Yes," I said. "And I'm thinking of condemning the place."

He laughed, and I looked up at him. Not *so* much up at him, because he was probably no taller than Jeremy. Five nine, maybe. Five ten. This was a very good-looking guy, but not dramatically so. Not in the contrasting, light-and-dark handsomeness of Jeremy, or even the suave Clark Gable, dark hair, dark eyes, mystery-and-secrets good looks that my Daddy had. This guy was light-haired. Not blonde, not dark, neither swarthy nor pale. This was not the curly-haired, muscular Athenian discus-thrower on the cover of my art textbook. That was Jeremy. *My* type. This guy was Roman. The profile of a Caesar stamped on a golden coin that begins the chapter on "Building an Empire" in *History of the Western World*. This guy was certainly attractive. He had fine aristocratic features. An exceptionally beautiful chiseled nose. He was practically the spitting image of Paul Newman. But he was not my type at all.

"It probably wouldn't be a bad idea to condemn it," he said. "I'm told the cellar, where they keep the sex-slaves, is infested with rats."

"They?" I said. "This isn't your house? You don't live here? I mean . . . I know nobody *lives* here . . . I didn't think anybody *lived* here. I just thought that . . . well, maybe a *few* people live here, but all these people couldn't possibly . . ."

That's what I do when I'm nervous. I babble.

He laughed again.

"No, I don't live here. A friend made me come. Said he'd show me around, introduce me to a few people. That we'd just stay a few minutes. Haven't seen him since we hit the door. That was an hour ago."

It was my turn to laugh. We'd both eased back to settle side by side against my wall. I sipped my drink. I think it was Rum and Coke.

"So," he continued. "Got a boyfriend here somewhere? Live in the dorms? What do you do when you're not inspecting buildings?"

"I didn't realize we were playing twenty questions," I said.

146

"No. And No. And real estate."

"Real estate!" he said, and I could tell he was not making fun of me. "Real estate? Really? You're an agent?"

"No. I'm not an agent. I'm kind of a . . . an assistant, I guess. I've been pretty much a secretary. But they're pushing me. They want me to get my license. I'm not sure. It was just a job, really, and now I'm not sure."

"*I'm* in real estate!" he said. "Commercial and industrial. I want to develop." He scrambled now to pull his wallet from his back pocket, to present me with a business card that said, in subtle engraved lettering, "Easton & Settler, Commercial and Industrial Real Estate," and below that, even more modestly, "Adam Harrison, Sales Representative." Don't laugh, chickadees, but business cards, back then, weren't cheap or easy come by. Only serious business people had business cards. And I was seriously impressed.

"So you're not in school either?" I asked him.

"No!" he said, triumphantly, as though it were a wonderful thing that two young people like us had risen above the fray, become immune to the pedestrian desire of wanting a college education. It seemed to him that we had a lot in common. But I didn't care anything about commercial real estate. I didn't even care about commerce. I was simply interested in houses.

"We should get together," he said. "Talk the trade."

"Sure," I said. "I'd like that."

I hadn't really deluded myself into thinking that this suddenly very sophisticated, and not entirely bad-looking, guy really meant what he was saying. But at some point he asked for my phone number and told me to keep his business card. We talked a good while longer. I remember less of what he said than of the soothing, mellifluous quality of his voice. I finished my drink completely and began to feel, if not really good, at least as we say in cotton country, "fair to midlin."

I had survived, sort of. I was thinking that my coming out venture had not been a complete disaster. But about then, coming from the stereo somewhere, barely audible over the noise of the crowd, I heard the Seekers singing "I'll never find another you." I didn't really have to hear the lyrics. I knew every word. And I stopped congratulating myself.

As I looked around now at the confident, stylish, vibrantly beautiful young co-eds and the swaggering, fun-loving males, I felt, momentarily at least, more alone than I had felt in months. There was a definite chance that when all was said and done, I would end in worse shape, not better, after my day of Janet therapy. I probably would have. Had it not been for the attentions of Adam and the fact that, accidental or not, with our hands braced against that comforting wall, our fingers touched slightly and neither of us made the barest move to sever that delicate connection.

At last Janet showed up, a little too pink-cheeked and hair-mussed for my newly acquired Victorian morals.

"Where have you *been*?" she questioned breathlessly. "I've been looking all *over* for you!"

"I know," I said. "And it's taken everything I could do for me and this wall to keep hiding from you."

She laughed, gave me that look, and I introduced Adam Harrison to my dear and deceitful friend, Janet Winston. They spent a bit of time weighing the relative merits of the University of Tennessee, Knoxville, against the practical, hometown college advantages. Adam didn't bother to enlighten her, but he winked at me once when Janet went off on a patronizing rant about how if you really wanted a good education you could basically get one anywhere.

On the way home Janet didn't tease me about Adam and I

granted her the same consideration about her lengthy disappearance. It had been a long day and Janet had genuinely put herself out there for me. Someday I would have to thank her for what she had done. For rousting me out of my self-destructive funk. For confirming what I had nearly forgotten about the redemptive power of friendship. For arranging the circumstances through which I would meet someone very, *very* important.

CHAPTER XII

The chapter that holds the end of the turbulent sixties is a raised ranch. Spacious and practical. Unattractive and ordinary. True, there'd been a one-year sojourn in a garden apartment. Not much garden to it actually, only a little courtyard with a crepe myrtle and some ornamental grass. But the building had been only two-story, sans elevators, with individual heat and air conditioning systems and windows that actually opened. I had been able to breathe a little better there. Made some progress of sorts. I have no pictures or tokens from that garden apartment. I made no friends there that I can remember. But I credit the time there as immensely valuable. As the short, sturdy, utilitarian little bridge that carried me over the last shallows of my cold, swift-running pain.

It had been there, in my garden apartment, that Adam and I had "courted," as Grandmother would say, taking it pretty slowly after that first winter meeting at the frat house. It had actually taken me until spring to finally fill him in on my short, sad little marital history. I guess I'd been afraid that it might spook him. It had certainly spooked one prince of a fellow, Clyde Hastings, the only other real date I'd had. Clyde had told me, after I'd shared my story on what was only our second time out, that some guys—not *him* certainly, but *some* guys—might find me "used goods." I'd never heard from Clyde again but he had given me a brand new perspective on my situation, one that had helped me, for months, to re-kindle the anger I was trying to grow beyond.

Fortunately Adam had responded quite differently to my story. He had gone from shocked, to sad, to angry, to sad again. Pretty much the same stages I'd been through, but Adam had managed it in hours, not months. I was grateful for that and grateful, too, that he didn't see me as damaged, or used.

At least I *thought* he didn't. The physical aspect of our relationship had been confused and problematic and I didn't know on whose doorstep to lay how much of the blame. Sometimes, when we'd been having a great time together, laughing and cutting up, I would feel almost whole, not healed exactly, but rather *restored* to the state I had been in before Jeremy. As though Jeremy and Natalie and all of that love and hurt had never even happened. There I'd be, chatting at dinner, dancing with Adam, enjoying myself at work or with friends, and then BOOM! Some phrase, some fragrance, a strain of music, would trigger the past and it would all fall down on me. Again.

I'd feel worse after those episodes. A Judas to the memory of what Jeremy and I had been. A shallow, easy little piece who couldn't even wait until the second season's sod had covered her husband's grave before she was dancing the night away. It was hard. I was young. And youth and grief don't get along so well.

Certainly I was sending Adam mixed signals. I would draw near to him, responding helplessly to his cologne, his beautiful mouth, some compliment that he had given to render me coquettish and stupid. Then I would withdraw, back away—suddenly it must have seemed to him, irrationally and capriciously—becoming cold and aloof for no apparent reason. Adam couldn't know that the band had just decided to play Jeremy's favorite song, that a waitress had just mimicked Merrilee's diction, or that something else—who knows what else?—had erased all my progress in an instant.

For his part Adam had been tolerant. Not just gentlemanly, but kind and empathetic. I really shouldn't have asked for anything more. I did, of course. It's the nature of the female beast, I think, to leave no emotional rock unturned. Adam's reserve worried me. Why was he so patient? So willing to wait while I worked my stuff out? Was there a game being played to which I didn't know the rules? Maybe he *did* think me damaged goods. Wasn't he attracted to me physically? Did he think, perhaps, that given what nymphos married women were reputed to be, the wait might well be worth it? Maybe our whole relationship was nothing more than a time-filling exercise: ambitious, attractive guy leans on pleasant, platonic friendship to fill dead space in career and romantic agenda.

I really didn't know the answers to any of my neurotic questions. But poor Adam was in the classic, damned-if-you-do, damned-if-you-don't dilemma. Clearly something would have to change. And it did, one Friday evening in February of '67.

For some reason Adam had insisted on picking me up after my real estate class. Classes were annoyingly held on Mondays, Wednesdays and Fridays and the Friday ones frequently delayed our weekend plans for dinner or making an early movie. It had never made any sense for me not to go home first, to freshen up a bit and then meet Adam at my garden apartment. But on this night he had wanted to change the routine, to pick me up from home and drop me off for class, to "mess around," as he put it, for two and a half hours by himself, and then pick me up again when class was over, while there was still enough daylight for us to be able to see.

"See what?" I had asked him.

"A house," he answered. Adam had been looking at houses, with my help, for weeks. He had been renting, with two other guys and a Labrador retriever, a barny old thing in the Overton Park area, but his career was taking off now, the roommates were getting on his nerves, and he was ready to buy.

"You've decided then? It's the townhouse. No. Don't tell me! I bet it's the Cape Cod on Duncan!"

The Cape Cod on Duncan was an absolute steal. Three bedrooms, two baths, not much yard to take care of, and a whole unfinished loft area upstairs where Adam had imagined a pool table.

"Nope," he said. "One you haven't seen."

Well, *that* hurt a little. Adam looking at houses without me? But what could I do?

Worry. That's what I did. And fidget. And let my mind wander while Mr. Arthur Bateman, broker and retired principal of Bateman and Chase, a highly successful—highly, *highly* successful—real estate firm, now demised for reasons I could readily imagine, tried to impress upon us the importance of not letting the client get away without signing a listing agreement.

"Never," he said, "Never, never, *never*! He had written "NEVER" in all caps on the blackboard and with each repetition of the word he stabbed it again with the chalk.

"If you've made a mistake, draw the line through it!" (Here he made a clear straight line through his "NEVER" and stabbed the board again.) "Initial it!" he shouted. "*Both* of you. Neatly above. Like so!" (Now he wrote ARB in small

154

block letters, high and to the right of NEVER.)

Sheesh. Bateman knew how to make a point. Even if that point was nowhere to be found in tonight's assigned chapter on "Mortgages and Deeds of Trust." He was a lot like those high school coaches turned history teachers who had spent all of our class time regaling us with irrelevant sports stories and then proclaiming, just as the bell rang, "Read chapter eighteen! Quiz tomorrow!"

I figured that Mr. Bateman's instruction didn't matter much anyway. We'd get the credit for the six semester hours required and the exam would be taken from the text. Passing the exam was the true hurdle in getting a real estate sales license in the state of Tennessee. I was studying earnestly, making Adam grill me on possible exam questions and getting other help when I needed it from the agents in my office. I'd been surprised to find that the math was not too daunting. There were no word problems in real estate classes. No trains leaving Boston at 8:15 p.m., bound for New York and traveling at 62 miles per hour, or anything like that. The math was pretty much straight-up arithmetic and we were allowed to use calculators.

It felt a little ironic to me, now that I was finally back in school, to be studying real estate instead of, say, *Western World Lit* or at least *Textiles and Patterns*. But Mr. Mitchner was paying for the classes and, assuming I passed, for the testing fees, too. As soon as I finished the courses, passed the exam, and got my first commission check, I planned to enroll in night school at Memphis State. I figured, that by taking two classes a semester and going summer sessions, too, I could still get a bachelor's degree by the time I was 25. That sounded pretty old to just be finishing college but I needed to keep working and I was going to be 25 anyway, right?

Bateman wrapped up the class with a horror story about some renters who had sold an owner's house, told us to read the next chapter on "Real Property Valuation," and finally set us free.

I clearly remember how handsome Adam looked that night. Apparently his natural penchant for neatness had been reinforced by his stint in the Marine Corps and his clothes, his hair, his car, the inside of his orderly briefcase, were always spit-and-polish perfect. I liked to study his profile when we were driving. No human being on earth had ever been given a more beautiful nose.

"Where is this mystery house?" I asked him. We were heading east, away from the river.

"Bartlett," he said. "You'll see."

I was shocked. Nothing Adam had looked at up to now had been that far out of the city.

"Pretty long way from your office, don't you think?"

"Maybe. But I'm rarely in the office. I'm in the car all day, all over town anyway."

He had a point. *Still.* Bartlett was the extreme north-eastern burbs. The city was definitely growing in that direction and directly east also. The river had it stopped to the west, and the Mississippi state line, only a few miles from where I'd grown up, cut off its official, if not its spillover growth, to the south. East was certainly where the future of the city's suburban real estate lay. Still. Bartlett seemed so far *out.*

And there I was, for the first time ever, smack in the middle of the Great Debate. I would hear it argued, from both sides, for pretty much the rest of my life. Suburbanites, spoiled by their light traffic, recreational amenities, and the convenience of shopping malls, groan at the thought of going in town for a play or a big league game. Townies think the suburbs are sterile and vapid, mocking a mentality that thinks a lawn is a crowning achievement. Burbies think the city expensive and stressful, laughing among themselves at the prices people pay to live in a cracker box surrounded by concrete. Townies think the homogenous nature of the suburbs tends to breed fear and racism. Burbies think the cities breed crime, bad air, crappy schools. Everybody is a little right, a little wrong. "Near" and "far", even "urban" for that matter, are much more states of mind than objective realities. The debate, probably, is what's actually dangerous, fostering stereotypes on both sides. If you get into real estate, though, expect to hear about it. Sometimes three or four times a week.

In actually less than half an hour we were there, in the suburban bedroom community of Raleigh-Bartlett, parked in front of a raised ranch. It was not new but certainly built in the last few years. The house was bigger than what Adam had been looking at up to now. Also a lot more boring. It had all the curb appeal of a brown and white shoebox.

Like many raised ranches, the ground level of this one was partially submerged below grade. This bottom floor was a milky brown brick, with a double garage to one side. The upper, or main level, accessed by a short flight of steps set in the house's exact center, was white horizontal clapboard siding. The little lengths of simple iron railing that bounded the steps and a single diamond-shaped cutout in the front door formed the sum total of all ornament or architectural detail on the entire house. No shutters. No awnings or porches or eves. No millwork or trim. Not even a single gable on the low-pitched brown-shingled roof. To someone whose favorite flavor of house was Neapolitan, sometimes even with nuts, cherries and whipped cream, this was definitely vanilla.

Adam was smiling, clearly expecting some sort of positive reaction from me.

"Well," I said, stalling. "This is interesting. Can't wait to see inside!"

There was no entry hall. Ranches, whether one-story or two, don't waste space on such nonsense. The living room was large, rectangular and carpeted in brown shag. The eating area of the galley-style kitchen was immediately behind the living room in perfect alignment with the little diamond window in the door. This arrangement, I conjectured, was not necessarily a negative if you and your family always ate tidily, and fully clothed, and didn't feel compelled to invite anyone ringing the doorbell to join you. There was a nice little powder room in the hall to the left of the kitchen (the previous owners had not exactly left it spotless) and one smallish bedroom which might serve as a nice little office. I was headed to the end of this hall, to what would logically have to be the master bedroom, when Adam grabbed at my elbow.

"Wait," he said. "Let's look downstairs first."

Sure. Why not?

We descended the stairs, carpeted in the same type of shag carpeting as was the main floor, except that the steps to the lower level had been seen as an opportunity point for changing the carpet color from brown to bilious green. This downstairs space, though, seemed massive—a really big rec room with a built-in bar, prefab fireplace, and double sliding doors to the patio. This room, apparently, was what had made Adam so excited and secretive. The whole Kappa Something house could party down here.

"Wow!" I said, with some real enthusiasm now. "This is great!"

And it was. The fact that the builder had found no other way to support this expanse than by putting a ten-inch metal pole in the dead center of the room, about four feet from the front of the fireplace, was annoying, yes, but Adam didn't really have much furniture anyway. He'd find a way to work around it.

There was one more bedroom, a full bath, and a laundry room on this bottom floor. A pretty big house, actually, for a bachelor pad.

Adam was beaming, apparently crazy about this room and the house in general.

"Come on," he said, tugging me to follow along, "now you have to see the master."

When we were back upstairs and he opened the door I saw the reason he had wanted to change our Friday night routine and how he'd been "messing around" for the time that I'd been in class. The master bedroom was nice. Spacious enough, with double windows on one wall, and mirrored sliding closet doors. But in the center of the room was spread a large quilted comforter on which sat a picnic basket and a bucket of iced champagne. Along the windowsill he had lined an assortment of candles.

"Oh, Adam." I said. "How sweet! And clever. And fun!"

We kissed. A long, tender kiss that left me a little shaky, and then Adam tugged me down to sit beside him and proceeded to host the loveliest picnic anyone ever had.

Adam had thought of everything. We had crystal glasses for the champagne, silverware and white linen napkins. He had even remembered the matches to set the candles dancing on the windowsill. We ate and chatted and laughed. We kissed a lot. We kissed between bites of fried chicken and deviled eggs. We kissed before sips of champagne, and after.

We kissed through the chocolate mousse that Adam's brilliant delicatessen had packed in my own, my Grandmother's, cut glass crystal custard cups. He apologized for filching them but I was deeply touched by the care that had gone into his planning.

At some point, giddy from the champagne, the laughter, all the kissing that had made the room, and me, unseasonably warm for February, I stated what I thought was the obvious.

"Well," I said, laughing. "It seems you've made up your mind. You're really serious about this house."

"Oh, I'm serious," he said.

And from the bottom of the picnic basket he produced a small jeweler's box. *That* kind of box, chickadees. *That* kind.

"I'm completely serious," he said, opening the little box and turning it to extend it, to offer it, to me.

He had not brought a radio. It was years before music would become so wonderfully portable and there was no electricity yet in the empty house. But when I recall that night I always remember music playing. I hear woodwinds and violins. An entire symphony played for hours, as our bodies, our skin, backlit by the light of the candles, flowed golden into one another in the mirrored closet doors.

When we finally left that night, that morning, another chapter of my life had ended and a new one was about to be written. I had changed my mind completely about the raised ranch that would hold it. It was an absolutely wonderful house. A few flaws, maybe. But we would work around them.

.

CHAPTER XIII

They were going to call it the "summer of love." In California there would be a great gathering. As many as one hundred thousand of our contemporaries would converge in a human tidal wave, coming ashore in a strange little neighborhood in San Francisco for a festival of youthful idealism like nothing the world had ever seen or would ever witness again. Even deep in the Bible Belt the call was being answered. Connor Laughlin and Myra Winston had heard the hype and were planning to spend spring break in the Haight. Myra was going, she said, to be part of a cultural and spiritual revolution. Connor, I suspect, was going for the sex, the drugs, the rock and roll.

For Adam and me it was a summer of love also. But our impulses were different. As energetically as many of our peers were working to turn on, tune in, and drop out, Adam and I were moving just as assiduously in the opposite direction, working counter to the counterculture in trying to legitimize ourselves and our careers, to become homeowners and taxpayers and to join, rather than reject, the great Capitalist Establishment. *They* may have wanted to be flower children. *We* just wanted to be adults.

My reasons were my reasons, that still mysterious complex of yearnings that made me want to nest, to find the place— one I could keep this time—that was not only legitimately mine but from where I could begin to build myself, that center from which I could give myself, to Adam and others, perhaps even children some day. Maybe I had translated my sense of motherlessness, which couldn't be fixed, into a sense of homelessness, which could. I'm not sure. My reasons felt strong, but they were fuzzy, not easily articulated, then, or now.

Adam's reasons were crystal clear. He had grown up hard. In pathetic tenement homes dominated by an erratic and abusive alcoholic father and a well-intentioned but ineffectual mother who had retreated into physical illness and mental health wards whenever she had felt overwhelmed. He had not shared that much of his childhood with me, but enough to make me understand. For Adam, the establishment wasn't something to be rebelled against. It was a special private club whose members held their heads up high, wore clean clothes, and always had enough to eat.

We wouldn't be going to San Francisco. But for our little wedding, in the small resort town of Heber Springs, Arkansas, I did, actually, wear a few flowers in my hair, and carried a few more in a ribbon-bound nosegay.

We spent our honeymoon in a little cottage at the edge of Greers Ferry Lake. Adam tried, unsuccessfully, to teach me to fish. I didn't care for it much but I loved to read on the grassy banks while he did. We explored the beautiful lake in a little rented outboard, cooked our own meals, and at night we made love to the lap of the water and the sound of the crickets. You want a word more blissful than "bliss." There are times that the language just fails.

We came home, to the raised ranch on Chantilly Drive, rested and happy, each of us in our own way eager to get on with it. Adam's company was growing, making a name for itself through the shopping centers and industrial complexes it was starting to develop, not just in the Delta, but as far away now as Missouri and Texas and Florida. I had my sales license now, too, and Mr. Mitchner and Terri Shorter—one of our younger agents, as blonde, beautiful and bubbly as any Alabama cheerleader—seemed to be genuinely interested in bringing me along, in "showing me the ropes," as they said.

I was career-conscious enough. Still a little befuddled, maybe, at how my first job out of high school had turned into such a serious adult commitment. But real estate gave Adam and me a shared interest, a common vocabulary, a context for talking about everything from economics to politics. It was, as they said in the day, our "groove."

I still had my secret little dreams. I was closer than ever now to being able to enroll in college. In the meantime, I had this house. Already a little obsessed with the idea of decorating, I had now been given an empty two-story, three-bedroom canvas. It was a bit like presenting an eager kindergartener with a big sheet of blank paper and fifteen pots of finger-paint. I just couldn't *wait* to get into it.

We had moved in with the best of his junk and mine and for bringing it all together Adam had given me a "budget"—a very grown-up concept in and of itself, but in this case it stood for four hundred dollars. Not much you think, unless you're made to recall that in 1967, the median household income was a little over seven thousand dollars, a gallon of gas was thirty-three cents and a postage stamp still cost a nickel. I intended to be very careful. To make wise and practical choices. But four hundred dollars was a king's ransom.

I had already observed, through the magazines, the model homes, the films and newpapers, how much fun and wit there was in the décor of the late sixties. Colors were vibrant,

163

patterns popped and swirled, art was wild and playful. Again, our generation exerted the influence of our massive numbers and our film icons, pop idols, and comic strip heroes showed up on everything from bed sheets to lampshades. You, chickadees, have no memory of such an unbranded world, but up until the '60s it was perfectly possible to walk around in clothing that didn't broadcast its manufacturer. Even, believe it or not, to buy your children a cartoon-less lunchbox.

Adam and I would participate to some extent in the trends and styles of the era. We would have our share of bean bag chairs and briefly a space-age molded dinette suit. I confess to having deep-ended for a while on the color orange, happily in fashion vogue then, and coincidentally the hallmark color of the University of Tennessee Volunteers. I recall wearing a lot of orange myself and I hung tangerine art nouveau wallpaper with a massive repeating flower pattern—better suited for a space the size of the Super Dome than for our tiny galley-style kitchen. In our big downstairs recreation room we would make a trendy "conversation pit" out of pillows in front of the fireplace—the support pole left us with few other choices—and we would hang pop art posters on the walls and faces of the Beatles, Mick Jagger, and Audrey Hepburn.

There was a lot that came out of those years that appealed to me then and that would influence, to a greater or lesser degree, all the houses to come. The Hippies had brought back interesting things from their pilgrimages, from India and Morocco especially, in carpets and rugs and accessories, but most importantly in fabrics. I loved then, and still do, the rich brocaded cottons and soft hand-loomed wools, the fascinating paisleys and batiks and the shimmering silks, in colors so electrically vibrant they radiated their own light. There was also a witty tongue-in-cheek approach to accessorizing that was born in that era, a youthful irreverence that reminded us not to take our surroundings, or ourselves, too seriously. They were fearless about mixing Victoriana with modern, with adding whimsical touches like a felt Fedora atop a bust of Beethoven or, say, putting a ruffled Elizabethan collar on a favorite ceramic dog.

There was a good bit, though, that I never indulged in. I skipped the blow-up sofa and the lava lamp. Throwaway furniture like Peter Murdoch's paper chair, struck me then, as it does now, as utterly stupid. And even though *House and Garden* magazine showed us how, I was never tempted to re-create a *Barbarella* room or the fantasy scenes from *Help!* I have never cared for plastic or chrome as furniture materials and I was not very happy about the era's clear disregard for wood. When the home furnishing styles of the late '60s and early '70s came into vogue again, as "retro" by that time as I was, I would see our molded dinette set in a furniture ad—perfectly duplicated, but at a hundred times the price we had paid for it, and still tacky after all those years.

But that's where I was, sitting in my bathrobe at the kitchen table pushing around paint chips and swatches of fabric, about to begin deciding what I liked and didn't, and how I would spend my four hundred dollar fortune, when Sophie's face began bobbing up and down in the triangle of the front door. I opened the door and looked around, wondering who, on a Saturday morning, might have brought her from her remote southern suburb to my nearer, and clearly more relevant, one at the far eastern end of town.

"Come see!" Sophie said, still bouncing like a kangaroo. "Come see my new car!"

Parked in my driveway was a battered blue and white 1960 Chevrolet Corvair. (I didn't recognize the make or model that morning; I am functionally illiterate when it comes to cars.)

Sophie pulled at me and I padded down the steps after her in my bathrobe and bare feet.

"Sophie, where did you get this car?"

"I bought it. It's mine!"

"You can't buy a car! You're only seventeen."

"Well, actually Nana signed the papers. But it's *my* car. Nana can't even *drive,*" she said disdainfully, kicking her foot into one of the wide white-wall tires, a car-shopping technique she had apparently just picked up. Sophie wore jeans, a tie-dyed tee shirt emblazoned with the peace sign, and her hair, this time, was in a pony tail of corkscrew curls.

"It's Horizon Blue!" she squealed. "The top is Ermine White."

"And what color is *this*?" I inquired, scratching at a decent-sized rust spot at the edge of the driver's side door. Sophie ignored me.

"Eighty horses!" she said. "And Powerglide!"

"Really? No kidding. But what *is* that, exactly?"

"Oh, I don't know," she said, not in the least offended. "But the boys really like it. Come on! I'll take you for a ride!"

"Uh, no," I said. "I'm not even dressed. Come in and tell me about it. Have you had breakfast yet?"

Sophie followed me reluctantly back inside, casting only one wistful glance over her shoulder. She talked, and twirled her car keys on her index finger, while I scrambled her some eggs and made toast and poured juice and coffee for both of us. She had gotten the money for the car through a combination of appeals to Grandmother and Nana, even from a loan from Maddie Laughlin who she planned to repay at ten dollars a week.

I was pretty impressed with her resourcefulness, a little miffed and partly relieved that she'd left me completely out of the process.

"And Maureen? "I asked her. "Did she pitch in?" Sophie rolled her eyes and sighed dramatically.

"Right," she said. "Like Maureen would care. She said I didn't need a car. Said it wasn't *necessary*."

I smiled. Stupid question. Of course Maureen would say that.

"But Daddy. Does Daddy know you've bought a car?"

Sophie's face flared pink but she didn't answer me right away and I waited while her flush faded and she pushed eggs around her plate with her fork.

"Daddy can go to hell," she said quietly. "He's never around anyway. Haven't seen him in six weeks."

There wasn't anything too terribly surprising about this, but what she said next would shock me.

"She's leaving him, you know. Maureen. She's had enough. There's a For Sale sign in the front yard of our house and real estate assholes tromping through all the time."

I let the real estate remark go by. I was too stunned that so much had transpired that I knew nothing about. It just went to show you how a few little things like falling in love, getting married, going on a honeymoon, and moving into a new house could take you out of the family loop.

"Oh, Sophie, I didn't know. Why didn't anybody tell me?"

"They didn't tell me either! Nobody ever tells me anything. I stand outside the door when they're arguing. I pick up the extension. I'm not as stupid as everybody thinks I am!"

For the first time I began to see what it had been like for Sophie these last years. I remembered how unwelcome the

167

pair of us had always felt in that house. But at least we had been a pair.

"But what are you going to do? All of you, I mean."

Sophie laughed.

"Well at least I get out of that fucking school," she said.

I didn't like her language. The F-word had a lot more shock value back then and it would never sound right coming out of Sophie's angelic face. This, however, wasn't the time for a lecture. And considering how I'd abandoned her, how could I possibly know what words her situation required.

"But where is everybody *going*?" I asked her. And then it hit me. If Maureen and Daddy were splitting up, then Sophie and Nana would be splitting up, too, and there would be nobody, nobody at all, to even consider Sophie.

"That's why we got the car!" she said, suddenly excited. "Nana wants to go back to Mississippi. They don't tell *her* anything either but she told me last night that she can see the writing on the wall. That's what she called it. The writing on the wall. She says she'll take me with her! I can go to school in Booneville. That's where her people are. She says it's really pretty there and her sister has a house. The kids there aren't stuck up or anything. They get out of school twice a year to pick cotton. Or cut it. Or something."

I pulled my robe tighter around me and looked out the second-story window of my raised ranch into the treetops, swaying in the March wind against a blue-gray sky.

"Sophie," I said at last. "You haven't thought this through." I remembered the nights of helping her with homework and how easy it had been to lose her completely if my actions, my voice, betrayed any exasperation or disappointment.

"What do you mean?" she said. "I can pick cotton!"

168

"Of course you can," I said. "But it's more complicated than that. We're not even related to Nana."

That was enough for the moment. I waited to let my point sink it.

"I don't think Grandmother and Daddy are going to let you go," I continued. "I can't see them letting you go off to another state. To finish high school living with a stranger."

As soon as I'd said the word I knew I had gone too far. If Nana, who loved her, who had been there for her day after day, washing her clothes and preparing her meals, listening sympathetically to her tales of how her school, her teachers, her parents, her friends, even her sister, didn't understand her—if *Nana* was a stranger, who then was not?

Sophie rose straight up from my kitchen chair.

"Nana isn't a stranger!" she said. "You're a stranger! You and your smart-ass, rich little hubby. You don't know anything about it!"

I rushed to fix it but she was already, keys in hand, striding across my living room, wrenching the front door open.

"Listen, Sophie. Wait! I didn't mean it like that! You don't need Nana. You can live with me! With me and Adam. You can . . ."

I followed after her, but it was no use. Before I could even stumble down our short flight of steps she was gunning the motor, backing out with two wheels in the lawn, missing the mailbox by a quarter of an inch.

Sophie wouldn't allow me to apologize or explain. For nearly three weeks she refused to return my telephone calls and was avoiding Grandmother, too. Sophie had been right about Nana not knowing anything either. My conversations with her were confused and uninformative. She seemed torn between wanting to calm me down and protecting Sophie's secrets—one of which she let slip in mentioning that Sophie was probably with her new "beau." I learned that Maureen had gotten a lawyer, that there was a buyer for the house, but nothing else. I didn't even inquire about Nana's own plans, whether or not she had really intended to take Sophie with her back to the cotton fields. There just wasn't any point.

But in Nana's protectiveness I realized that she, too, would be losing something important. Sophie had been made motherless in infancy. She had found brief substitutes in a busy grandmother and a hired black maid. These had been supplanted by the custodial country personage of Nana, who was now being ripped from her by the accident of another marriage ending. Sophie was getting a raw deal. But Nana was, too. Sophie and I, but particularly Sophie, had been as close as Nana had ever come to grandchildren.

By the end of March I was half crazed with worry and rose early on a Saturday morning to drive to Whitehaven, chancing it that somebody, anybody, would be home on Lochinvar Drive to fill me in on the path that my family's disintegration was taking. My old friends were preparing for Easter break departure—Janet to the Gulf Coast, Myra and Connor, if the rumors were true, to the West Coast. My junket had the dual purpose of hearing their plans and wishing them well.

The old neighborhood looked beautiful. Quiet at that hour, and tidy as a magazine spread. If a new brood of children had come along to replace our old mob, someone was teaching them to put away their toys and bikes and not to trample the flowerbeds. Azalea bushes and spring bulbs were already blooming and the morning dew glistened on the greening carpets of lawn.

I felt odd when I reached the front door, wondering whether I should knock, ring the bell, or use my old key. These streets, these yards, the open spaces within and around Fairfield Estates, had always been mine. But my sense of ownership, of belonging, ended at this door. I knocked. In a few minutes Nana answered the door, clapped her hands together in delight and then smothered me in her ample bosom and the soft warm puddings of her arms.

"Land sakes!" she said, "Come in this house, child! You by yourself?"

"I am," I said. "But do *you* have company?" There was a late model car in the drive. Not Daddy's. Certainly not Sophie's new acquisition.

"Oh, Lord no," she said shaking her head. "We're moving out of here, didn't you know? Truck going to be here this week, she says."

I followed Nana into the kitchen, past a tower of cardboard moving boxes stacked in the living room floor. God, I thought. *Boxes*. Somebody in this family should find out who makes them and we all should invest heavily.

In the kitchen Maureen sat at the built-in breakfast booth, a coffee cup in one hand and a cigarette in the other. I hadn't known that Maureen smoked, but then there was a lot I didn't know these days.

"Well, good morning," Maureen said. There was unmistakable sarcasm in her voice and she leaned back in the booth and glowered at me, her eyes narrow and accusing. It was only March but Maureen wore sandals and khaki shorts and a kind of Rosie the Riveter kerchief thing on top of her auburn hair. She was really a good-looking woman. Exceptionally beautiful legs.

171

"Good morning," I returned, avoiding her eyes. I didn't blame Maureen for being angry but I hadn't come here for a row.

"New car?" I questioned.

"Not new," she said. "Just a car. Your *father* took the Plymouth."

I was still standing around, wondering if it would be presumptuous of me to sit down in the booth. Nobody apparently was going to offer me coffee.

"So what brings you slumming on a Saturday morning?" Maureen asked. There was an energetic lift to her voice this time and also a mocking smile. She tapped her cigarette with a red manicured index finger.

Nana set a cup of coffee on the corner of the booth. I sat down across from Maureen.

"I was hoping to catch Sophie," I said.

Maureen laughed, and exchanged a quick glance with Nana. Nana turned away, busying herself with something at the kitchen sink.

"Your sister," Maureen said, "is not here." She paused and took a deep breath. "She hasn't been here to sleep or to go to school. She hasn't been here to help with the packing or anything else. She has taken a few clothes. Her guitar. *My* good suitcase!" She lifted the cigarette to her lips. It trembled in her fingers and ashes fell to the table.

Nana turned from the sink to face us, wiping her hands with her apron.

"She'll be back," Nana said. "She's just got a new beau, that's all."

"Who *is* this new beau?" I asked her earnestly. "What's his name?"

Nana looked puzzled. "Lester?" she offered. "Was it

Lester?"

"Mother!" Maureen scoffed. "That was my father's name." And then, to me, she said, "He was a son-of-a-bitch, too."

"But his *name*!" I almost shouted. "Don't you know him? Has anybody called *his* parents?"

"That's just it," Maureen said. "Nobody seems to know him. Not even Maddie. Sophie's only taken up with him lately. Just about the time she got that damned car!" Now Maureen scowled menacingly at Nana. Nana shook her head sadly and turned and walked out of the kitchen, still wiping her hands as she went.

My heart was racing in my chest and I was afraid of what I might say next. I picked up my coffee very carefully and followed slowly after Nana, trying to leave the impression with Maureen that I was still under control. I walked out of the kitchen, down the narrow hall past the bathroom, noting how the packing activity had already called out the dust bunnies from their secret hiding places, freeing them to dance their drifting waltz across the hardwood floors. Ahead of me Nana softly closed the door to her bedroom.

There wasn't, I realized, anything to be accomplished by bothering her. She was obviously as guilt-ridden as I was and she didn't really know any way to help. Instead I walked to the door of our old room and looked inside. The room had been stripped almost bare. The café curtains were gone and the ugly bedspreads purged, only the mattresses left on the maple bunks. The room seemed shrunken, too small to have ever contained the energies of both Sophie and me, let alone all of our toys and clothes and paraphernalia. I remembered the nights, more than a decade ago, when Sophie and I, small ourselves then and newly homesick for Thelma and Grandmother, had held each other in that lower bunk, plotting our escape from this house. Well, we'd done it. Both of us. Neither of us, I supposed, in the best possible way. I tried to think a blessing for whomever occupied this room next. I hoped it would be a little girl. I hoped she wouldn't be homesick for the last place and that they'd get her a canopy bed.

When I returned to the kitchen I found that Maureen had been crying. Her nose was red and her eyes still welled with crystal tears. Puzzled, I put my hand on her shoulder.

"What's wrong?" I asked, hoping I wouldn't have to listen to the litany of my father's sins.

"It's my fault," she said. "I told her."

"Told who? Told what?" I sat down again across from her in the booth.

"Sophie." she sniffed. "She was mad. We were fighting. I shouldn't have told her. But she called me such horrible names!"

I wasn't getting this at all but Maureen was clearly suffering. I reached across the table to lay my hand on hers.

"What are you talking about Maureen? I don't understand."

"I told her what your Daddy had said. What he told me once."

"Maureen, you're not making sense. What did he tell you?

"That Sophie wasn't his. That he'd never thought so."

Suddenly I felt my heart do a frightening levitation. It had lifted itself up, to beat high, in my throat, in my ears. I pulled my hand back like someone who'd been burned.

"And you told *Sophie* this?"

Maureen didn't answer. She convulsed now into jagged sobs, crying so hard that she was fairly gasping for air. She dug at her eyelids with her red manicured nails.

174

I didn't care. I could scarcely hear her anyway for the pounding in my ears.

"Maureen!" I shouted. "Shut up! *When* did you tell her this? *When*?"

"*That* day," she stuttered. "The day she ran away."

CHAPTER XIV

Our own summer of love was a little sadder, not nearly so eventful as the reports of the one in San Francisco. Still, we were newlyweds and Adam was gentle and patient with me. In the beginning I'd had terrible dreams about Sophie, too terrible to tell anyone about, but Adam had held me in the night when they came and in the daytime he had listened to me ramble when I couldn't get her off my mind. I had made no decorating progress at all over the spring but as the days grew warmer and the dreams came less frequently I began to take a little interest again. There had been no *bad* news about Sophie after all. No calls from the police or reason to believe she'd been in any kind of accident. By June I had developed a simple, but baseless, theory. Sophie was at the beach. Biloxi or Gulfport. Panama City maybe. She was shacked up with a bunch of stupid but harmless teenagers, and before school started again, if not sooner, she'd show up, suntanned and repentant.

I painted the powder room, hung living room draperies, re-framed old greeting cards and sheet music for a grouping over the couch. We didn't hear from Sophie in July.

In August I tented our bed with gauzy Indian cotton, made a batik bedspread and bright silk pillows, and window valances from paisley shawls. We checked with the city police and the country sheriff's department to make sure there was no news and just to confirm that they were still looking. Detective Kellogg, with the city, reminded me of the tens of thousands of runaways that were missing all over the country. An officer with Shelby County made a perfunctory check and told me that no "bodies" matching Sophie's description had been reported. The dreams returned for a week or two but Adam kept talking me through it. It was just the nature of their work, he said. They didn't mean anything by it.

That fall and winter I would get to experience a few "firsts" with Adam that I had not even shared with Jeremy. Halloween came and we handed out candy to the neighborhood children from our own front door. It was a pretty cool first, actually, if you'd only ever been on the receiving end of the deal. We played scary music from an eight-track tape running just below our open windows and Adam wore a black cape and full vampire make-up. He enjoyed himself way too much, I thought, in frightening the smaller children.

We were invited to share Thanksgiving with Merilee, Grady and baby Lyle in their new three-bedroom brick home in Collierville. Grady and his partner had opened their own garage and Merilee was working three days a week in a beauty shop off the square. Lyle got to go to work with her, occasionally crawling around on the cutting room floor. Merilee cracked us up with her stories of finding "black roots," and specimens of "frizzy perms," in Lyle's baby diapers. We had a nice time. Everyone was cordial and Merilee and Grady tried hard, a little too hard, to translate their old friendship with Jeremy into a new one with Adam. But it wasn't the same. It wasn't ever going to be. Merilee and I would never really lose touch. But when we hugged goodbye that November evening we both knew, in the way that women know these things, that we were closing a door that wouldn't re-open.

In December Adam and I put up our first Christmas tree and I cooked my first Christmas dinner with all the trimmings. It was not half bad even if Grandmother had helped with the dressing and my turkey had turned out just a tiny bit dry. But Christmas, too, was a bittersweet holiday. Except for Grandmother's brief mention of Sophie in her fervent and lengthy blessing, it was almost as though she'd never been. Never been part of Halloween or Thanksgiving or Christmas. Never belonged to this family or its choppy, disconnected traditions.

But Sophie was on my mind all day. Optimistically, in the course of my Christmas shopping, I had bought her a cashmere sweater, a pair of cloisonné barrettes shaped like butterflies, and a chord and lyric book for the Rolling Stones. On Christmas night, after Adam had driven Grandmother home and I had put away all of the leftover food and cleared away most of the dishes, I went to turn off the lights. The living room looked almost bare, bereft now of the holiday clutter. There were only three packages left under the tree. I could not have accepted it had I known it then, but for four more years those packages would be the first gifts set out under our annual Christmas tree and for four more years they would be last of our holiday items to be packed up and put away.

January began with an optimistic President Johnson telling us that the challenges of Vietnam had been met. It ended with the Tet Offensive, the North Vietnamese reaching even the grounds of the US embassy in Saigon, demonstrating that no end of the war was in sight.

We woke, at the beginning of February, to see on the front

page of the morning newspaper, in what would become one of the most iconic images of the war, an AP photo of a suspected Vietcong being shot in the head in full view of an NBC cameraman. The nightly news will provide the film footage. We have color television now and the news broadcasts are becoming graphic and bloody. The war is never far from any of our minds these days but still it is playing out in Southeast Asia, half a world away. We have our own local problems to deal with.

The city sanitation workers had been on strike in Memphis since the middle of February and by the middle of March we were beginning to realize exactly what services these twelve hundred or so previously invisible workers had performed for our city. Garbage was starting to pile up on curbs and against buildings. Backstreets and alleyways were taking on pungent odors. Husbands had begun leaving for work with bags of trash, charged with disposing of them far from home and when they were sure no one was looking. My home town, which frequently billed itself as "the nation's cleanest city" wasn't looking so clean anymore.

For me the most telling thing about the strike was the slogan that the striking workers had adopted to communicate their cause. It was nothing about better pay, pensions or benefits, nothing about better working conditions—what working conditions could have been more deplorable?—not even about the healthcare that might have offered some protection against the lice and maggots and disease that infested their workplace. The slogan that appeared on the cardboard placards of the marchers, that showed up on national television to the city's, to the nation's, undying disgrace was simply, "I am a man."

I don't remember much about the politics of the strike. I

know that Mayor Loeb was dead set against it and that the city council's sympathies were divided along purely racial lines. Only three, I believe, of the thirteen council members were black. I don't even remember thinking much about how much difference ten cents an hour might make in a person's life—a person like Thelma's husband Nolan. But I do remember those signs.

I remember, too, the feeling that began to take hold of me that spring, the uncomfortably guilty sense that while our own lives, mine and Adam's, seemed to be coming together nicely, the rest of my family, in fact the whole rest of the world, seemed intent on falling apart. Adam's mother, who I had scarcely come to know at all, had passed away on New Year's Day. We had made the simple arrangements and he had attended her little service dry-eyed and stoic. In truth I didn't even know Adam himself well enough then to understand that his demeanor masked not just sadness but anger. She had lived a life of joyless passivity, never finding the means or the strength to escape her lot. Now, just as Adam was arriving at a place where he might have provided her some comfort and peace, she had surrendered completely, opting out of the struggle of living but also depriving him, cheating him, of the chance to bring his childhood story to any better end. Adam's father, who he had not seen in years, didn't appear for the funeral and I, for one, was glad.

There was Grandmother, too, to worry about. She had been "retired" by the millinery department at Silverstein's and we had helped her to move, one last time, to another nearly identical old quadriplex only a few blocks away. This one was cheaper, she said. Safer, too. And her friend from church, Mrs. Bartow, lived on the upper floor. All that seemed fine, a comfort actually, but each time I visited I found her uncharacteristically slow about settling in. I knew what it meant to have no interest in unpacking the boxes. Her curio cases had not been repopulated with the Dresden angels and the Hummel figurines. Her heavy drapes lay piled in the corner. She always brushed off our offers to help and it was *me* now, checking up on *her* by telephone, at the ritualized after-school time.

Sophie's absence was the worst, of course. Adam and I, Janet and Myra and David, everyone we knew, engaged in varied speculation about where she might have gone, what she might be doing. Nobody, not even the police, had managed to discover anything, not even the name, of her mysterious "beau." Nana had not, after all, returned to her people in Mississippi, but had moved into a city apartment with Maureen. I never visited them. I was still years away from trusting myself not to wring Maureen's neck. But I kept up some contact with Nana by telephone, thinking that it might be she above all others that Sophie would go to. Logically I knew that Sophie probably wouldn't know where they lived now anyway.

Daddy and I were completely estranged also but given our minimal contact over the last few years it was hardly a thing to notice. He lived alone, Grandmother thought, in an elegant new condominium complex on the Mississippi bluffs. Local glitterati and rock stars, even Cybil Shepherd they said, lived in that building. Nobody believed that Daddy could manage those staggering rents alone and he never invited anyone to visit. He wasn't shopping for a new mother for Sophie and me anymore, but he was still shopping, and obviously doing pretty well at it.

More than one dark cloud seemed to be collecting ominously above us that spring but there would be a break, or at least a different type of cloud, to divert us in the middle of March. On the eighteenth, four days before my twenty-first birthday, Dr. King made his first visit to Memphis. King's interest in the strike was viewed differently, depending upon where you stood in the dialectic. For some, but not all, whites, it was seen as interference, an exploitation of a purely local problem for the sake of a much bigger, and dubious, political and social agenda. For some, but not all, blacks, it was seen as hopeful, the sign that national sympathies might actually turn the tide. For almost everyone, there was fear. Our little local problem was exploding. The strike that Dr. King was to lead could easily mean trouble.

But on the morning of my birthday it began to snow. Snow, even then, in the South was a cause for celebration, the happy excuse for leaving work early or skipping the next day, for rushing the grocery stores for white bread and milk, for eager anticipation of hours, maybe days, to be filled with nothing you'd already planned. Whatever you'd had on your calendar it certainly hadn't been a wet and raucous snowball fight. It hadn't been sliding down an icy hill with the neighborhood children or making ice cream from stuff that fell from the skies. You had not scheduled the unexpected intimacy of cuddling with the kids, snuggling with a lover. Snow in the Deep South is always a party. But snow like this one, late in the spring when the daffodil and tulip and crocus have already made their colorful resurrection, well, *that*'s a jubilee—a reminder that dull and plodding creatures though we are, surprises can still happen. Life is not so predictable after all. By the time it was over, sixteen inches had fallen, blanketing the city and making the record books as the second-largest snowfall in the city's history.

Our snow day, my birthday, was to be a true holiday, spent

with my husband and the best of my best friends. The call to my office had found only one agent on the premises, busy taking calls from others who wouldn't be venturing in. Adam had left the house early but had returned in a couple of hours, finding that almost none of the project crew he managed had shown up on the site, and sure by then that the weather wasn't going to break. At about 10:30 Janet and Myra and David blustered into our living room, practically giddy with their private jokes and full of exaggerated accounts of the wrecks and slides and fender-benders they'd witnessed on the way. We cobbled together a late breakfast, interrupted by one inspection of David's muffler and a short macho snowball war and then we girls began immediately to wash and peel, chop and dice, for a big pot of vegetable soup.

Vegetable soup. What can I say? Every culture has its version, every family its variation. The soup kitchen staple. The fallback meal of the poor. But also the unexpected gift of guilty professional parents to families they really do, actually, care about. The one simple dish in America that take-out chains, fancy restaurants, even the most famous of corporate soup conglomerates can't possibly reproduce. Because good vegetable soup can only be made at home. Nothing perfumes the house, warms the heart, fills the stomach, or communicates love like a slow-cooked, homemade, nutritious, delicious, pot of vegetable soup.

Mind you, chickadees, I don't expect to. But if I ever end up on death row—forced, or allowed, to choose one last meal—bring me vegetable soup. Bring it with or without beef. With or without crackers or corn muffins. Serve it in a tin cup or a Limoges china bowl. Just make it taste like Grandmother's. Like the soup I'm used to. The flavors I associate with cold days and unexpected snow. With happy weekends when everyone's at home. Like the soup we made that snow day in 1968.

We served our soup. It was spectacular. The guys ate in silent reverence, asking for seconds and thirds, complimenting us not so much with words as with the animal gusto that thrills the heart of any cook. Adam produced a birthday cake, the real reason, he confided, for his morning's venture out. We washed down our cake with cold Budweisers, and David, the only one of us now for whom the beers were illegal—and the only one of us at the moment in danger of being called to Viet Nam—noted the obvious irony.

We moved then to congregate downstairs—the rec room that was Adam's pride and joy. We burned the pre-fab fireplace all afternoon long, jumping when its metal shaft popped and groaned. We had all grown up without fireplaces at all. The noises struck us as funny, as part of the ambience.

We played music and brought out first the word games, which Janet and I were particularly good at, but we soon switched to the board games to give the guys a chance. We had decided early on to take a break from television. There was too much of war and bloodshed on TV. There was too great a likelihood of triggering Myra, now a fervent Eugene McCarthy supporter, into an unpleasant political diatribe.

In that panorama of my life, this day, too, will play among my happiest days on earth. Except for one small event. One short window-opening moment on the future that I should have heeded. That I should have granted more serious attention.

"Pay me," Adam said to Janet, who had landed on Adam's Park Place, already developed with three hotels.

"Here," said Janet, handing him six hundred-dollar Monopoly bills, not nearly enough to pay the debt. "I'll owe you the rest. Let me take my turn."

"No." Adam said emphatically. "Pay me now or you're out."

We all looked around, a little startled with Adam's seriousness, the extent to which he was treating the game as real.

"Adam!" I said. "She'll give you an I.O.U. Won't you, Janet? Here, write it on this!" I held up a soggy paper napkin, a leftover from Christmas that proclaimed "Peace" in ivy-twined script.

Everybody else thought this was terribly funny, laughing and rolling backwards on the pillows, our knees still holding our Indian-style postures.

"No," said Adam again. "She pays me or she's out!"

Slowly we all righted ourselves. There was a brief tense moment of quiet. And then Myra pulled a Myra, in this one rare case, making things better, not worse.

"Whoops!" she said, deliberately flipping the board into the air, sending the cards and the little metal tokens flying in every direction, everyone's money, the deeds to their real estate holdings, floating down in intermingled wreckage. For a few seconds we held our breath, our eyes darting nervously between Myra and Adam.

"Tornado?" Myra said sheepishly. And finally, Adam smiled.

We all laughed this time, the kind of tummy-holding laughter that leaves you breathless and teary. Everyone helped to pack away the games and Adam handled some not-so-gentle ribbing, even delivering a joke of his own when he pretended to be stowing some of the Monopoly money away in his own wallet.

Everyone, of course, was happy to spend the night. We put

186

Myra on the daybed in Adam's office, and just in case they should be so inclined, Janet and David within visiting distance on the rec room couch and the downstairs guestroom. That's something I was never sure about. To me, after all those years, the idea of sleeping with David seemed almost incestuous. But I would never be completely positive that Janet shared my view.

We would enjoy that respite—that short, chilly little break in the heated onslaught of events that were still to come that year. On the day that Dr. King returned to lead the march that our snow had postponed, I was in the office, looking through the newest listings, trying to make sure I hadn't missed anything.

"Hey, what's going on down there?" Mr. Mitchner said.

He was looking down into the street from one of our office windows. Terri and I, and the husband and wife clients who'd been waiting in our reception area, all rushed to a window. Below us, on the sidewalks five stories down, there was a moving river of people, almost all black, all headed in the direction of Main Street.

"Turn on the radio!" Mr. Mitchner ordered. But even before we found a local station, started to hear of the riots that had broken out on Beale and Main, the telephone had begun ringing, all of the buttons of our five incoming lines starting to flash at once. One of the calls was for me, from Adam, who had learned of the trouble ahead of us from the radio in his car.

"Don't leave!" Adam said. "All of you stay inside. I'm out east but I'm coming to get you."

I tried arguing with him. My own car was downtown, parked in a lot not two blocks from here. But Adam wasn't having it and I had to agree to stay put. The calls kept coming, from frantic husbands and wives and parents and kids. Most of our staff was not in the office at all but out there in the city somewhere, trying to sell a house. We all helped to field the calls, assuring concerned friends and relatives that we knew that everyone, everything, would be just fine.

We didn't, of course. We listened to the radio, and watched the stream of people and the snarl of traffic from the windows. Reporters told of widespread looting and described streets littered with bricks and broken glass, spattered with blood. We could envision the scenes of riot. We had watched them in Harlem, Watts, Newark and Detroit. We just couldn't imagine one here.

When Adam finally arrived there were only the three of us left. Our clients, the Morgans, had waited with us for perhaps another hour which Mrs. Morgan had spent weepy and nearly hysterical, telling her husband over and over again that she wouldn't be moving to this wretched, awful city, that he couldn't make her and that she'd leave him first. Mr. Mitchner and Terri and I had done everything we could, but when poor Mr. Morgan had broached the idea that it was probably safe to leave, we had readily agreed. The radio said that Dr. King had aborted the march. There was a considerable police presence on the scene now and no need to drive in that direction to leave the downtown area anyway. Mr. Mitchner would walk Terri to her car, where he'd tell the attendant to keep an eye on mine, and Adam and I could go home.

When we reached the lobby floor of our building I saw John Parker, our building's night watchman, looking through the double glass doors at the passing sidewalk traffic. The river of people had dwindled to a trickle and most were now walking in the opposite direction, away from Main Street and the river, still wearing the cardboard placards, proclaiming, "I am a man." John was a pleasant, jovial fellow, always whistling, always there at the end of the day to acknowledge us by name, to open the door and to say warmly, every single time, "Y'all have a good evening now, you hear!"

I smiled when I saw him, early at his post, and I remember thinking that he might have learned more than anyone about what had actually happened to make the march turn violent. But when John turned to face us he was not wearing his usual smile, not flashing his perfect white teeth. There was a sinister scowl on his face and when his eyes locked with mine I saw no hint of recognition. Only a burning accusation, even hatred. He backed away from us, making no move to open the door, offering no farewell greeting.

I clutched Adam's arm as we joined the little stream of returning marchers on the sidewalk.

"Were you scared?" Adam, asked, and I had to answer yes. I had not honestly been really frightened until a moment ago, until I had taken John Parker's stare. But now I was scared. And I thought of Sophie. Who could possibly explain all of this madness to Sophie?

CHAPTER XV

Mayor Loeb wouldn't officially declare an evening curfew until Friday. Curfews were something else we had never expected in our city, but Adam and I, and the vast majority of our fellow Memphians, were not much inclined to leave home that night anyway. We bolted our doors and settled in before our television sets to watch on national news what had been happening only blocks away from Mitchner and Hogan. More than two hundred people had been arrested, dozens injured, one person had died. The property damage would not be officially reported for days but the cameras showed the blocks of looted stores and the streets littered with glass and debris. Eerily the footage already looked archival, like something we'd already seen.

Martin Luther King was interviewed. This had not been what he wanted. Not in keeping, he made it clear, with the philosophy of non-violence that had managed to accomplish so much up until now. Had he given up, stayed away, history—not just our local story, but indeed human history—might have been very different. But he said he was coming back.

It's strange what you remember. Stranger still what you forget. I have forgotten completely what Adam and I talked about that night. What touchstones of agreement or divergences of opinion we discovered between us as we watched our city, our little local problem, being x-rayed before the whole world. But I vividly remember one local reporter making a very big deal about what he thought was the extremely expensive downtown hotel room that Dr. King had stayed in. The implication was that the motives of Dr. King, that champion of the poor and disenfranchised, could not really be so pure, so genuine, if he required such costly lodgings. The King retinue must have heard of the broadcast, too. When they came back they would book something more modest. A twenty-nine-dollar-a-night room in the Lorraine Motel.

Saturday, the 30th of March, was our second night of curfew. The city had called out the National Guard and President Johnson had offered us riot assistance, too. There were some scattered outbreaks of looting and violence, but for the most part that Friday's march was calm and orderly, in keeping with Dr. King's goals. We all began to breathe a little easier.

On Monday I have errands and appointments, each important enough to require rousing myself, shaking off the surreal lassitude of the terrible weekend. The first is to drop off my registration package for summer semester at Memphis State. I linger at the high counter in the Registrar's Office for several minutes after an assistant has already taken my packet. It seems like there should be something more. A band maybe. A bouquet of roses. At least a photograph of the Chancellor shaking my hand. I'm smiling as I cut across the grass quadrangle to head back to my car. In a few more weeks I'll be "college" as Merrilee would say.

The second appointment is serious business. Terri has asked me to show a townhouse to a lady who was moving up from Searcy, Arkansas. It was Terri's own listing but she had told me that the commission was mine in the event this lady took the place. The "lady," already standing on the sidewalk when I arrive, is not much more than a girl, younger surely than I am, except that she has a baby on her hip, a padded diaper bag over her shoulder.

"Good morning, I'm Bobbie Lee Kent," she says, in that soft, slow, musical syrup of an accent that, born-and-bred Southerner though I am, can still surprise and delight me.

"And this here is Samuel." She holds out her baby's arm, jiggling it up and down so that his hand seems to be waving.

"Hello," I reply. "I'm Lacey Harrison with Mitchner Hogan. I hope I didn't keep you waiting."

She is blonde. Both very short and small-boned. The chunky infant on her hip looks like he could weigh a third of her tiny mass. Her voice, her face, reminds of Merrilee except that Merrilee would tower over this girl and is definitely, I can already tell, a world more assertive.

"Oh, no," she said. "I just came on early. I'm not so good with directions, you know. I always plan enough time to get lost!" She smiles at me and hikes the chubby baby up a notch on her hip.

We enter the townhouse with the key Terri has given me. It is still years before the electronic lockbox will simplify this process, making the collecting of keys unnecessary, even keeping the digital record of who has come and gone.

It's a bad idea, chickadees, to show to a client a place that you haven't already previewed. You run a considerable risk in embarrassing yourself and harming your broker's reputation. Say, for example, that one day you usher an elderly couple from upstate New York into a just-listed condominium that contains a plugged and flooded toilet, a living room still furnished with stained mattress, used condoms, and bong pipes. You will be sorry you hadn't previewed first. Lucky for me this is a sweet little place. Clean as a whistle and smelling only lightly of curry and patchouli.

Bobbie Lee checks the kitchen first, looking deeply into the drain of the single ceramic sink and then inspecting under the counter. She opens the door to the oven, which fortunately looks as though it had never been used, checks the tiny pantry, and then peers into the little back yard with a thoughtful, faraway gaze. In the dining area she stops to look down hard at the carpeting and cocks her head at some picture in her mind. I try to imagine her furnishings and wonder how the brown-beigey color could not possibly work.

"It's pretty neutral," I offer, because I'm new at this and frankly don't know what else to say.

"Would you mind?" she says, thrusting out her baby, leaving me no choice but to take the meaty, smiling Samuel. Bobbie Lee produces a seamstress's tape measure from the diaper bag and proceeds to measure the shortened wall between the living room and kitchen pass-through.

"We've got a piano," she tells me. "Marvin, my husband, he plays."

Samuel is staring at me intently. He reaches fat fingers to pluck at my earrings.

Bobbie Lee takes the stairs, leaving Samuel and me for what seems an inordinate amount of time to get to know each other. Instinctually I bounce him, move around with him in the empty place, pointing out, idiotically, the features of a two-bedroom, fee-simple townhome to a baby. My voice has assumed the cadence, the high falsetto timbre, that I remember finding in my bag of tricks from my baby-sitting days. But I feel myself an imposter and wonder when this kid will figure me out and start to scream the alarm.

Eventually Bobbie Lee descends the stairs. She seems surprised to discover that I'm still in possession of Samuel.

"Oh, goodness!" she says, assuming charge of the hefty baby who is still transfixed by my face. 'I'm sorry," she says. "But you know how it is."

Then, perhaps in reaction to my blank expression, she asks, "You got any kids of your own?"

"No," I say. "Not yet. But we're planning to."

Did I say that, really? Or has memory, unreliable transcriber of the past, put that in the record because of things that happened next.

I might never have recalled Bobbie Lee Kent or her baby. I might never have remembered (or made up for the sake of remembering) our conversation at the townhouse, had it not been for my third appointment of the day. This one was with an obstetrician, a new one—I couldn't even bear to think about Dr. Graves. I'd had no appetite for a while and had been queasy in the mornings for several days. My period, maybe, was a little late. I was never very good about keeping up with it and it seemed always irregular this past year. But my concern was with something other than the possibility of pregnancy. It was with whatever mysterious female failing had caused me to let go of Natalie. I had not gone back to Dr. Graves for my recommended "six weeks check-up." In truth I had never discovered the brokenness, the possible malignancy I harbored that had caused me to kill my baby.

This doctor's office is pleasant and homey, the coffee table strewn with copies of *Look*, women's magazines, and old issues of *National Geographic*, but instead I find the morning's newspaper and while away my time reading the horrifying details of the My Lai massacre. I'm thinking that I should go, that there is really too much to do today and this

195

gynecological thing can wait. For a few years at least. Until the world is a better place.

I've already stood up, about to make my escape, when the receptionist calls my name.

"Mrs. Harrison? The doctor will see you now."

Because I'm a new patient I'm led first into the doctor's study. Dr. Barrow is an uncomfortably handsome middle-aged man who rises to shake my hand. We get through the introductions, the preliminaries, and then I have to tell about Natalie. As much as I know, which isn't very much.

"We'll have to get your records from Dr. Graves," he tells me when we're done. "But in the meantime, let's see how you're doing."

In the examining room I will submit to the indignities of the posture, the metal stirrups, this strange man probing my private insides. I have never known whether these are occasions for conversation or for remaining silent and clinically inert. *So, were you surprised to hear that President Johnson won't be seeking re-election? Terrible weather we're having, isn't it?* I study the poster on the wall showing the stages of fetal development.

"About seven or eight weeks along I'd say. Everything seems fine."

Logically I know that I must have responded. That the doctor must have projected a due date and given me standard instructions. Did the nurse, when I made the next routine appointment, offer me congratulations?

There are two pregnant women who walk out of that office. Both of them are me. There is that other me, of memory. That eighteen-year-old, unwed, unemployed, high school senior who floats out of her first visit to the obstetrician in a romantic rapture. Who doesn't know really—

196

not at that moment and not for absolutely sure—if she may not have to spend the next seven months hidden away in the hills of the Ozarks in a home for unwed mothers. That one who knows nothing, fears nothing, and will find nothing remarkable about all the pieces to the future falling into easy place.

There is this present me—this married one, the one that has just come of legal age and has a husband, a job and a three-bedroom house in the suburbs. This one resents the intrusion of that other one, the image of her dancing down the sidewalk, the sly smile fixing on her stupid face, daring anyone, begging everyone to be let in on her secret. That naïve little ditz thinks pregnancy has made her invincible, untouchable, even holy. This me should be happy, too. But because that one was, this one can't be. This one can only be afraid.

On the way home from the doctor I am stopped at East Parkway by a bizarre convoy. Traffic has been halted so that a line of tanks driven by National Guardsmen can make its slow rumbling way down the parkway. The street is one of those archetypal picture postcard southern boulevards, shaded by ancient trees and lined by beautiful old homes. Memory wants to tell of Spanish moss draping old magnolias even though I know that's another city, another postcard. This much is true: The city has just installed embedded lane markers. They are little orange plastic nothings in the noonday sun, but highly reflective and useful little safety devices on a rain-slick street at night. I have read about them in the paper and followed the civic debate about whether they will reduce enough accidents, in preventing drivers from hitting the median, to merit the taxpayer's expense. The tanks, the armored personnel carriers equipped with 50-caliber machine guns, file past the front of

197

my car. The guardsmen, cradling their rifles, look down at me through my car's windshield. Their smooth young faces are stern and unreadable. One or two of them look directly into my eyes. I watch as the convoy rolls past, its great weight crushing, one by one, the new lane reflectors into exploding puffs of orange dust and plastic.

Is this an important memory? What does it mean? Why have I held onto it when I've let so much go? This much is true: That evening I won't tell Adam about my visit to the doctor. This doesn't feel like the right day, the right time.

Surely I would have told him by the weekend. Surely I would have if I'd been able to sleep those next two nights. If Adam hadn't come home troubled by a disappointing business setback on Wednesday. If James Earl Ray had not found Dr. King in his rifle site on Thursday evening.

The curfews imposed at the end of that first week of April were much stricter than those we'd had in March. Only essential emergency services were exempt. Grocery stores, gas stations, restaurants, and theaters were not considered to be offering emergency services. To her credit, Memphis bore her infamy with quiet resignation. Most of us were still in a paralyzing stupor of disbelief, of sadness and humiliation. But the rest of the nation erupted in seismic rage.

You've read about those days of April in your history books. You know there were riots in more than a hundred cities. You can look up the statistics on the deaths and the injuries, the stores and livelihoods destroyed, the tolls on neighborhoods and business districts that wouldn't recover for decades. What the books can't describe to anyone who didn't live through it was the mind-freezing task of trying to make sense of it. It was like watching a war movie—an armed conflict taking place on a Hollywood set. There was the enormous cast running and screaming through the burning streets, the soldiers with fixed bayonets dodging sniper fire, the frighteningly realistic special effects of flying bricks, rocks and Molotov cocktails crashing through storefronts, the directors going too far when they set Marines behind mounted machine guns on the very steps of the nation's capitol.

Except that it wasn't a movie. We actually *were* at war. With ourselves.

By Friday of that week I am becoming haggard with sleeplessness. My dreams, which don't wake Adam anymore, are always different, always the same. The world is imploding on all of us. Sooner or later I wake, gasping for breath, just as an avalanche of bricks and glass and sliding mud comes crashing down on Jeremy, on Sophie, or on me.

In the thin early hours of Saturday morning Adam finds me standing barefoot in the kitchen in only my nightgown and yellow elbow-length RubberMaid gloves.

"What the hell are you doing?" he asks me, which is a good question. But he is not likely to understand the answer. Not this morning. Not ever.

"I'm cleaning," I tell him. And I am. I have only started on the oven. But I have plans for the range top, the inside of the refrigerator, the pantry shelves and kitchen floor. Then I will attack the bathrooms, the grout between the tiles, the toilets and the tubs.

"Come back to bed, Lacey," he pleads. "You can finish that tomorrow."

No. I can't. Or maybe I can. But the momentum will have to carry me that far. I will clean past sunrise, through the whole day, and long after sundown. I will clean until I am beyond exhaustion. Until I have examined, but not answered, all the questions that plague me. Until my anger has been calmed by the back and forth rhythms of scrubbing, until my fear has been diluted in water and solvents. When I am done, or when I am forced to concede that I can go no longer, I will have affected nothing great. The world will not be a better place. But I will have put my house at least, *my house*, in order.

CHAPTER XVI

In the middle of May I register for my first college semester. By going two nights a week from 5:30 to 8:15 I should be able to take two classes. English composition is a given and I had been planning to take Biology as a nice contrast but at the last minute I scratch that out and write PolSci101 on the form. Still, I'm uncertain. I start over on a new form, re-write Eng101, but this time I put Hist110 below it. Lucky for me the line is long behind me and there aren't that many blank forms left on the table. Needless to say, my major is "Undeclared."

Adam has been apprised of his impending fatherhood, and while he had initially been a little underwhelmed by the news, he is getting used to the idea. Actually now he brings it up more than I do, asking me how I'm feeling, wondering out loud if we shouldn't move his office downstairs so that the nursery can be near our bedroom. October is far away and there's plenty of time for that. But his questioning has spurred me to *some* action at least. I have arranged a special meeting to break my news, simultaneously, to Nana and to Grandmother. I will take them to lunch, to a quaint little midtown tea room and we'll visit and catch up.

At the door of Maureen's apartment Nana greets me, still in housedress and apron. She is beaming delightedly but I get the eerie sense that maybe she doesn't actually recognize me.

I've cut my hair. Lost a little weight. Her eyes, probably, are going.

"Nana, it's Lacey! I'm here to take you to lunch."

"Land sakes!" she says, abashed. "I didn't know you would get here so early. You're not speeding in that new car, are you?"

I don't have a new car but it doesn't matter. To some people a car is a car.

"Nana," I say, stepping inside onto the small parquet square that forms the foyer. "Why don't you change? Put on something a little fancier." I don't want to hurt her feelings but she's seriously underdressed for the place I have in mind.

"Ha!" she says, lifting her apron slightly with both hands as though she is surprised to find herself still wearing it. "I was going to! I didn't know you was going to get here so fast. Just sit yourself down. Would you want something to eat?"

"No," I tell her. "I'm fine. You change. I'll wait right here."

I sit down on the familiar Danish Modern sofa and look around. Most everything here I recognize but there are a few new furnishings and accessories. There is a little Chippendale desk at the window and in the corner a floral-covered Queen Ann chair. A glazed porcelain Chinese vase rests incongruously on the end of the stick-legged coffee table. It occurs to me that Daddy may have overly influenced the furnishings of our little ranch house in Fairfield Estates. That Maureen's own tastes may actually have been less contemporary, more traditional. Too bad he'd let her have her way about the ugly maple bunk beds.   Actually, I realize, I don't know much at all about Maureen. Maybe I never did. I certainly don't know where she works now. Whether or not she is seeing someone. Whether she has forgiven herself for

202

what she said to Sophie.

Nana reappears in another housedress. This one is slightly crisper. The apron is missing. It will have to do. On the drive to Grandmother's though, I begin to gather that Nana is not quite the person she once was. She is happy and chatty, glad I imagine, to be out of that small apartment for a bit. But some of her remarks are cryptic, even nonsensical.

"I forgot about that dog," she says, laughing. "I reckon he can wait for his supper."

There had been no dog in the apartment and the likelihood that Maureen, who would never allow Sophie and me to have pets, should have acquired a dog at this stage in her life was well beyond incredible. I am less perplexed, but more troubled, by Nana's reference to *that good-for-nothing Jeff Stoner*. Jeff Stoner, I clearly recall, was a character in one of her favorite soap operas when Sophie and I were small. And even the fictional and adulterous Jeff Stoner, shot deservedly through the heart by his wife, had been dead for at least ten years. When we arrive at Grandmother's House, to find her impeccably attired in black silk dress, single-strand pearls, black patent heels, I am starting to feel, as you chickadees might say, more than a little "creeped out."

We're seated immediately in the charming little tea room, all of its patrons women, only one or two of whom even glance at Nana's housedress. There's been no opportunity to privately share my concerns with Grandmother and I resolve to let things run their course, to see if Grandmother picks up on anything odd about Nana. For quite some time they enchant me, these two lovely women of a gentler, more civil era, in their cordial but formalized exchanges, the way they still address each other, in spite of our long histories, as "Mrs. Archer," and "my dear Mrs. Winters." After we're served our tea and the light fare that stands as lunch in such ladylike places, I make my little announcement. They are both comprehending and delighted. Grandmother, who never raises her voice, even shares the news with our waitress, audibly enough that it creates a generalized twitter and a smattering of applause from nearby tables.

They are happy for me. I want to be happy. Possibly I've over-reacted. Possibly Nana is having an off day. But then, with a finger sandwich paused halfway to her lips, she drives a cold dagger deep into my heart.

"That sweet little Sophie," she says musingly. "You have to wish the good Lord had let *her* baby live."

Grandmother blanches. We stare at each other and then back at Nana. My head has gone light. I feel wobbly in my chair.

"Mrs. Archer," Grandmother says at last. "I think you must be confused."

Nana apparently doesn't hear her.

"How old do you reckon that child would *be* now?" Nana asks intently, her brow deeply furrowed with the strain of remembering.

Grandmother dabs at the hollow of her throat with her napkin. She leans forward, low to the table and speaks again, almost in a whisper.

"Mrs. Archer," she says. "Hush!"

Nana's face crumples, the wound visible in her eyes. She looks at me for explanation.

"It's ok," I tell Grandmother. "It's ok."

And so I explain. I don't know how I do. I don't know why the fates have arranged it so that I will have to say all of it and aloud. But I do. The child, I say, would be almost two and half. The child, I say, was a girl. I don't know whether or not I

204

say that the child's name, had the child lived, would have been Natalie. I don't suppose I add that the child's father is dead also. I know that I say this:

"But Nana. It wasn't Sophie's baby. It was mine."

For a second Nana's face is still stricken and confused. Then, astonishingly, she smiles.

"Aw," she says, "I just had it mixed up." The relief in her voice is ironic and painful but I take it as a measure of how much she loves Sophie rather than of how little she loves me.

I drop Nana back home first. She is happy and garrulous again on the ride and her conversation, for the most part, makes sense. I resolve to get her out more, to be, since I can never really be her granddaughter, at least a better friend. She had spent years taking care of Sophie and me. In my head I acknowledge the burden of that debt. In my heart I feel it lightly, if at all. It is almost—can I say this?—the gratitude of a prisoner for his food. But I will maintain the connection a while longer. There is always the chance that Sophie will seek her out.

In the car again Grandmother and I are quiet, but it is the easy quiet of two minds reflecting on the same ideas. The soundless communication of thoughts working, but no friction in the effort. We say nothing at all until I pull her alongside the curb before this year's quadriplex.

"Thank you for a lovely luncheon," she says. (It was always "luncheon" with Grandmother. Never just "lunch.")

"You're very welcome," I say, wryly amused at our own sudden formality.

"And I'm sorry about Mrs. Archer."

"Me too," I say, certain that both of us understand all of the ways that we mean it.

"But I'm happy for *you*, darling!" she adds brightly,

leaning over to kiss my cheek, the familiar whispery scent of her lilac toilet water tumbling me backward through the years.

Wait! I suddenly want to say as I watch her walk up the sidewalk. *Stop!* I think, as I see her going away from me, a small black-clad woman in patent shoes and matching handbag, moving slower than I recall, a weariness in her step that doesn't belong to Grandmother.

Let me come in! Let me come home! I don't say, because it's grown late and there is this other house, and this man waiting for me across town. Because most of all, worst of all, Grandmother's House—this one, any of them—won't really feel like home either and if I follow her, I'll have to remember.

For reasons I can't recall Bobbie Lee Kent and her husband do not choose Terri's listing. But through the sheer dumb luck of simply being there to answer the office telephone a little after hours on a Wednesday evening I acquire clients all my own. This is a newlywed couple looking for a townhome. I happen to know of a lovely one, I tell them, and I'm able to describe its features fluidly, having so recently practiced my presentation on the curiously attentive Samuel. I show them two more, but this is the one they like. With lots of help from the others I get through my first closing and I have the fun of congratulating happy first-time buyers and the thrill of depositing my first real commission check into the bank.

Adam takes me out to dinner. He seems proud and impressed. This real estate thing actually seems pretty easy. (I will have plenty of reason to re-examine this assumption in the years to come.) It's the college thing, surprisingly, that turns out to be a little harder.

The history is going well. I like my teacher, Mr. Chester Hansen, a young teaching assistant who is passionate and earnest about American history and seems to really care about whether or not we absorb its lessons. There's a substantial overlap between this first course and what I supposedly learned in high school but I find there are plenty of gaps in my knowledge, an abyss in my real understanding, and I enjoy being taught by someone who is more interested in the subject matter than Friday night's football game. The approach to scoring well on college history exams appears to be the same one that worked, when you applied it, in high school. You pay attention in class. You read the material. You study a bit. And *voila!* You receive the A you so richly deserve.

Something, however, has gone a little awry with the English. On the third night of class our professor, Dr. Agnes Ketch, returns the graded papers from our first composition assignment. In my desk, not in the very first row, but more judiciously chosen in the second, I'm already working hard to feign humility. Dr. Ketch uses a "curve," she says, for the first three assignments, to offer some hope, she tells us, that every last one of us won't fail the whole course. Unlike Mr. Hansen, Dr. Ketch has been at this a while and doesn't pull any punches. I'm unconcerned with her brittle exterior, certain that it hides a heart of gold and the lifelong yearning to discover the next Virginia Wolfe. Or Dorothy Parker. Or maybe Eudora Welty. In truth, these are essays we're writing now and I haven't had the opportunity yet to develop my poetic or fictional style.

As Dr. Ketch passes out the papers my classmates begin to emote in moans and groans and a couple of low-level profanities. I'm wondering if they'll dislike me after they see my grade. But it isn't going to be a problem. When Dr. Ketch deposits on my desk the paper I've written, in answer to the burning question, *Do school uniforms provide an educational advantage?* there is a large, unmistakable C+ written in red at the top.

Nope. Nein. Nyet. Obviously a mistake.

Hadn't I mentioned to Dr. Ketch in our friendly hallway chat after first class that I had been a pioneer of the Advanced Placement program in high school? Actually, had I not been so busy getting married that I'd failed to take the exemption exam I should have skipped her stupid course entirely. I know that I'd told her that I loved English. That I was a writer. A HUGE reader.

Maybe she was testing me. Pushing me, because of my precocious abilities, to reach greater heights than expected of the plebian hordes. But my paper was a bleeding bandage of red ink. I had taken some liberties with unorthodox punctuation that had not amused her. I had misspelled a couple of words. To one of my finer philosophical points she had written "*Logic?*" in red in the margin. A comment at the bottom, in barely legible, but very red, script, said "*Not a bad first effort. But pay attention to mechanics. Avoid rambling discourse in favor of critical thinking and better organization.*"

OK. Maybe I'd have to give her the point on mechanics. But me? Ramble? When Dr. Ketch posts the range of scores on the blackboard I haven't even made the top of the curve.

On the way home from class I pull my car over on the shoulder to throw up. I'm not sick exactly. I'm just sick. Myra Winston, one of the most lackadaisical students I'd ever known, is about to graduate from the University of Tennessee. Janet and David are rising juniors. Sean Laughlin, my chess buddy, is somewhere up in New England doing stunningly in pre-med. Even Timothy Booker, a sloppy, mediocre writer from newspaper staff has a column now in a monthly local magazine.

Adam is still up when I get home that night. Ask him now, give him the opportunity to slide a tiny bead here and there along the picaresque chain of the past, he'd do it differently. He'd be sound asleep when I enter the door, slamming down my schoolbooks on the kitchen table, clomping heels-hard down the galley kitchen, slamming the refrigerator door once I've extracted my Tab.

"What's wrong?" he asks innocently.

"Nothing!" I say. Bait in the female trap. Take it, you're doomed. Ignore it, you're doomed.

"Lacey!" he says, not standing up yet, but making it clear in his voice, his posture, that he's going to take the bait. "What's wrong?"

"I flunked my first English composition," I finally tell him. After a dramatic silence. After I have taken a long, slow sip of my Tab at the kitchen sink, and managed to put a martyr's resignation in my voice.

"You flunked?" He says, genuinely startled. "You got an F?"

"No, I didn't get an F!" (Annoyed, long-suffering sigh) "I got a C plus. Basically, I flunked."

"That's great!" he says. (Big mistake. First indication that he's not really listening.)

"Great?" I query sarcastically. "You think a C plus is *great*?"

"Well, sure," he says. "If a C is average, then you're doing fine. Better than average."

Average. That's what he'd said. Adam has now defined the

debate. Am I going to go there, to challenge him so early on its central tenet? You bet I am.

"Really?" I parry. "Average is *great*?"

"Well," he hesitates, suspecting probably that he's being edged into a corner. "Sure. There's nothing wrong with average."

"So," I respond, smelling blood, "you'd be happy with an *average* career? If Mr. Brinkman tells you next week that your performance has been *average*, you'd be just fine with that?"

"Uh . . . well, no," says Adam. (He's slumping now at the kitchen table.) "No. I guess not. But that's different."

"Really?" I say. "How is it different? In what way, exactly, is it *different*?"

My voice is too loud, undeniably defiant. I'm asking for it and I know it. On some level I already know I'm going to be sorry.

"Because I'm talking about work!" he says, suddenly belligerent. "You're just talking about a stupid English essay!"

(S*tupid*. Poor choice of words. The opening to go for the jugular.)

"So work, *your* work, is valuable? My work, if I should choose to make it writing an essay, is stupid?"

(Well done, Lacey. Are you satisfied now?)

Adam stalks off first. He gets official credit for making it the first night ever we will lie soldier-stiff in the marital bed, an unbreachable few inches between our bodies.

If you still love each other, and we did, part of the work that goes on in this awful time— once you've calmed down and find yourself feeling lonely and ashamed—is a complete review of the dialogue. You replay what you said. You listen again to what he said. Your voice on the tape is strident and shrewish. His voice on the tape is calm and reasonable. If you still love each other, and we did, part of the work to be done in these awful times is self-examination. How much of this had I set up, using the C+ as a straw man?

What I had brought to that silly argument—what I had set down, prepackaged and time-bomb ticking between us—was the knowledge that Adam isn't all that crazy about me going to college anyway. He's vaguely jealous of my classmates, my teachers, the experiences I'm having in night school. He's definitely bothered by the fact that all of it—this whole college pipedream that I'm obsessed with—doesn't seem to calm and satisfy, but rather to agitate me, the ideas I'm picking up infecting me with a fevered restlessness. *His* package, Adam's time-bomb, is the knowledge that I'm a little jealous, too. His career seems real and very adult. He makes good money, meets important people. He is helping to build shopping centers, warehouses, industrial parks. Serious stuff compared to the sale of one townhouse.

But we hadn't really exploded anything yet. We had only been petty and childish. One of us had anyway. I was sorry for my part and tomorrow I'd tell Adam so. But by God, I wasn't going to let Dr. Ketch defeat me. I could learn to write a college essay! I wasn't about to settle for "average."

I finished my review of our first real fight and let myself surrender to sleep. I was certain by then that sometime in the night, our bodies, our unconscious minds, would cross the imaginary breach. They would if we loved each other. And we still did.

CHAPTER XVII

"I was thinking of white," Mrs. Inman says, holding up a pristinely pale sample of high-pile carpeting for my inspection.

Our firm has been given the exclusive marketing and sales rights to a new subdivision not seven miles from my own house on Chantilly Drive. Terri and I spend long days in the model home, busy in flurries with speaking with clients, driving them around to look at lots and partially constructed houses, soberly writing the occasional contract, which Terri and I, once the clients have safely pulled away, celebrate with very un-sober whoops and hollers and dancing around the model. I am the one who gets to sit with clients at the model's kitchen table, helping the newest buyers to pick paint and tile, Formica and floor covering.

This woman, the mother of three stair-step boys who are now roughhousing in the model's living room, flicking about the construction mud caked on their shoes in the process, is considering white.

"And maybe red for the countertops?" She chooses a small scarlet piece of Formica from the chained ring of samples.

"Sure," I say. "White is . . . nice."

Mrs. Inman is a large pink-faced woman. Little beads of perspiration glisten above her lip and there are great damp circles under the arms of her flowered sundress.

"But maybe a little impractical?" I offer. "What do you think of this?" I push a more neutral, definitely more dirt-colored sample across the table. "It's called Prairie."

"Prairie?" she says, taking the sample but wrinkling her nose. I intuit that it's not the color, but the name, that she objects to. I rifle my mental filing cabinet, trying to think of a carpet color in our offerings that will hold up under Mrs. Inman's rowdy boys but has a prettier name.

"How about this one?" I suggest, picking another dark neutral with barely perceptible paprika flecks. This is *Sedona Sunset*."

Mrs. Inman smiles. Now we're cooking. I can already see her conducting tours of her new little house, pointing out coquettishly that her carpet is *Sedona Sunset*.

"And red for the counters?"

The chip she is holding is almost neon. A ghastly choice, I think, unless you're decorating the corner diner.

"Well," I begin again, "maybe something a little less exotic?" I realize instantly that I've made another mistake. Exotic is exactly what poor, plain, domestically overburdened Mrs. Inman dreams about.

Gently I take the ring of laminate samples out of her rough-knuckled hands.

"This is nice," I tell her, selecting a brown and tan mottle with nearly the same little orangey undertones as the carpet. "It's called *Grecian Isle*."

Mrs. Inman smiles again, taking the selected chip back from me, looking at it rapturously as though it were the Hope diamond.

Now that I know the formula it's easy to guide her through the other choices of trim and paint colors, linoleum for the kitchen and tile for the bathrooms. When she's gone and I write up her selections on the form for decorating options, it reads like a travel brochure.

I am garnering a great deal of satisfaction from my work these days. Were it not for the morning sickness, which stubbornly persists through May, and shows up at times other than mornings, I would almost be in heaven. I love watching the evolution of houses go from grating to footings, slab to framing, drywall to finishing touches. The aromas of some of the stages—the sweet fragrant smell of just-cut lumber, the chemical scent of spackling and paint, the stinging dye-smell of new carpet—can still trigger a spate of gagging and nausea. But Terri covers for me if I'm having one of those days. So far, so good.

I have ascended from a B minus to a B plus on the last two of Dr. Ketch's curved essay assignments but it doesn't seem that it's getting easier. For weeks all of my spare time has been devoted to writing and re-writing essays. Early in the morning, late and night, in the spaces between clients dropping into our model home, I write, scratch out, start over. I've stopped being clever with punctuation. I practically sleep with a dictionary. I have to believe that the A that I'm shooting for is out there somewhere but I'm wondering if it's in another nebula.

At the end of May Adam and I make the drive to Knoxville to attend Myra's graduation. It's a boisterous and fun-filled weekend and I get to re-connect not only with Myra and Janet's parents, but with dozens of cronies from high school, some from Myra's class, some from mine and Janet's. On Saturday night Janet takes us on a drop-in round of fraternity parties, taking credit, each time she introduces us, for being our matchmaker. I'm a little less envious of all of it now, less sensitive now that I'm finally in school myself. Adam and I reminisce about our first meeting. We dance and hold hands. The campus scene is fun, we agree, but it doesn't compare to what *we* have. Not to the satisfactions of careers already taking off. The comforts of our own house. The pleasures, Adam reminds me with a lascivious wink, of really great sex.

Wait! Hadn't I thought this before? Hadn't I once before grown smug and complacent? Started to get used to being happy? Isn't that the way you tempt the Fates?

In early June one of the old dreams wakes me. The clock reads well after three but Adam is not in bed. I had left him watching the late returns of the California primaries. I find him, holding his head in his hands, still sitting before the downstairs television. The voices on the TV are confused, unusually loud. The camera swings and sways wildly.

"Adam, what's happening? What's going on?"

He lifts his head and I see the shock, the bewilderment.

"They've shot him," he says. "Someone has shot Bobby Kennedy."

Adam had fallen asleep on the couch, even before the network had ended its coverage, once it had become clear that Kennedy had won the primary. Only minutes before my arrival the television had leapt into action again, waking Adam with the hastily captured scenes of mayhem in the pantry of the Ambassador Hotel. I sit down beside him to watch the unfolding of yet another national nightmare. It's too late to look away when the camera catches Robert Kennedy's face, his head cradled in someone's hand. His eyes are still open but the life flows out, into a massive pool on the pantry floor.

It won't be official for hours, but this hope, too, is already lost to us. On Saturday we will listen to Ted Kennedy deliver his brother's eulogy at St Patrick's. We will watch the footage of the slow funeral train rumbling back to Washington. Thousands of mourners line the track, young and old, black and white. I remember a very old man, a World War I vet in the drab woolen jacket and cap of his own war, standing in rigid salute. Mothers and fathers and children clasp hands and weep silently beside the track. A teenage girl holds up a sign. "Farewell, Bobby."

This time the long transport of the Senator's body will require something a little different in the way of a state funeral. This one must take place at night. Floodlights illumine the scene at Arlington Cemetery. The mourners hold candles in the dark. The folded flag goes to Ethel Kennedy. She is pregnant, too. But she has other children who will remember him. She doesn't have to sit, empty and ended, while the body of her husband goes into the ground.

This can't be right. Why does it seem that this whole terrible year keeps looping back on itself? Maybe this is what it means to be a grown up. The discovery that happiness is only a teasing respite between funerals. For days I will clean in the evenings on Chantilly Drive. In the model, during the four days of rain that follow the funeral, I dust the furniture, scour the bathrooms, reorganize my files.

One Monday I am called to come to my new obstetrician's office. Dr. Barrow has received my records and wants to explain to me what I had not been told, perhaps what I had not wanted to know, about Natalie. I'd had a complication of pregnancy known as *placenta previa*, a condition in which the placenta is covering, or too close to, the cervix. Dr. Barrow protects the brotherhood and will say nothing critical about my previous treatment. He does acknowledge, shaking his head, that he doesn't know why my condition had not revealed itself earlier. Many, many such pregnancies, he tells

217

me, go on to result in healthy, full-term babies, even if delivery is typically by C-section. So that's the good news. The bad news is that I am at some risk for a repetition of heavy bleeding not only during the pregnancy but at and after delivery. The good news is that there will be no more invasive ob-gyn examinations. The bad news is that there won't be any more sex, either.

Adam takes my diagnosis in perfect stride, only blinking a couple of times when I tell him the bit about the sex. He is an optimist, Adam, and sees no reason to get overwrought. He buys us a little television for the bedroom dresser, takes down the gauzy tenting—which I learn he never liked much anyway—and proceeds without further discussion to begin moving his office down to the bottom floor.

His preparations will seem prescient, almost as though he had known what was coming. Three weeks later, after nothing more than walking around at Adam's company's Fourth of July picnic, I start to spot. Adam and I rush from picnic to emergency room and then wait, hours, for the doctor. I'm OK. The baby is fine. But Dr. Barrow decrees bed rest. As in complete bed rest. As in, flat-on-your-back-and-don't-get-up-for-anything-but-the-bathroom bed rest.

And so, my chickadees, comes an ugly part of my story. I could easily skip it. Probably no one would ever know. But if I omit this part I am in danger of allowing other lies in.

In the very first weeks I do pretty well. It's almost like an unexpected vacation to be sent to bed without being sick. To lie back, propped on my pillows, and to be waited on hand and foot like a princess. I read and write letters. Paint my toenails. Find myself unwilling drawn into the plots of the daytime soap operas. But the days drag on. The novelty wanes. Rapidly the princess becomes bored and irritable.

218

Little by little, day by day, she becomes more selfish and demanding, shorter of temper and sharper of tongue. In truth, she becomes a perfect bitch, and she just can't seem to help it.

It would be impossible to overstate how much sympathy there is for my plight. Everybody in my little world does what they can. Grandmother calls me several times a day. Often I'm rude to her, breaking her heart, and knowing it, when I tell her not to call back. I receive gifts and cards from Adam's co-workers which I never deign to acknowledge. Friends from my classes drop by—I use the term loosely, because Chantilly Drive is miles and miles from school. They bring me the last of summer school assignments. The take-home exam from Mr. Hansen's history class. The last graded essays from English. I have finally managed to eke A's out of Dr. Ketch but she insists on giving me an *Incomplete* for the semester. Her handwritten note, on monogrammed paper but still nearly illegible, says that we will "resolve" the incomplete next semester, after we're able to talk. The hatred I feel for her borders on the homicidal. Particularly since I'm unable to get out of this bed to register for fall semester. I cry and fume and rail. Adam bears the brunt of it.

Terri persists in trying to support me and my flailing career. She brings me presentation posters and samples so that I can make coordinated decorator boards of colors and materials that will look good in our little subdivision. I use scissors and markers and rubber cement to make more arrays than they can possibly use. There is, finally, not much difference between a palette of slates, and one of charcoals.

I wear Adam down in my demand for books. He gets me texts I will not need for years from the Memphis State bookstore and makes twice-weekly trips to the public library. Hardy, again is my novelist of choice. I have moved into his lesser known works now and get the old satisfactions from *A Pair of Blue Eyes* and *The Woodlanders*. But in *The Hand of Elthelberta* Hardy betrays me with a happy ending and I decide to put him away for good. Perhaps I'm being unfair to him. I'm not really seeking companionship in my misery this time. I'm seeking fortification against it. I know this will turn out badly. I just don't know how long it will take.

In my spiral-bound English essay notebook I write multiple versions of my last will and testament. Some of them are witty and sardonic. Others are more honest and heartfelt, even sloppily, embarrassingly, sentimental. None of them, really, are centered on the disposition of my worldly goods. I don't give a rat's ass about stuff right now. But all of them are perfectly punctuated and dictionary-verified. After I'm gone, they'll find no misspelled words.

If there is any good, any personal growth at all, that comes from this horrible time, it is the lifelong sympathies I will develop for the chronically ill, the bedridden, that will stay with me forever. There is nothing so hard as doing nothing. Physical inactivity is an affront to the life force, the beating heart and pulsing blood, the muscles meant to work, not waste. I have dreams of running. Of climbing steep hills. I fantasize about just being able to dash to the mailbox.

Curiously the child inside me doesn't share my lethargy. The baby rolls and tumbles, kicking and punching and prodding from within. This seems like even more activity than I remember from Natalie but I don't know how to feel about its rambunctiousness. On the one hand it seems a good thing. A sign of vigor and health. On the other hand I fear that its gymnastics will disrupt something, rush us too soon to the hospital. On an even other hand I wish, sometimes, it would just let me sleep at night. I am never really tired, but always a little groggy, and like an old dowager I nod on and off all day.

For more than two months I live like this. For more than two months, *we* do. Adam's nerves are frayed. He can't do enough for me. He can't do anything right. At my insistence he sleeps now downstairs, a low-tech walkie-talky type of intercom connecting us. Most nights I turn it off. In the morning he'll pretend to be angry, but the absence of its static will have allowed him, at least, to sleep.

It is Janet, again, who comes to my rescue. Janet, again, who takes my psychic pulse, who sees right through my whiney bullshit and cuts to the core of my fears. It is a Thursday, I think, when she comes by. But how can one know this, when all the normal cues, the little spikes and dips that correspond to normal weekly activity, have all been flat-lined by the monotony of a life being spent, every single day, in bed. Our dialogue goes something like this:

Janet: So, how's it going?

Me: Fine. I had a wrinkle in the sheets on Tuesday, but I handled it. I'm fine.

Janet: You know he's worried about you, don't you? Adam's a little scared.

Me: Really? Screw Adam. He's got nothing to be scared about. It's not his gonads they're going t eviscerate.

Janet: Eviscerate? You're such a weirdo. Who talks like that?

Me: You're the campus cutie. You tell me. Don't they use polysyllabic words at UT?

Janet: Polysyllabic. Nice! You always were a weirdo.

Me: You're repeating yourself. What can I do you for, short of sharing the bedpan?

Janet: No shit! You have to use a bed pan?

Me:	No. I don't. I can get up when I need to.
Janet:	That's good. I can't imagine dumping. I mean, lying down and all.
Me:	You always did suffer from a lack of imagination. Probably why you wasted half of tenth grade on Ricky Wyndham.
Janet:	Yeah. Wyndham was a waste. He's selling cars now. Somewhere out in Germantown. I hear he's gotten really fat.
Me:	Too bad. But he was a waste.
Janet:	Yeah. He was a waste.

[Companionable silence.]

Janet:	So you want a girl or a boy?
Me:	I want out of this bed.
Janet:	[laughing] Yeah, I hear that. But, say, it's a girl. Where's she going to sleep?
Me:	What do you mean, sleep?
Janet:	Adam says you haven't bought anything. You don't even have a crib or anything. Not even diapers for God's sake.
Me:	You've been talking a lot to Adam. What does Adam say?
Janet:	Adam doesn't know what to do, Lacey. Adam's a man.
Me:	Yeah. Adam's a man.
Janet:	Yeah. Adam's a man. But he's in this, too, Lacey. Isn't he? I mean, *isn't he?*

And so Janet saved the day. Again. Adam *was* in this but I had forgotten. Whatever happened he would be there too.

222

Unless Uncle Sam re-activated his unit, really, really fast, Adam would be there beside me. He would share in the urgency, the rush, of running alongside wheeled gurneys and then the numbing tension of waiting. He would be there to listen to their supercilious medical explanations, to have swinging double doors shut in his face. There would be somebody, besides Grandmother, to defend me against the white-coated fiends. And when it was over, all over? Well, Adam would share in that, too.

"Listen," I told her, after we were done, after I'd acquiesced to her busybody interference and agreed that she, or she and Adam, would secure the bare necessities for bringing a baby home, "Keep the receipts. Save every lousy price tag!"

"Sure," she said, closing the door to my cell behind her, "Don't worry. I'll save the receipts."

So Janet and Adam become a team. For six weeks, off and on, they meet at, or go together to, the furniture departments, children's stores and fancy department stores—those venues for infant and juvenile wares that served back then before Babies R Us had become a one-stop shopping wonderland. In the evenings, those when I'm not pretending to be asleep, they show me their purchases. One night it's a simple layette, a supply of basic cloth diapers. On another there's a set of baby bottles, packages of pacifiers, a spindly little infant seat for bringing a newborn home. Adam and Janet are united and businesslike, always making lists at my kitchen table, happily planning their next rendezvous, as though it is their baby, not mine, they are preparing for.

"It's enough," I tell them, when they bring me hooded towels and washcloths.

"Enough," I say, when they show me a boxed starter set of baby oil, powder and lotion, cotton balls and swabs. But there are always a few more things, only a few more essentials to necessitate one more shopping spree for my husband and my best friend.

Janet, the blue-eyed and flaxen-haired, seems to have become more gorgeous than ever. She is trim, tan, and hard-bodied when she shows up in short skirts, hot-pants, tight stone-washed jeans. I, on the other hand, am a fat, flaccid sow. There are only two nightgowns now that will cover my swollen, ugly body but I would die before I asked Janet to pick me up another. Usually my hair is straight and greasy. My breath always stinks.

By the end of summer they have substantially outfitted the nursery. There is a bassinette and a crib, a small chest of drawers and a changing table, even ball-fringed curtains which I had not sanctioned and which I'm not sure I even like. In the daytime now and again I pad into the little room, fingering the unopened packages of tiny T-shirts and receiving blankets, a plush white rabbit one of them has placed in the crib. True to her word, Janet has left the price tags on everything. A little giraffe lamp weights down a stack of receipts.

At the end of August there is also something different to see on my little bedroom television. I have never paid attention to a Democratic National Convention before and I don't expect much in the way of good theater from this one, but I'm interested in the process. Anti-war sentiment had brought down Lyndon Johnson, but neither Myra's peace candidate, Eugene McCarthy, nor George McGovern seemed to have the traction. Bobby Kennedy had been shot. Nobody, I thought, could really take George Wallace seriously. Hubert Humphrey seems a shoe-in. But the convention itself surprises me by its contentiousness. Many of the delegates are frustrated and refuse to support the nominee. There is clash and conflict on the floor but the real drama will play out in the streets. National television will capture yet another history-altering event of that long and terrible year. From my bed I watch the Chicago police shouting orders through bullhorns and then wading into the crowd swinging clubs. I see demonstrators and bystanders, beaten, maced and arrested, many of them bleeding as they are dragged to the paddy wagons by feet, arms, and hair. Those images, your history books will tell you, inspired a conservative backlash that doomed Humphrey's candidacy. For me, and millions like me, they kindled an impotent anger and deepened a growing distrust and suspicion of government. Everything that long, hot summer seemed only a pointless charade.

But the thing about summer is that it morphs into fall. One day I realize that I have made it to September. A familiar refreshing crispness wafts through the bedroom window. I feel unusually energetic, even hopeful. I will take my shower before Adam gets home. I'll wash my hair and shave my legs. I'll surprise him tonight with a wife who is clean, wearing make-up, practically human.

The shower is long and wastefully decadent. I let the water run forever while I shampoo my hair twice, three times, rinsing and conditioning and rinsing again. I shave my legs standing up, holding the wall with one hand while I accomplish the nick-less, if not perfectly thorough, job. I feel wonderful, completely revived. Maybe I can find something to put on besides the mammoth nightgowns. Maybe, if I shouldn't really cook us a meal, I can at least make a big salad for dinner. I have just turned off the water and reached for a towel when I notice the bright blood circling the shower drain.

Adam, who is almost never in his office, is fortunately there today. He makes it home quickly. We remember to call ahead to the doctor, to put my overnight bag into the trunk of the car. On the ride to the hospital, Adam is white-faced and quiet and I feel for him an aching love, an anguished pity. I try to reassure him. It's probably nothing, I tell him. They'll probably send me right back home. But I feel the folded stack of towels between my legs growing cold and wet. By the time we arrive at emergency I'm feeling faint, but for Adam's sake I struggle, push back hard against the coming blackness.

I remember being lifted and moved, Adam receding, growing small in the distance. I remember the overhead lights in the corridor whizzing by in staccato flashes. I remember clawing at someone's face and will have the proof under my fingernails that I had managed to draw blood. I remember strong arms holding me down, strapping me so that I have no way to fight. And then I remember . . . nothing.

I know that I've been gone a very long time. That I've been days and days in the darkness, in a place where stranger's hands had gripped and pulled and tortured me and stranger's voices had called my name over and over before they had finally given up and let me be. Yet I haven't. It's still the same day and only dusk when I'm finally able to keep my eyes open long enough to get my bearings. To realize that I'm in a regular bed in a private room and to find Adam slouched in the chair in the corner. His eyes are closed but still he looks terrible. His face is gray and haggard and his matted, frizzled hair, if he didn't look so sad and exhausted, would almost be funny.

He senses that I'm awake and gets up stiffly from the chair. He comes to the bed and bends down to place a feathery soft kiss on my lips.

"I'm sorry," I tell him. And truly I am. For the first time in months I hurt for Adam more than I do for myself.

"Sorry for what?" he asks. And then, in that kind of miracle of good timing that happens once or twice in a human lifetime, a green-garbed nurse pushes into our room.

She is bringing me Justin Matthew Harrison. A little small maybe. The expression on his tiny face a little churlish and peeved. But otherwise, in all other ways, absolutely perfect.

CHAPTER XVIII

We will have two homecomings of sorts. The first, after four days, is mine only. Justin, we're told, is just below the arbitrary guidelines for a premature infant and will have to stay in the nursery for a few days more. I travel three times a day to the hospital to feed and hold him, imagining each time that he is happier than the last to see me. He is taking to my breast well and I think that I'm the one responsible for his rapid recovery of the near pound lost after his birth. But another woman, a mother already of two, who shares our preemie predicament and rocks and feeds her own baby beside me in the little nursery annex, says no. Probably not. They feed the babies between times. If we don't get out of here soon, she warns me, all the nursing progress will be undone. The babies will get lazy. They'll only want the rubber nipple and the formula sold in stores. She is a valuable first mentor to me and we become, for a short while, intimates and friends. I'll wish that I had kept her name. Even now I'd like to thank her.

On the next to last day before the hospital finally releases our son I'm surprised to see a familiar figure peering through the glass into the hospital nursery. The dark-haired, handsomely dressed man is my father. He presses a blue-bordered card up to the glass, pointing to the plastic cart that holds my Justin. For a second I think of backing away, turning back down the corridor and waiting until he's gone. I don't. Who knows why better judgment sometimes prevails?

"Daddy?"

He turns around. For one heartbeat there's an astonished caught-in-the-cookie-jar look on his face and then he smiles that movie-star smile, flashing the straight white teeth he didn't pass on to me.

I approach him and we hug. I want to control this reunion. To be stiff in his embrace, formal and aloof. But he holds me tight and kisses my cheek and it feels too good. I find my throat closing up, my eyes filling.

"Lacey!" He says, patting my face with a square of handkerchief. There has never, not ever, been any occasion on which my father has not possessed a clean, carefully laundered white pocket handkerchief. "What's wrong? Are you all right?"

"I'm fine," I sniff. "Hormones, you know."

"This!" he says turning again to the glass, his arm still around my waist, "This is one handsome boy!"

My father and I stand side by side and look through the nursery glass, commenting on my son's perfection. To be perfectly objective, there is nothing more, or less, handsome about Justin than any of the other babies in the nursery. Truthfully, the one little Asian child and the two black babies look considerably less mottled and apoplectic. But this one is mine and objectivity is overrated.

"Yes," I sigh. "He's beautiful."

My father knows next to nothing, I think, of the trials that have led to this viewing of his grandson. He knows little, or very little, about Adam and me, about our lives or our jobs. He has never been in our home. Except what he's heard from Grandmother, he has no notion of the damage he's done.

230

"Have you heard anything from Sophie?" he asks, still peering through the glass.

"No. I haven't." I say, and I feel my heart hardening anew against him. He is the reason, really, why Sophie is out there somewhere. I take a step towards the nursery door. To escape, without seeming to, the trap of my father's embrace.

"You would tell me, wouldn't you?" He asks earnestly, turning now to face me. "You'd tell me?"

Did his voice break slightly? Was that something like regret, even guilt, in his eyes?

"I have to feed my baby," I tell him, briskly, turning the knob to open the nursery door. But then, as an afterthought—who knows why better judgment will sometimes prevail?—I say, over my shoulder, "Come see us."

Adam and I bring our little boy home. I've made slow but steady recovery from the C-section and the months spent in bed, and I've used my days of hungry waiting to organize the nursery, to remove all of the price tags, to clean again everything I've had the energy to clean and to spray what I couldn't with Lysol. Grandmother and Myra, Terri and the now almost forgiven Janet are there to welcome us. Adam makes the presentation, bearing the light bundle of a lifetime's responsibility a little stiff and awkwardly as he follows me into the house. They swarm and crowd, gush and sigh, touch and coo, queue up for the chance to hold him first, second, third, while I, so very recently the spoiled princess, recede to the fringes to bask in the attention being lavished on a small stranger and to feel rightfully, happily, a queen.

In the days that follow we learn by going. I've had the

advantage of getting to know my son a little in the nursery annex but now I must teach myself to dress and bathe him, to read his gnomish expressions and the meaning of his squeaks and grunts—to gauge the intensity of his discomfort, his hunger, his every need on the nearly infinite scale of baby noises that range from soundless cherubic slumber to undeniable, furious wail. Adam makes steady progress in conquering, or concealing, his anxieties and awkwardness, but Grandmother, who stays to help me for a few days, handles Justin from the first with the practiced confidence of a pro.

I am grateful that she is there for me in those early days. To answer my questions and to help me out when I tire. Especially to let me sleep without worrying. Daddy has had a bow-bedecked rocking chair delivered to the house. My heart softens again. I will call him soon, I think. Maybe Nana and Maureen, too.

I miss Sophie terribly. And it saddens me to think she is missing this. But in some fantasy album in my head I see a picture of my sister holding my son and I believe it will come true. I am awash now, flooded you might say, not just with new optimism but with a new appreciation for what *family* means. For what family *can* mean.

It's the confidence of that new optimism, I think, that makes me take the risk. That, and the warm sweetness of a late afternoon scene in the living room a week after Justin's homecoming. It's the sight of my grandmother rocking my son in that new chair. She is patting his diapered bottom gently with age-speckled hands, humming to him an old tune that I thought I had forgotten, but remember now in the deepest part of me. In some tactile recollection of being held myself by this woman, her hands patting me in time to this same tune.

232

"Tell me about my mother," I say, the words coming from no conscious volition, surprising me as I hear them, and for just a moment, one beat only, the rocker pauses before resuming its soundless easy rhythm.

"What can I tell you darling?" She says. She looks at me over the tops of her glasses but she isn't frowning. Her voice is calm and willing. I sense that at long last she will not put me off. That I can pose the questions that Sophie and I had stopped asking even in our own childhoods. I am a mother, too, now, and the answers are my right.

"Why did she leave us, Grandmother? Tell me what happened."

I don't think I'm mistaken in thinking she almost smiles.

"Oh, my," she says, leaning her gray head back on the rocker but keeping her rhythm, still patting little Justin's bottom in the same easy time. "It was such a long time ago, Lacey. And not so easy to explain."

"Try," I tell her. "Try."

I move to sit on the couch. I am sitting to the side, slightly behind her. She won't have to see my face. I wait.

"Your mother was very young," she begins. "Young and very pretty. She was a cabaret, a night club singer. One of those places where people go to dance and drink."

I stiffen. Grandmother, of course, does not approve of places where people dance and drink.

"She did have a beautiful voice," Grandmother adds. "And very ambitious. Your Daddy was crazy about her."

"But you," I offer. "You didn't like her."

"Oh, goodness," Grandmother laughs. "Of course I liked her! I didn't like the way they were carrying on in those days. The both of them. A whole *pack* of them actually. Running around to those places all night, your father sleeping the day

233

away. I tried to talk to him. Lord knows how I prayed about it. But he was young, too, and he'd come through the war." She pauses and looks at me over her shoulder, across the top of her glasses.

"A lot of those boys were restless then. They'd been all over the world. They'd seen things they oughtn't to have even known about."

"But they get married," I say. This much of the story, surely, I know.

"They do," she says. "But not right away. The two of them are courting. He's there in that place every night where she sings. He brings her around on Sundays for dinner. And then, for some reason, there's a break-up. I never understood it but for a while there your Daddy is just crazy. He just loses all reason. The boy doesn't eat or sleep or look for work. Two jobs already, good ones, he's lost, courting your mother. You can't prowl all night like an alley cat and keep a decent job!"

There is a rising ire in her voice and the rocker's pace has picked up. She lifts Justin to her shoulder. I wait. In a few minutes she is rocking slowly again, lightly patting his back.

"And then one day they both just walk in the door. Just like that. Stars in their eyes! They tell me they're married. They want to know if they can both stay, with me, until they find a place."

"And you let them? They live with you?"

She pushes her glasses up on her nose and laughs.

"*Let* them? They're still there, the place on Tutwiler, when they bring you home from the hospital."

"Was she a good mother?" I want to know. This is the question, perhaps above all others, that I've always wanted to ask. The one question, fearing its answer, which I had thought I would never pose.

234

She turns around to me again. She smiles.

"She was a good mother, Lacey. She loved the both of you. But it was hard for her. She'd had these big plans. And she was used to all that attention. To being in the spotlight. The applause, I guess. Those sequined dresses . . ." Her voice trails off. She leans her head back on the rocker again and closes her eyes.

"One day I came in and heard her singing. Not like the little lullabies she used to sing to you, but one of those night club songs, and she's really pouring her heart out. And I'm so glad about it because she's been down and sad for weeks. But I find her in front of the mirror. She's all dressed up in one of those fancy dresses with her hair all piled up and she's singing into the mirror like she's on stage. With a hairbrush for a microphone. I don't mind. I'm really glad that she's feeling better. But when she sees me she just goes wild. She just starts screaming and ripping at her dress and pulling her hair. She cried and wailed that night for hours. Until Dr. Chilton got there and gave her a shot and she finally went to sleep."

I see a tear trail down Grandmother's powdery cheek. I go to sit beside her on the floor by the rocking chair. She strokes my hair.

"She was never the same with me after that, Lacey. I'd never been much help to her. *That's* at my door. But I had the department to run. And your Daddy was always on the road. But it was like she couldn't abide me after that day. I never told anyone. As God is my witness, this is the first time I've ever spoken of it. I thought it was nothing. But it was something to *her* and before long they got their own place. They moved out."

"Did they move to a house? I mean a house, not an apartment?" There had always been a fragment, a piece, of another house. I had never been sure that I hadn't made it up.

"Yes!" she says. "A little frame house on Holmes Road. I'm surprised that you can remember. You couldn't have been more than three."

"I don't remember very much," I say. But I trust now the images of a sandbox under a tree. A puppy only touched through a wire fence. The white bars of Sophie's crib.

"She had a girlfriend. A girl from the old nightclub days. They called her Kit, I think. No. Cat! That was it. Maybe short for Catherine. Now *that* one I didn't care for. Didn't think she was the right kind, if you know what I mean. But sometimes they would bring you and Sophie to me on a work night. She and Cat wanted to get some dinner, she said. Go to a movie. I didn't see any harm. Your Daddy was always on the road. I didn't see any harm."

"I guess I don't either," I say. "Why is this Cat person important?"

"Because of the accident," she says. "When the train hit them on Perkins, it was this Cat who was driving. Your mother was in the back seat."

There is a long vacant silence. I can hear her take in air before she speaks again.

"Your mother, and a man," she says.

And slowly it all sinks in.

This is the reason that no one had ever been eager to share the story. The reason that Sophie and I, so very early, had learned not to ask about our mother. Unknowingly, even as babies, we would have had been touching the tender bruise of Grandmother's guilt. The open wound of our father's shame. And later, the sensitive scar of his anger, and his doubt.

So much now makes terrible, perfect sense. So much now has its own sad logic.

Justin fusses on Grandmother's shoulder. I stand and kiss her cheek before taking back my warm and wriggly son.

"Thank you for telling me, Grandmother," I tell her. "It means a lot. It does."

CHAPTER XIX

The dirt in Georgia is red. An orangey-red dirt and not really dirt, but clay. If that is something you know only in theory—because, for instance, you saw *Gone with the Wind*—and a fact you find unremarkable, then you obviously did not grow up in the Mississippi Delta. From where I came from, dirt was black and that's all there was to it. The dirt under the old magnolias on Grandmother's street, a few inches down in the back yards and open fields of Fairfield Estates, in the little back lot behind the duplex on Ellison Street, in the small front yard and sloping woods behind the raised ranch on Chantilly Drive, was black. Or some degree of black. It was certainly not red. Not cold and clammy. Not so sticky you could throw a pot with it.

I was told that the indigenous color of Georgia's indigenous dirt was a function of iron oxides. Warm humid climate weathering acid crystalline rocks on rolling hills for eons of time. Old soil, I was told. But chickadees, it was new to me. I could not quite get over it—its outrageous color and its obstinate stickiness. The way it followed everything into the house, streaking your carpets and clothes and children's toys.

The color and texture of Georgia's dirt was probably the biggest culture shock I had when we moved there from Tennessee, but it certainly wasn't the only one. Georgia was still the South. The climate was comparable, the vegetation recognizable, the food, traditions, and culture familiar and comfortable. But Atlanta was definitely faster-paced. More urbane. More sophisticated. There was a lot more "cosmos" in the cosmopolitan. It was different.

The question that everyone, Grandmother, Janet and Myra, Terri and my other friends. would ask me for months was, "How do you like Atlantans? Are the people nice?" Sure, the people were nice. But very few of them were Atlantans. The city, in the early '70s, if not the ultimate melting pot, was a powerful magnet, pulling from the Midwest, other parts of the Southeast, but especially from the Northeast, with the lure of good jobs, cheap housing, and a high standard of living. Had Sherman known how many Yankees would eventually make their homes in Georgia, he might have kept the matches in his pocket. In point of fact it would be more than a year before I actually *met* anyone who had been born and reared in Atlanta. It would be longer than that before I saw a peach growing on a peach tree.

As most unwilling transplants do, I spent the better part of that first year wearing my attitude on my sleeve, playing the "this town just ain't like *my* town" game. There were plenty of ways, I thought, that Atlanta paled in comparison to Memphis. These people, for example, seriously believed that the Chattahoochee, only a fast-running creek next to the mighty Mississippi, deserved to be called a river. The place was all rolling hills and city blocks shaped, not like squares or rectangles, but more like dodecahedrons. You always ended up lost, miles from where you'd started, on a street named Peachtree or Roswell, but not the right one. All their stores had funny names. Yet they managed, somehow, without a Piggly Wiggly. Most absurd of all was the fact that they

240

thought they knew something about barbecue. It was wretched! They didn't even serve coleslaw on it, and what the hell was this Brunswick stew?

Remembering makes me laugh. But it was a good initiation. It would give me a special perspective later, a tender tolerance for the clients from Michigan who missed the snow. The Okies who hated the humidity. The New Yorkers who decried the fact that there was almost nothing in the way of theater and that you couldn't buy a good fresh bagel anywhere in town. Chicagoans would rail at the difficulty of finding a taxi. Philadelphians would be appalled at our ignorance of the steak sandwich. And almost everybody, more and more as the years went on, shocked and dismayed at our massive urban sprawl, at our surprising long-distance commutes.

By then I understood. It's hard to leave your home town. But it does get easier. Most of those cultural deficits we would remedy over the next few decades. The summer heat, obviously, we were stuck with. But a year or two of watching four distinct seasons unfold here could convert even the most stubborn of transplants. In the city itself, in the Appalachian foothills to the north, and just beyond the recently-plowed fields of the suburbs, there are enough old hardwoods to make fall a riotous glory. Atlanta, in the spring, ablaze with azalea and dogwood and cherry blossoms, can make anyone religious. In summer and the dead of winter there is always the softening green backdrop of the ubiquitous pines, and even they, sometimes, bear the surprise of snow on their branches. Atlanta is a beautiful city. But it took me a while to appreciate it.

I had not wanted to come here. Initially I'd balked, simply stonewalled at the idea of leaving my home, my friends and family. It was impossible. Out of the question. There was Sophie, especially, to consider. Every month, every year that passed, seemed to sever some thread of connection, to pluck up some breadcrumb from the trail she might follow to someday find her way home. Maddie was married now. She had moved to St. Louis. The Winstons were leaving the old neighborhood. Almost nobody, it seemed, would be where Sophie had left them.

I knew the transfer could be important—a career and monetary opportunity that was hard to pass up. They wanted to promote Adam into marketing. To make him responsible for scouting new development opportunities from the vibrant business nexus that Atlanta was becoming. I didn't want to stand in his way. But at the same time it was clear that they would not discard Adam if he opted not to move. The choice, I was made to believe, rested in my hands. I agonized, acquiesced, then reversed my thinking and retreated, exercising my female prerogative to change my mind every day or two.

The tipping point had finally come when Adam had mentioned school. The goal of graduating at 25 had already been adjusted. There had been the semester lost by my confinement and failure to register, the next semester postponed while I nursed Justin and got my Mommy feet wet. I had cleared my Incomplete and managed to squeeze in two more night school semesters, but a year and half had gone by in the process and I was only a few measly credits closer to my goal. But now Adam proposed that after the move to Georgia we would be able to afford, even without my income, a little household help. I could actually take a full schedule. It sounded plausible. I was almost seduced.

I agreed only to a scouting trip, just to assess the housing options, and Adam and I flew off to Atlanta. Mr. Mitchner had arranged for an old college pal of his, Nate Plunkett, to pick us up at the airport and to show us around. Nate was an enormous Santa Claus of a fellow, even if his own white beard was short and trim, and even if he wore a green polyester leisure suit and butterfly collar sport shirt instead of Santa's usual garb. A transplant himself fifteen years ago, Nate had acquired an encyclopedic knowledge of Atlanta. He told us that we are in the home of Margaret Mitchell, the Rambling Wrecks of Georgia Tech, and of course, Coca-Cola. But he also shared some interesting lesser-known facts. Who knew that Atlanta had a law on the books making it illegal to tie a giraffe to a street lamp? Who knew that the state fish was the wide-mouth bass? He pronounced a street spelled "Houston" as *hows-stun,* and rendered Ponce de Leon Avenue into something I couldn't repeat. But he was pleasant and funny and he definitely knew his way around. Were it not for the fact that he passed gas so frequently that I was forced to ride in the back seat with windows down, Nate Plunkett would have been the perfect buyer's agent.

Adam and I spent three whole days absorbed in my favorite pastime, looking at houses. I was amazed at the enormous size of some of the suburban subdivisions. I was a little surprised at how much the Federal and Colonial influences dominated the architecture. But I was absolutely *shocked* at the price range of the homes that Nate was showing us. Adam and I had not discussed a housing budget. But apparently he'd discussed it with Nate. And apparently we were moving up.

We began by looking at re-sales, and inside the urban perimeter, but only one excursion to one of the city's many burgeoning suburbs where your buying dollar practically doubled, convinced us that we would be buying new, and in the burbs. Adam would be opening a new branch office, hiring a very small staff here, and we were in the enviable position of being able to find a house first and office space later. Nate took us everywhere, individually addressing each of the five metro counties, crisscrossing and doubling back when I wanted to return to compare something just seen with a house we'd found that morning.

I was especially drawn to the northwestern development and to one neighborhood particularly in eastern Cobb County. It was a smaller subdivision than many we'd seen, with rolling curvy streets and cul-de-sacs and more trees spared than usual. The houses were all square and angular, mostly Georgian Colonials, with medium pitched roofs and flattened, plain or fluted, columns beside a center door. Some had the Federal flourishes of Palladian windows or fanlights and there was an impressive variety in brickwork and color but still they were a lot alike. This formal symmetry had never really been my personal cup of tea. Not since the days of wandering Grandmother's streets, peering up at the interesting and complicated old Queen Annes, wondering what might be inside them. The ability to look at a house from the street and know, with a high degree of accuracy, exactly what its floor plan was and how every room would be used, had always struck me as a little disappointing. But my bias was romantic and emotional, not practical at all. There was good reason that this classic architecture and the arrangement of bedrooms upstairs, living area down, had endured since the time of the colonists. And Atlanta builders and buyers seemed to love it. In real estate parlance, Nate tells us, they're called "five, four, and a door."

In the evenings, in our hotel room, Adam and I reviewed

244

each day's tour. I'm not sure exactly how I got swept away. How window-shopping these beautiful houses had caused me to lose my reason. But by the end of the second day we were both already talking like the transfer was a foregone conclusion. And by the time we boarded the plane for home we'd put earnest money down on one of those Georgian Colonials, just at that stage of construction where I could choose the decorating options and get built-in bookcases in the study.

On the flight home I'm in a rapturous fog thinking about this wonderful house. About its spacious rooms and beautiful appointments. The absolute dream of a kitchen! When we pick up Justin from Grandmother and walk back through the door of our raised ranch on Chantilly Drive, the place is claustrophobically small. The floor plan, really, is impossible. The spillover of Justin's toys and baby paraphernalia can only go to the living room. I'd never realized how much I hated taking the laundry downstairs to wash it, only to bring it back up to put it away. There's that kitchen table practically on the front porch. And, we don't even *have* a dining room. True, there was no single room in the new house as spacious as our downstairs rec room. But there's that stupid pole in the middle of it. And I'm suddenly mortified that I'd ever thought an oversized poster of Mick Jagger was an objet d'arte.

So we're going. I've got to get this house ready for the market. I've got to go back to Atlanta to pick my colors and tile and floor coverings. I've got to pack and arrange a long-distance move. I am only halfway through re-painting this living room and there are the unopened rolls of bathroom wallpaper that now, I suppose, I ought to return.

Suddenly my life seemed all loose ends and unfinished projects. I hadn't had a chance to scout a school in Atlanta and to have my records and transcripts forwarded. Justin was due for a check-up. Even though I'd been pitiful little help in the last year I'd really wanted to be here for the final sale and close-out celebration of mine and Terri's little subdivision. And there was one piece of business particularly that I was tormented about leaving unfinished. This was my own, very private, search for Catherine Glozer.

About a month after my talk with Grandmother, on my first half-day excursion without Justin, I had gone downtown to the offices of *The Memphis Commercial Appeal*. In the microfilm archives from 1951 I had easily found the report of the accident in which my mother had died. The collision had occurred a little after 10 p.m. at a train crossing that the article called "unregulated." I wasn't sure if that meant unmarked, as in, without the usual flashing lights and drop-down barriers that normally protect railroad crossings, but I thought it was a pretty good bet. The article said that Anna Winters, of Memphis, and a male passenger whose name was being withheld pending notification of next of kin, had both been pronounced dead on the scene. The driver, a Catherine Glozer, also of Memphis, had been transported by ambulance to Baptist Hospital where she was in serious but stable condition. I was able to find one follow-up article, and also my mother's obituary, but I found no later obituary for this Glozer person. Apparently she had survived. And for the better part of the next year I would be intermittently, rather subversively, preoccupied with finding her.

This was the kind of challenge, chickadees, which should make you appreciate the internet. The investigative tools at my disposal at the dawning of the '70s were not just crude in comparison, they were practically nonexistent. I had already eliminated the obvious. I had searched the telephone directory, finding no Catherine, but a few Glozers with pairs of initials that included a C. I had called them all. A couple of the calls led to swift but polite dead ends but I had one, excruciatingly lengthy but fairly amusing, conversation with a Carl William Glozer, who wasn't Cat himself but who had known someone who went by that name—a buddy who had worked with him on the line at the Firestone plant and who'd been in a minor industrial accident which had left him short the tip of his index finger. A great guy, that Cat, but finally, we'd both conceded, probably not the one I wanted. A lovely older lady with a slight British accent spoke to me at length about her own cats, three of them, and gave me some good insight into the feline psyche. I talked to a young woman who told me that she thought Catherine Glozer was a famous ice-skater—an avenue of research that I briefly pursued but one that didn't pan out. I recall this, and share it with you, only by way of reminding us that it was a kinder, gentler time. Folks back then were not quite so cynical and suspicious. They had not yet been telephone-marketed to death. Nobody needed Caller ID to tell them who they didn't want to talk to. A phone call in the morning, or late in the evening when children were already abed, was a social opportunity. A chance to connect. It took me weeks to get through all of these conversations. Some of them were a little strange. But some of them were lovely.

There was one listing, one only, that I couldn't completely eliminate because the telephone number had been changed to a private listing. I did visit the address, a midtown quadriplex actually, not terribly dissimilar from any of Grandmother's houses, except it was on a heavily trafficked, less shaded street. There were broken bottles and trash in the gutters. The mailboxes showed signs of jimmying. I had knocked and rung the bell, been unanswered, and finally walked away wondering just how much difference there might be in rents between this place and Grandmother's latest digs. Location, location, location.

At the library I secured the telephone books for the nearby towns and communities in Mississippi, Arkansas, even Missouri, and made dozens and dozens more phone calls before I finally became discouraged. The fact of the matter was that Catherine Glozer could be half a world away by now. Or, having married and changed her name, she could be living right down the street and I would never know. For a while I put it aside.

I wasn't really, truly—this part may be received suspiciously if you choose to—trying to clear my mother's record. I wasn't looking for a way to expiate her sins. What I wanted, I think, was simply to talk to someone who had known her. To get the perspective of a contemporary, a friend. Actually, I'm not sure what I wanted. Except that I wanted to find Cat Glozer.

A couple of months later it dawned on me that my real estate knowledge might have some investigative advantages. Whenever I got the chance, and a babysitter, I searched property records, deeds, workman's liens, tax records— everything I could think of in the public domain that might have recorded *Glozer, Catherine*. Nothing. For another while I put it aside.

Then, only a couple of weeks before the move was scheduled, on the very day we received a contract for the sale of Chantilly Drive to a nice couple with tow-headed twin boys, I'd had another idea. I had run across the card given to me almost three years ago by Detective Jack Kellogg with the city police. He had been my contact for all the disappointing inquiries about Sophie. Kellogg had been a little tactless sometimes, but he had always been patient and considerate of me and I knew the police could find out things that regular people couldn't. The problem was that there was no connection between the missing persons case on Sophie and my own little crusade to find Catherine Glozer. So, I wasn't exactly truthful with him. Actually I lied through my teeth. I told him that we'd learned that Sophie had been in contact with Catherine Glozer just before her disappearance. We didn't know why, or exactly when, but we thought it might be important. Even if my ploy didn't turn up Cat Glozer it might serve to renew the effort to find Sophie. I had made sure Jack Kellogg knew where Adam and I were moving and how to reach us. He had told me he would check it out and I ended my call with a little fresh hope on two fronts.

Amid the clutter of packed boxes and dismantled furniture Adam and I throw a little farewell cook-out to say good bye and thank you to the friends and closest co-workers we were leaving behind. We eat burgers and beans on paper plates. While Terri and Adam and a couple of others from our offices talk real estate, David and Janet and I form our own little huddle, making jokes and swapping stories about how far we've come since the halcyon days of Beautiful Fairfield Estates. Janet is dateless tonight because she's going with me tomorrow to drive my car, and Justin, to Atlanta ahead of the movers. But David has a new girlfriend who Janet thinks is something of a snob, or a twit, or another of Janet's monosyllabic pejoratives. Actually I like her just fine and can pretty much figure why she must feel a little like the odd man out. We go back a long way, the three of us. A very long way.

It's the first time since weaning Justin that I've had the inclination to drink. It serves to make me overly sentimental and nostalgic. Before the night is over I'm convinced that I'm making a terrible mistake. Everything I really care about is here, not in Atlanta. My friends are here. My job. My father is just getting to know his grandson and Justin adores his great grandma. Even the little flaws in my raised ranch are, tonight, terribly dear to me. We'd worked around them, hadn't we? What in the world was I thinking?

But it's too late for transfer remorse. Ten hours from now the movers are coming to take it all way. Two days from now Janet and I will start to unpack boxes. And to start cleaning the Georgia clay from everything we own.

CHAPTER XX

Imagine, if you can, our pioneer fore-parents, having convinced themselves that a better, brighter future lay over some unknown horizon to the west or, say for the sake of illustration, about three hundred and twenty six miles east, southeast. They can be sure that the adventure will be a collective, communal endeavor. They will caravan together in their covered wagons, supporting each other when they are threatened by tribes of long-haired natives riding Harley Davidsons or when confusing landmarks and the primitive directions they've been given to their new home send them sixty miles in the wrong direction. Among them are strong leaders and wise elders who know how to scavenge for fast food along the wilderness trail, what to do when their caravan runs out of gas in Gadsden, Alabama, or when a small child riding behind them in the wagon chokes on a piece of Tootsie Roll pop. On arrival there will be many hands to share the labors and the rough, arduous work of making a home in the wild new land. While some of them stay put, keeping the hearth fires stoked, watching the small ones so that they don't stick bobby pins into unprotected electrical outlets, there are plenty of others to assume the harrowing tasks of finding the water department, putting down deposits to get the telephone turned on, roaming the strange wilderness to locate the right post office to find out what the hell has happened to the mail.

If there is one time in life that you don't want to find yourself friendless, it's during the great adventure of moving. If there's one sure way to find out who your friends really are, ask them to help you move. Janet was simply invaluable. Particularly so since Adam encountered a business emergency that required his presence in Memphis for several unexpected days. It was the kind of business emergency that would predictably present itself over the next years whenever we really needed him. But this time, at least, I had Janet. For ten days she helped me unpack boxes, make beds, arrange cabinets, find the myriad essential objects, like can openers, that separate us from the other primates and facilitate civilized life. When the gas man balked at lighting the pilot because something or other wasn't "code," Janet flirted to the edge of indecency, inspiring him to make the repair himself rather than leaving us hot waterless for days. She entertained Justin while I made the excursions necessary to get us functional in the new house—excursions that perhaps should have taken under an hour but that I managed to triple by constantly getting lost. Chickadees, kiss your GPS.

On the last day before Adam would arrive, and before I would reluctantly put Janet on a homebound plane to Memphis, we had spent the afternoon in the course of shelving—and re-shelving—books. I had been dismayed to discover that she had unpacked three boxes without any regard whatsoever for the patently obvious distinctions between American Lit and British Lit, between Art History and Art Linkletter. She had also failed to consider the matter of relative literary and cultural importance. I had always liked my most important books to be shelved sort of centrally, easily accessible to me and at a nice eye level for visitors who might want to peruse my growing and, I thought, increasingly impressive collection.

"So which of these, Miss Debbie Decimal System," she asked me," is actually more *important*? In one hand she held up my copy of Betty Friedan's *The Feminine Mystique* and in the other, *Better Homes and Gardens Favorite Ways with Chicken*. It was a good question, actually, and one which we discussed at length that night.

"The problem with you," Janet explained, "is that you're so conflicted."

We are sprawled on the family room carpet with glasses of wine and the white cartons of Chinese take-out still scattered across the coffee table. Justin sleeps, guarded on the couch by a row of protecting pillows. His arms lie relaxed at his sides, his hands small open blossoms, pink petal fingers curving upward around the paleness of tiny palms.

"And the problem with you," I reply, with less than my usual sarcasm, "is that you don't *see* a conflict."

Janet and Myra are both second-wave feminists. As yet neither one of them, nor any of the other millions of Americans who'd grown pretty comfortable with the idea of female suffrage, have any idea that the efforts on behalf of women's rights in the '60s and '70s would one day be labeled *second wave*. No more than the feminists after the '80s could expect to be called *third wave* because they sought to consider race and class. Myra is stridently, almost fanatically committed to passage of the ERA and sees this now as the central issue of our times. In fact, the causes of women have almost superseded her anti-war activism and she currently hates Phyliss Shlafly almost as much as she does Richard Nixon. Myra insisted that she would never marry. She espoused free love and open relationships. She is an active member of NOW, a frequent demonstrator, and has even stopped wearing make-up.

Ideologically speaking, Janet sympathizes. But that's as far as it goes. Janet—she has told me more than once—shares the philosophy of Elizabeth Bibesco who thought that you didn't have to signal a social conscience by looking like a frump. Janet does plan to get married someday. Maybe even to have children. But Janet envisions an egalitarian partnership, a perfect utopian balance of home and career.

"Most of it is a simple matter of distribution of labor," Janet tells me, moving one of the old rec room pillows under her head. The pillow is stained, flattish, and clashes horribly with the new carpet.

"Where women undermine themselves," she continues, "is in their own lack of self-respect. They simply fall victim to the old patterns, to their parents' rules. They just don't have the courage to assert themselves, to demand their own right to self-fulfillment."

"Most women are just like you," she goes on, "conflicted between wanting power and wanting protection. To quote Sally Kempton, it's hard to fight an enemy who has outposts in your head."

Because these are the rules of the game, established when the two of us were not much older than twelve, my job is to refute, to challenge, to debate—even to play devil's advocate where necessary, just for the fun of it. This time, though, I'm not really playing. I'm interested in, even threatened by, Janet's ideas. I'm also offended as hell by her condescending, tutorial attitude.

"And to quote somebody else," I counter. "Your theory is crazy. But it's not crazy enough to be true. It just doesn't work that way, kiddo. The distribution of labor, as you put it, includes a good bit of labor that a man can't do."

"Oh, I don't mean *that*," she hurriedly assures me, as though *that* were really a small part of the issue at hand. "I mean all the nitty-gritty stuff. What gets Myra's bunch so riled up. I mean the shit work. The cleaning the toilets. Ironing the shirts. I mean, *that* can't really be what it's all about, can it?"

Janet has just spent the better part of ten days helping me do some of the "shit work." I'm not sure I understand her point.

"Maybe not," I admit, using two of my eyes to carefully refill our wine glasses and the third, the mother's eye, to check that Justin is still sleeping peacefully. "But the shit work takes time. And somebody's got to do it."

"But women make it such an *obstacle*," Janet says, suddenly sitting up from her pillow. "They make those stupid domestic functions so *central*. Like the relationship is just the necessary enabler. Like a man should be ashamed of himself to cum on the fancy bed sheets he's paid for!"

She has just used some of the same exact language, the same phrases, that I've heard Adam use in our discussions on the subject. She could only have picked up this language in their special time together, when they were preparing for Justin's arrival and I was a fat sow in the breeding pen, ineffectually waiting to die or disappoint.

"But those stupid *domestic functions*, as you put it, are the energies that *make* a home. Men want it both ways. They don't want to bring their bosses, even their football buddies, into a dump!   But they don't want to assume any responsibility for seeing that it isn't."

Now I'm sitting up, confronting Janet a few feet away. Our inclined foreheads almost touch. I've got more to say.

"You said something about demanding self-fulfillment.

But what you meant was the male standard of self-fulfillment. Defined by General Motors and AT&T. That we don't have the guts to stand up to our husbands, to negotiate the shit work, so we can *both* be chairman of the board."

It was Janet's turn to be confused.

"Don't you see?" I explained. "It's not the work. It's us. Women are still shit and so everything we do is shit work. Nursing, teaching, caretaking. Nurturing. Creating instead of destroying. Hell, even cleaning! Everything we do. Everything we're instinctually, biologically, morally, *naturally* inclined to do is still shit work because it's women who want to do it."

It was Janet's turn to be offended.

"So the problem is that I've sold out? That law school is *male* self-fulfillment and that if my heart were really in my vagina I should really want to teach kindergarten?"

"No," I say. "Of course not." And then I'm stuck. Because secretly some part of me wants to say, *yes, yes you would*.

And another part of me knows that isn't true. Janet is right. I'm very conflicted.

"No," I concede. "I just don't like this dissension in our own ranks. I mean, as long as we're denied equal wages, equal opportunities to compete with men in *their* world, operating under *their* value system, how crappy is it that if we try to eke out a little self-fulfillment from raising kids, from making a home, that people, especially other women, put us down for that?" Yeah. That was closer to what I really wanted to argue.

"But you Harriet Homemaker types can be just as judgmental!" Janet fairly shouted. And she was right. There was plenty of blame to go around. The dissension in the ranks would grow considerably worse over the next decades but the "new" problem we were addressing still wouldn't be solved. One day women would sit at the head of the Board and carry guns into battle alongside men. But the gender bias for shit work wasn't going away.

"Maybe so," I said. "But sometimes it feels like we're under siege."

And then I thought Janet got really personal.

"Well, maybe it's because you're such perfectionist snobs." she said. "You *can* put the ketchup bottle on the fucking table! You don't have to run yourself ragged making sure everything is color coordinated." (This from a woman who wouldn't dream of leaving the house unless her purse matched her shoes.)

"And," she continued." You don't have to be so obsessive. You don't have to clean everything within an inch of its life!"

Well. While I appreciated, sincerely, everything Janet had done for me in the last ten days, I sense that it's a good thing—a really good thing—that her time here was almost over.

"Fine!" I said, fully aware now that for some time I've been arguing not just with Janet, or with Janet and Myra and Adam, but to a great degree, with myself. "Cherish your little notions of the negotiated domestic life. Of experimental marriage!"

I think I scored some enlightenment points with that one. Experimental marriage was an expression that had recently cropped up for an arrangement in which—don't laugh—the husbands would help with the housework.

"But you know what? " I went on. "Damn it, some people *like* to clean!"

This was not then, nor has it ever been, entirely and completely true. But I do like things to *be* clean. And I certainly see the superior therapeutic value of mindless, repetitive cleaning over breaking dishes or throwing things all over the place that you'll just have to pick up later.

"See what I mean?" Janet said. "You're so conflicted."

"I'm going to bed," I said, standing to collect my sleeping son but pointedly leaving the take-out trash just where it sat in the family room. "I'll see you in the morning."

We made up. Janet and I had always made up. Always without any sloppy sentimentality. Usually without even an acknowledgement that making up was necessary. I know that we both felt a little somber, slightly chastened when we hugged good bye at the airport. As I watched her disappear through the jetway and then began my trek back to the parking garage, I was already experiencing the first tinges of withdrawal, the sad and slightly panicky feeling I'd always had when Janet and her boyfriend had dropped me off at school, when she had abandoned me at a party, even when, in my confinement with Justin, she had kissed my cheek and sashayed out the door, leaving me to wonder whether she and Adam might have a happy future together one day, whether already they'd laid the groundwork. As we walked away, while I seated Justin in the car, I could almost see her, stowing her overhead carry-on, settling into her seat and buckling up, exhaling a long exhausted sigh of relief, and then shaking her head in bewilderment. *Poor Lacey*, I could hear her thinking. *So much promise. So much potential. So much conflict.*

The marketing adjective that always described East Cobb

County, in the same way that "beautiful" had become permanently prefixed to Fairfield Estates, was "prestigious." But some of the qualities that worked to make East Cobb so prestigious were exactly the same ones that served to make my negotiated agreement with Adam—the plan to get a little help with the housework so that I could go to school—practically unworkable. The first obstacle was that there was nothing, *absolutely nothing*, in the way of public transportation from the city. This isolation protected us, I suppose, from marauding bands of juvenile delinquents who might otherwise have been tempted to hop a bus and bring their crime spree to our far northwestern suburbs. It apparently ensured the prestige of our near lily-white community in keeping blacks, who could have afforded the homes but simply didn't have a car, from moving in. But it didn't help very much in securing a qualified domestic.

What I'd had in mind, of course, was someone like my grandmother's Thelma. Someone exactly like Thelma. Someone who was intelligent, even-tempered, scrupulously honest, hard-working, resourceful and calm in emergencies, skilled in the simple household arts of cleaning and cooking, and who, without added monetary incentive, would also love and protect Justin as though he were her own.

Unfortunately, many of the Thelmas of the world had decided to give up their centuries-old corner on the domestic servitude market and let us white chicks fend for ourselves. The civil rights successes of the last decades—again with a significant amount of help from our own bloated generation—had enabled black women to find jobs that were better paying, less stigmatized, and carried a much higher prospect for promotion than "day work." We were about twenty years away from the effects of globalization and the influx of third-world nannies and Latino immigrants who would take the next shift. The early 1970s was simply not a good time to be looking for domestic help in an affluent suburb without even bus service from the city. No one in East Cobb apparently wanted my job, with or without its prestige.

So that was one fly in my ointment. In inquiring into local colleges and universities I soon discovered another. Even though we were homeowners and taxpayers, the Georgia Board of Regents considered me a non-resident for the purposes of university enrollment for a period of one year. The difference between resident and out-of-state tuition, while a pittance compared to today's college costs, seemed astronomical. Or at least Adam seemed to think so. I got nowhere in the discussion.

"It's not just the money," Adam had said. "It's the principle of the thing."

"But Adam, you promised! That was the deal if we moved here."

"Lacey, be sensible! Why pay all that extra money for classes that will still be there next year? It's not like you've got a *deadline* or anything!"

He was right, of course. Adam's logic, when it came to money, was always irrefutable. And while I did actually have a secret new deadline, I had grown quite used to thinking of a diploma as a continually receding target. It hurt, a little, to think that Adam couldn't see that there was another principle involved. But he was right. It was only sensible to wait.

So there I was. Bazillions of miles from home. Friendless in a strange town. Unable to secure any household help. My long-thwarted dream of becoming a college graduate thwarted again for another year. I did, under the circumstances, what any sane, resourceful and highly conflicted person would do. I threw myself into decorating.

Unfortunately, the '70s were not such a good time for decorating, either. On careful review of the decade, I have now come to the unavoidable conclusion that everybody back then, at least everybody connected in any way to home furnishings and fashions, must have been smoking dope. Just pull out any old 1972 copy of *Better Homes and Gardens* that you might have laying around and you'll see what I mean. First of all there were the retina-scalding color schemes. Peppy combinations of orange, hot pink and lime green. Red, yellow, and orange. Fuchsia, pink and orange. Purple, red and orange. If you were more conservative, or had grown tired of orange in the '60s, there was plenty of red and black. Someone had invented pre-pasted wallpaper and the industry celebrated with an explosion of dayglo wallpapers, metallic wallpapers, flocked wallpapers, textured wallpapers, shiny vinyls and gigantic geometrics. If wallpaper didn't float your boat you could stick up other things. Contact paper. Sticky-backed mirrored tiles. Squares of cork, Formica, balsa, aluminum, practically anything.

Mirror-topped coffee tables were all the rage. Their buyers, I assume, did not have children but did have domestic help. And gallons and gallons of Windex. Hanging swag lamps and suspended macramé tables filled the empty air space beside your inflatable sofa and there were lots of chairs shaped like human body parts.

It was also the decade that taught me to run whenever I heard someone use the words "fun" and "fabric" in the same sentence. There were a lot of fun fabrics. Happy fake zebras, leopards, tigers, ocelots, and other plush or hairy fabrics that resembled no animal on earth. Gleeful geometric fabrics and huge cheery prints, covered in the playful, ubiquitous daisy,

261

printed in color wheel pairings that, up until the '70s, had not only never been intimate next door neighbors but had never even attended the same cocktail party. Shag carpet was bigger than ever, even in the bathroom, and to pull it all together you could paint your bathtub purple.

This was the era of the popcorn ceiling, of harvest gold and avocado kitchen appliances, of the sectional sofa (need swag light here), of plywood veneer paneling, and perhaps the decade's only redeeming invention, the aesthetically dull but undeniably comfortable reclining TV chair.

So. What do you do when you find yourself in a highly traditional Georgian Colonial home in the midst of decorating current that that is best described as hallucinatory? You ignore it and go antiquing.

For months Justin and I, and Adam too when the job could spare him, went to antique shops, junk and thrift stores, estate sales. I had decided to rise above all trends. To return to the time-honored designs of the past and the rich warmth of real wood. Janet had once told me that if I had a choice between actually going to heaven and reading a book about it, I'd pick the latter. It was true enough that it had taken me a little while to get the joke. I read books by the score on antique furniture and on early English and American cabinet making. I studied joinery and finishes and learned to tell the differences between machine-made and hand cut and to scout for dry rot and insect damage.

I actually had been able in the fall to pick up one more class—a Biology and its accompanying lab. The one class had cost as much as the pie-crust occasional table I'd passed up to take it and I'd had a near nervous breakdown in trying to get to class, or make up my absences, when Adam forgot or was unavoidably detained. The logistics of going to school were still defeating me but I was desperately in love with my house.

A year after our move to Georgia our house was still not finished. Neither houses nor people ever get finished. But it was looking pretty damn good. I'd bought a few pieces, reproductions of course, of English and American traditional designs. We had a Queen Anne dining room table, only gently used, but the six Chinese Chippendale chairs surrounding it were late eighteenth century Honduran mahogany, so beautiful that I made unnecessary detours through the dining room just to caress the mellow white-flecked wood. I'd ordered some drapes and made some curtains, sans daisies, and to accessorize I'd found wonderful old botanical prints, china pieces and other knick-knacks in junk stores. I had astonished myself with the way I could carry a color in my head for weeks, ensuring that the matte of a picture frame back at home would exactly match the color in a non-returnable fabric remnant purchased clear across town.

In a trip to a central Georgia estate sale that we'd turned into a long weekend holiday, I'd secured a nineteenth century carved partner's desk which, for many years, would be my pride and joy. Adam was a little dubious about the price we'd paid—a dealer from northern Florida had been bidding against us—and I went several hundred dollars above my absolute, *absolute* top dollar price. I learned a lot about auctions that weekend—that they are much more emotional adventures than financial ones—but I would not ultimately be sorry about the price. When hard times came, and come they would, that desk would be better than an early dot com stock option. I would grieve to see it go. But it would pay for two years of Justin's college.

By the end of that first year I had used up the entire

budget, larger this time, that Adam had given me and also most of the savings I'd stashed away from my subdivision commissions. I still had practical and aesthetic holes to be plugged. But on those afternoons while Justin napped, those evenings I spent alone when Adam was out of town, I would walk through the rooms of this creation-in-progress and feel deep, visceral pride and pleasure. The little vignettes like armchair, table and lamp would seem as lovely to me, in the lighting and color and composition of their parts, as any painting I'd ever seen. But this one I had painted. And my painting held a functional chair and light to read by and a useful but graceful table bearing a Chinoiserie box with mints inside. How wonderful it seemed when function and form came together, when you could live and work and play, with, around, and *inside* art of your own making.

By the end of that year I had almost forgotten that I had once not wanted to move to this interesting and beautiful city. I had almost forgotten my disappointment about not being able to go to school right away. I had definitely forgotten, in the excitement of preparing for the long weekend of our trip to Augusta, to pack my birth control pills.

CHAPTER XXI

A six hundred mile round trip journey in a car with an active toddler isn't all that easy and I wouldn't make it home those first few years as often as I should have. I had missed Grandmother's last birthday and skipped our five-year class reunion but when Janet let me know that Connor had been killed I knew that I'd be making the trip. I had already packed for Justin and me and had plans to leave at dawn when the phone rang. It was May. A few days after Nixon had announced the invasion of Cambodia. I know because I'd been reading the paper at the kitchen table, learning the details of what would become known as the Kent State massacre.

The story itself was horrifying. Four students had been killed by National Guardsman and nine others wounded. But what struck me that morning was the picture. The young woman who leaned over the body of one of the dead students. She was not a student herself, the paper said, but a fourteen-year-old runaway.

"Mrs. Harrison?" the voice on the phone inquired.

"Yes," I said. "Detective Kellogg?" I had recognized his voice immediately and immediately begun to steel myself against the chance of more bad news.

"We located your Catherine Glozer," Kellogg said.

I am relieved. This is not bad news about Sophie. But momentarily I'm also confused. I had almost forgotten about this second, tangential task I had asked the detective to undertake and I had not heard from him in months.

"You did? Really? Where did you find her?"

"Well, right here. She lives over on Madison Avenue. The owner of the building says she's been there for years. I could never catch her at home but I finally ran her down at her place of business. A bar she runs on the south side. The Cat's Cradle they call it. Kind of a neighborhood place. Nothing great but it seems legit."

For a moment I feel annoyance. The old apartment building I had visited, the phone book address of the C.K. Glozer who had not been at home, had been on Madison. Apparently it had been the right place all along. I had just given up too easily.

"Funny thing, though," said Kellogg. "She claimed not to have spoken to your sister. Said she didn't recognize your sister's picture. And frankly I believed her. But then when I mentioned your name she acted pretty strange."

"Strange?" What do you mean, strange?"

"I mean strange like she'd seen a ghost or something. Like she was putting something together. But whatever it was she wouldn't tell me."

I could feel my pulse rising and my face growing warm. There was no doubt in my mind now that Jack Kellogg had found our mother's old friend.

There was a long dead space on the line. I could hear Kellogg breathing.

"Mrs. Harrison? Is there something you need to tell me?"

"Tell you?" I echoed, stalling. Of course Kellogg was suspicious. I had actually used him and now I had to decide whether or not to tell him the truth. But if I did, and my deceit made him angry with me, would he stop looking for Sophie?

Fortunately he asked me another question. One I could answer truthfully.

"Do you *know* this woman?"

"No!" I hurried to assure him. "I don't know her at all." I was about to say that I had never seen her in my life but I realized that this probably wasn't so. I just didn't *remember* having seen her.

"It was just kind of strange," he said again. "She seemed pretty interested in your names. With the names *Sophie* and *Lacey*. She said it a couple of times. It was funny, you know. Kind of strange."

I backed the phone away a few inches, taking a second or two to collect myself. To be sure I could answer casually.

"Well, yeah," I agreed. "That *does* seem strange." I waited, hoping Kellogg imagined me wondering, too. Wondering what it was about our names that could possibly interest Cat Glozer.

"Anyway," he said finally, "That's all I got." And it seemed then that I had gotten away with my mischief. Kellogg made some small talk. I made a point of thanking him for his efforts on behalf of my family. Before he hung up he promised to let me know of any developments and told me not to give up hope.

Hope. Of ever seeing my sister again? I would never give up hope. Not unless, or until, I had to.

I won't recall so much this time about the details of Connor Laughlin's funeral. The script, by now, has become familiar to all of us. There is a slightly larger military presence at this one. Connor is a legitimate war hero and will be posthumously awarded the Medal of Honor. The chaplain speaks of Connor's sense of humor, his devotion to his fellows, the audacious and unhesitating act of courage that had saved other lives. No one doubts the truth of the chaplain's words. But this man didn't know Connor. Those of us who gather afterwards, in the small rooms of the Laughlin's house in Fairfield Estates are the ones who knew Connor. There is Janet and Myra and David, of course, David's parents, old relatives and neighbors, some of whom I don't know or recognize, but most of whom I do. Maddie is there with her copper-headed newborn. Indeed all of the Laughlin clan, except their patriarch, is again under one roof. Mr. Laughlin's heart attack last year has cheated Connor of the chance to impress the old man in a really big way this time.

For a while we are in the mode of classic wake behavior. We greet each other with low voices, catch up in solemn respectful tones, eat daintily of the feast always provided to nourish the first stage of grief. Justin and a little girl about his same age weave in and out among adult legs, finally settle themselves to giggle under the tent of the tablecloth.

Everyone has remarked on how much he resembles Sophie. I am a little surprised by the strength of their assertions. My father's doubts, for nearly three years now, have been my doubts also and have suggested a simple explanation for the fact that Sophie and I were always so dissimilar. I thought I had seen Sophie in my son also but I could never convince myself that I was not projecting this likeness onto his face because my sister was so much on my mind. He has always been brown-eyed like me but his hair grows lighter, curlier every month.

In a while the Laughlin's rooms begin to thin and women

have begun to clear plates and put away the glut of food. Mrs. Laughlin, now obese and diabetic, has been encouraged to take a rest. Justin and his new little girlfriend have been put down to nap on a quilt on the floor. We find ourselves, the twenty-somethings who are there from the old gang, from school, from Connor's crowd, gravitating to the backyard where we make a circle of kitchen and lawn chairs. The open highway behind the houses on Lochinvar Drive has all but disappeared. Fences and hedges and tool sheds have turned each home into its own little island. The house from which Sophie and I had begun our suburban adventure is not even visible from where we sit.

We swap stories about Connor, some of which are ridiculously funny and not so flattering but we know he would find them a tribute. We tease David about his apparent inability to find a girl who can stand him more than a couple of months. I share a little about Adam, our adjustments to Atlanta. I get to surprise even Janet with news of another baby on the way. She first lifts her eyes heavenward and places a hand theatrically over her heart, but then she gives me a little wink and the thumbs-up sign. I share nothing about antiquing or my house obsession which seems now, in this context, superficial and petty. Yet anyone with a piece of gossip about an old school chum is encouraged, obliged, to share it. This time our talk stays away from all things political. We don't approach the war that has taken Connor, the student strikes and uprisings that are happening everywhere.

It is almost dark when we exchange our last hugs and our last promises to get together, to do better about keeping in touch. Most of those promises we won't keep. I will not see most of them again. I will never again spend another afternoon in Beautiful Fairfield Estates.

Against the sad backdrop of Connor's funeral there will be some bright spots in that long weekend trip. I will have one entire fun-filled day with Janet, packed with shopping, lunch, more shopping and drinks. By the time I get back to Grandmother's house she and Justin have bonded so intensely that it's Grandmother, not me, he wants to change him into pajamas. Grandmother, not me, who should read the bedtime story. Daddy would be coming to see Justin on Sunday morning before our departure, but the next evening, a Saturday, I enlist Grandmother's babysitting skills again. I'm just going to meet up with a few of my old real estate friends here I tell her. Another lie. But this one is for her sake, not mine.

The Cat's Cradle is on South Willett in a part of town well past its middle class heyday. The building is at the end of the block, a small side parking lot connecting it to the street and while it's early yet for this type of establishment there are only two other cars in the asphalt lot. I enter the front door between plate glass windows plastered with neon beer signs and wait for my eyes to grow accustomed to the dimness. One wall is a long burnished oak bar, backed by the typical mirrors and glass shelves storing the ceiling-high inventory of liquors and wines. A young man behind the bar is busy with something behind him. There are small free-standing tables and chairs in the center but the other wall is anchored by large red leather banquette seating, all empty now except for a graying middle-aged couple who stares at me pointedly as I stand inside the door. I feel a momentary flutter of panic. I've never actually entered a bar unaccompanied before. I'm overdressed for this place in my funeral suit. I'm not sure at all why I've come here or what I hoped to accomplish. But I press on, walking to the middle of the long bar, hoisting myself on a stool, smiling pleasantly when the barkeep eventually turns to see me.

"Good evening," he says. "What can I get you?"

"Gin and tonic," I say, pleased with myself that I could think of something so sophisticated, and so fast. In those days, when I drank, it was always something sweet and frothy. I had never had a gin and tonic before. And I wouldn't ever order one again.

"Coming up," he says, but then almost apologetically, "Would you have some ID?"

"Sure," I say, and produce the Georgia driver's license that will give us something to talk about for the next fifteen minutes.

The bartender, who introduces himself as Phil, I think, has a buddy who lives in Atlanta. They've prowled the night life scenes in Buckhead and at Atlanta Underground and Phil thinks it's the greatest place on earth. To most of his questions about whether or not I'd been there or seen that, I have to tell him no. But it sounds like fun. I'll check it out. When this has gone on for a decent interval and I've taken three or four miniscule sips from my bitter drink concoction I finally ask my own question.

"Listen," I say. "Would Cat be around tonight?"

"Sure," he says. "Back there," pointing to the far end of the room. In a smoke-filled shaft of light I can make out a woman, brassy blonde, head down over a pile of papers in the last red banquette.

"Thanks," I say, pushing Phil a five dollar bill and sliding myself carefully, drink in hand, off the tall bar stool. Cat Glozer seems unaware of my approach. She doesn't even lift her head in the long minute I stand beside the booth.

"Ms. Glozer? I'm sorry to disturb you." Now she looks at

271

me. Her face is some past its youthful prime and yet still striking, still beautiful were it not for the inch of deep scar that undercuts one cheekbone.

"I'm Lacey Harrison," I say. "Lacey *Winters* Harrison."
Still she stares at me. She lays the pencil she's been holding down on her papers and leans back in the red leather booth.

"Yes," she says at last. "I can see that. I can see that you are."

I don't wait for her to invite me. I sit down across from her and place my drink on the table.

"You knew my mother," I say. "I was hoping we could talk."

"I knew her," she says. "I killed her. Is that what you're here to talk about?"

I drop my head. It's the only way to break the hold of her stare.

"No. Of course not. I know it was an accident."

"Really?" she says. "And how do you know that?"

"Because I went to the newspaper. I read the stories. The crossing wasn't marked, was it? And it was dark. It was an accident, wasn't it?"

She sighs. The look in her eyes softens and she lifts her gaze now over my head, onto some unfocused place near the dark ceiling.

"It *was* an accident," she says. "Your mother was my friend. I wouldn't have hurt her for the world." She drops her eyes back down to her papers.

"But that doesn't change anything," she says. Her voice is flat and dismissive, as though her part in this conversation is over.

I wait. I let the silence between us grow. I feel it swell and expand, feel the danger involved in what I say next, in what, if

272

I don't speak, might be lost forever.

"I didn't care about the accident," I say. "I didn't come for that."

She lifts her head again, this time looking me directly in the eyes.

"Tell me about her," I say. "Tell me what she was like."

And she does. Cautiously at first. Skeptically. But little by little Cat Glozer and I begin to feel our way toward understanding. Word by word, phrase by phrase, in the difficult silences that fall between us, she comes to see that I haven't come to accuse her. That I've come on another mission—to scavenge bits and pieces from which I can form even a crude mosaic of my mother, any picture at all to fill the empty frame of memory.

In the hour, maybe more, that I sit with her, the little place starts to fill up behind us. Music begins to play and a low undercurrent of conversation flows beneath it, punctuated now and again by a burst of female laughter. Once the young bartender approaches her but she flicks him away with her hand and we aren't disturbed again. Almost everything I know, everything I will ever know, about my mother I learn from Cat Glozer on that one May evening. I learn that my mother had suffered a terrible childhood and had severed her connections to her own family even as a teenager. There were secrets there, Cat Glozer implies, that even our father didn't know. But she also tells me little anecdotes from the time of their friendship, funny little stories from which I absorb some sense of Anna Winter's high good humor and her playfulness, and others, not so funny, that suggest her struggles with depression and despair. I learn that my mother was an incredibly talented performer and that she may have lost her only chance at stardom when I came along. Cat wants to know about Sophie's disappearance and I tell her everything, even how Sophie had come to know about our father's suspicions.

"Listen, honey," she says. "Anna was no angel. But your father didn't make it easy for her. He was so damned jealous. He liked it that she was stuck there all the time. He didn't want her seeing any of her old friends and he wouldn't bring her back to the club even on weekends. Even for a little diversion." Her teeth are clinched and a muscle in her jaw twitches.

"But I tell you *this*," she says vehemently. "He was a fool to doubt that baby. Anna was practically a prisoner after you were born. When she got out at all, I was right there with her."

"But the other man?" I ask. "The man in the back seat?"

Cat Glozer smiles. The scar moves higher on her cheek.

"Stu Woolsey," she says. "Trombone player. I was giving him, and Lana Witt, our little cigarette girl, a lift home. We'd just piled in that way when we left the club. Nothing more than that. I had just dropped Lana off and Stu was next. Stu didn't make it home. Neither did your mother. But that's all they had in common."

So that was the story. Cat Glozer herself had been seriously injured in the accident. She had spent more than two months in the hospital. She had never known the track my family's thoughts would take from the trombone player in the back seat, but when she had been well enough to explain no one would talk to her. Even Grandmother, Cat told me, had said to "leave it alone." Our mother was dead and buried. The pictures of her lost or destroyed. The little objects she might have touched, things she treasured, all disposed of.

When I left that night Cat Glozer let me hug her and the

composure she had maintained through all her tale fell away. Her shoulders shuddered in my embrace and my neck and cheek were wet where she rested her head. I felt nothing to forgive her for but she must have felt a little forgiven. I was glad to give her that if I could, but she had given me more. I had something now to go in my frame.

On Sunday, after our breakfast, I packed up our things while Daddy and Justin played on the rug with the new toys Daddy had brought. When there was nothing left to do but bundle Justin into the car I sat down on the edge of Grandmother's claw-footed settee and told them the story. I related the entire progression of events that had led me to Catherine Glozer and every detail, almost, of our meeting the night before. Throughout my story Grandmother sat impassive, only plucking from time to time at the crocheted doily covering the arm of her chair, but the range of emotions that passed across my father's face was something to behold.

I don't know what other questions they could have had for me but I didn't stay to answer them. If there was to be further discussion it would be private, between just the two of them, after Justin and I were well down the road. There was still a pale stupor on both of their faces as we said goodbye at Grandmother's door and I left, feeling strangely light, almost exultant. Maybe that nonsense was over now. If only I could tell Sophie.

CHAPTER XXII

There is war in the Middle East, the threat of scarce oil, and a looming energy crisis. Government deficits are staggering, the largest in history, and the dollar, too, is at an all-time low. Rising prices have everyone worried and a new term, "stagflation" has been coined to describe the scary combination of slow economic growth and high unemployment. Sound familiar, chickadees? It should. But we're talking the '70s here. More than thirty years too soon for history to repeat itself, to demonstrate, yet again, that we don't learn from our mistakes.

At the height of my house pride, when I still have all those little functional and aesthetic voids to fill for the color center spread I expect to one day provide for *Traditional Homes* magazine, Adam and I hit our own little stretch of stagflation. Investors are getting nervous about pushing ahead on planned development. Projects are being dropped or postponed and cutbacks being made in staff. Adam isn't really worried about his own position. But he'd hoped for larger office space this year. That won't be happening. And neither will a new car. And the antiquing junkets need to be squelched.

I can deal with it. At seven months pregnant I'd cut back on my running around anyway and now I have society, a whole sisterhood of neighborhood women, to entertain and amuse. Compliments of three-year-old Justin and the phenomena known as "play dates" I have gradually come to know my neighbors, or at least my neighbors with preschoolers, and the job that consumes so much of Adam's time and energies seems a little less adversarial. The toddler connections from the play groups have uncovered other more individual connections and I have friendships now with more than a dozen women from all over the country. True, we're all still white. All solidly middleclass. Diversity in prestigious East Cobb still didn't encompass much more than the rare Jewish couple or the novelty of a New Jersey accent. But there is Laura Duncan, former lit major at USC, to swap books with. Ginger Buchanan from Boston who knows a world about antiques. A score of others for coffee klatching, trading recipes, playing mindless bunko and serious bridge. We depend on each other in emergencies and for the freedom to run short childless errands. The casserole brigade greets newcomers, illness, and bereavement. There is an endless stream of charity, school and community causes that require our skills and our hands. The neighborhood has a comfortable, small town feel and for a lot of us, transplants a long way from home, it is the only extended family we have. One day Hollywood will depict the suburbs as a soulless wasteland of empty materialism and moral decay and I'll run my review, trying to see if I can remember where the Sopranos lived in Emerald Hills. Maybe the model for that vapid subdivision is somewhere. But it wasn't our neighborhood. I knew a few frustrated housewives. I was one myself from time to time. But desperate? Phooey. We were too busy for that.

The buffering effect of female friends will make this third pregnancy easier, a lot less frightening. There have been people to recommend a doctor, to share experiences and advice, to inquire and sympathize. Even in the short time since Justin's birth, pregnancy and delivery have become slightly less pathologized. The hospital here allows fathers in the delivery room, has rooming in for the babies, and offers support rather than resistance to mothers who want to nurse. So far my expected complication has not presented itself and the doctor says there is chance, a slight one, that if I take it easy I may be able to skip the bed rest. We'll see, he says. We'll see.

By November I am pleased as punch with myself. I have already carried this child longer than Natalie or Justin and while I'm big as a house I think, I'm a tidier, tighter big, by virtue of spending more of my days on my feet than on my back. My due date is three weeks away, exactly Thanksgiving and I'm trying to decide if that's a good thing or an inconvenience. Daddy has promised to bring Grandmother to Atlanta for the holiday and I'm imagining how I'm going to juggle it all. What I would like, of course, is a spotlessly clean house, a perfectly cooked meal, and an adorable new baby to present to them on their arrival. This is exactly what I had told Janet on the telephone last night. So that we both could have a good laugh. I will settle for just getting this baby here safe and sound.

Justin and I are in the side yard, just at the back of the driveway. He's abandoned his Big Wheel in favor of a dirty softball left in the yard by some older child. He lifts it high over his head in a huge throwing wind-up, releasing it just right so that it plops to the ground behind his back. I'm deadheading chrysanthemums—a row of them I had planted last year that have exploded this fall in a profusion of white and gold blooms. A battered pick-up truck slows in front of the house, hesitates and moves on. Justin sticks with his game, once or twice actually throwing the ball forward. He may not be a jock, this kid, but you've got to give him points for persistence. I've accumulated a nice little pile of dead blooms and leaves and am about to go to the garage for a broom when the rusty pick-up comes round the block again. This time it pulls into the bottom of our drive. It's not the kind of vehicle that any of our neighbors would be driving. Magazine salesman, I think. Maybe encyclopedias.

The driver's door opens and a solidly built middle-aged woman wearing western boots, jeans and a plaid shirt exits the truck. She leans back into the cab and presently extracts a sleepy-eyed child, a little girl, two or three years old, which she deposits upright in the drive, bending to whisper something into her ear. The child teeters for a moment, blinks, breaks into an incandescent smile, and begins to toddle in my direction. I notice, barely, that the other door has also opened, that a tall young waif of a girl is getting out, her hair hidden by a baseball cap, her movements graceful but cautious as they all approach. It's the child that has my attention. She has brown hair, shiny as glass, and green eyes, and the creamy ivory skin, well, of an angel. It will take a full minute, maybe more, before she stretches little arms to me, before I am able to lift her up, knowing by then exactly who she is. Knowing that this is my sister's child and that Sophie, at last, is found.

You might think, chickadees, that the next part of the story should be the tale of celebration. Of the prodigal's welcome, the prodigal's homecoming feast, the sharing of the prodigal's saga. We would, eventually, get to all that. And there was, right there, that very day, a short, wildly spontaneous celebration of delight and jumping for joy. Some jumping, specifically, up and down on a concrete drive. Enough jumping that, coincidental or not, three women and two children got to observe a spontaneous deluge of amniotic fluid onto the driveway and our prodigal celebration came to a sudden, jaw-dropping end.

About fifteen minutes after my sister's return—for which I had waited four years—Sophie and her Clara, me and my Justin, and Zelda Evans, the saintly soul who had returned my sister to me, were scrunched into the cab of Zelda's pick-up and we were all on our way to Northside Hospital. We had accomplished this feat with a minimum amount of hysteria and without anyone having to sit directly on my lap. But we had not brought my overnight bag, my purse, or anybody's telephone number.

By the time Adam got home, shortly before seven, finding us gone and no dinner ready, Anna Elizabeth Harrison had already made her entrance into the world. She had done so with the barest minimum of fuss and nuisance and had already been greeted by her Mommy, her brother Justin, her Aunt Sophie, her cousin Clare, and the best family friend we would probably ever have. When I reached Adam, interrupting him in the middle of a hilarious episode of "All in the Family," I guess I began the explanation for my absence too far down the story line.

"Honey," I said. "Could you come up to the hospital? Justin wants to buy his sister and his cousin a surprise from the gift shop. And I need a little cash to get our pick-up truck out of the parking lot."

The details of Sophie's odyssey would become known slowly. Some of them I would never learn and I'm probably better off for not knowing. By her own admission there are gaps in the saga even for Sophie. They had departed—she and the mysterious beau—for San Francisco, that destination that had been so romanticized by Myra and Connor and the media. Sophie had actually been there, had even, as it turned out, attended the same concert at the Monterrey Fairgrounds that Myra had come home raving about. But their paths, in the mob of over 60,000 stoned and jubilant youth who attended had, not surprisingly, ever crossed.

Maureen had been absolutely correct in observing a link between Sophie's new beau and the new car. The new beau had actually sold it to her and the relationship had developed— Sophie would eventually figure out—from his realization that there might be a way to keep his beloved Corvair as well the money she had paid him for it.

She had known him only three weeks before his motives and her own vulnerabilities had coincided perfectly. She had failed another semester of school, a secret which she was still keeping to herself, when she had learned of our family's impending collapse. I then had made my own little contribution in informing her that she would not, in all probability, be allowed to pick cotton in Mississippi with Nana, and then Maureen had supplied the last straw with the information that her father doubted his parentage.

It had taken her a long time, she would tell me, to realize that a half-sister was a great deal better than no sister at all but by then she had been afraid, and later incapable, of coming home. What amounted to almost two years of her absence could be accounted for in time spent incarcerated. She had first been arrested in the city. The mysterious boyfriend was long gone by then—with the Corvair and most of the money—but he had been replaced by a ragtag group of other friends, runaways, too, most of them, who were living a communal, hand-to-mouth lifestyle. The first charge had been merely vagrancy. Sophie had lost her belongings, her guitar, and all identification, but the judge had refused to send her to Juvenile and she had been incarcerated with adult women where she had gotten into more trouble, and the thirty-day sentence had been extended by months. The second arrest had been for possession, a weekend trip, Sophie admitted, when she had been "strung out" and despondent and gone along only on the promise of work. But the prior record had shown up. She had served eighteen months without receiving a single visitor, even a postcard from friends or family, relying only on Zelda to feed and care for her child, to hide her, as she said, from "the system."

It wasn't that Sophie had never attempted to contact us. She had tried calling Grandmother's old number, a month after the switch to the next quadriplex. This one she'd figured out, knowing Grandmother's propensity to move very few years and that as a single older woman, always a little fearful, she had never allowed her number to be listed. She had sent a letter, appealing only for a bus ticket or for Grandmother's telephone number, to the address of Daddy's failed business. Obviously, the letter had been returned. There had been a call placed to Chantilly Drive at that exact time of our move to Georgia, in that precise four-day period when the old phone had been disconnected and the new one not yet in service. There was more. A heartbreaking, tragicomic string of coincidences—one that could never have happened in David Kirk's dull and stable family, but that had happened easily in ours. Just as I had feared, almost nobody had been where Sophie had left them. I couldn't even bare to think about how many weeks, or months, or years, that our reunion might have been delayed had the Kirks not stayed planted in Fairfield Estates. Had they not been at home to tell Zelda and Sophie that we had moved to Atlanta, and to produce our address from their Christmas card list.

In the cast of characters that had played parts in Sophie's nearly four-year drama there were plenty of villains. There were plenty of victims. There was more than one clown.

But there was only one hero. *Heroine*, I should properly say. That was Zelda Evans, operator of the little half-way house where she had first befriended my sister. The heroine who had started her on the right track and who, in spite of Sophie's second disappointing screw-up had still protected her child. Had fed and clothed her and guarded her mother's image. The good simple woman who had helped Sophie really straighten up and, hardest of all it seemed, had managed to convince her to wait out her California probation so that she would be free and clear to travel, to come home and start again.

We were early risers, Zelda and I, and one morning, while the rest of the household slept, we shared coffee, and more, in the quiet house.

"She's not a bad girl," Zelda said, as though I had ever thought so. "She's just a little too trustin', if you know what I mean."

I knew. Sophie had always trusted too much. Always been easily shocked by the things people could do.

"I lost a baby in the system," she continued, seemingly eager to tell this part, her own role in Sophie's saga. It was the second or third time this phrase, *the system*, had surfaced. I was getting the idea that my concept of the system was naïve, very different from Zelda's and Sophie's.

"They took her away," Zelda said. "And I couldn't get her back. It takes money for lawyers. To fight back and all. I was almost on my feet. Had a job and everything. But they came at me with the adoption thing. With this nice rich family dying for a baby and I thought, who am I? I'm just the mother. But I can't give her all that stuff. A house and a swing set. Toys and books. Maybe even college."

Zelda looked at me studiously, intent on making sure I understood.

"I know she had it better," she said. "I'm not sorry. It's just that I think about it sometimes and I wonder if she ever thinks her mama didn't love her. That nobody wanted her and nobody cared. That's a hard thing to carry, don't you think? The notion that your mama didn't love you?"

"It is," I agreed. "A very hard thing."

And if I am sometimes lost and confused in Zelda's musings, I am crystal clear on this. It is, indeed, a hard thing to wonder if your mama really loved you. I am lucky, at last, to know that mine did.

"You could just tell it wasn't like that for Sophie," Zelda said. "She talked about you and her grandmother. About this Nana and a Thelma person who'd been there way back. I knew she had people."

"Yes!" I said. "She had *people*."

And then, because that was so ridiculously funny in this packed-to-overflowing house, because Zelda and I have shared a cathartic, profoundly female exchange, because it's just too lovely the way that everything—*everything*—had finally worked itself out, we found ourselves laughing uproariously, unable to explain ourselves at all when Sophie, the children, wandered into the kitchen.

I had been able to spread the news of our prodigal's return, and of Lizzie's arrival, in one fell swoop, not immediately, but as soon as practicable after Lizzie and I had come home and my Georgian Colonial was filled to bursting with big people, little people, talk and commotion.

I called Grandmother first. She injected a dozen "Praise the Lords" into our conversation before I turned the phone over to Sophie. We called Daddy next. He was happy, too, but my conversation with him was more formal and strained and I walked away after handing Sophie the receiver. Janet and I spoke privately, running up a serious long-distance bill. Lastly I called Maureen, who said almost nothing but wept quietly into the phone. I got the idea that Maureen may actually have come around to missing us. That after freeing herself from the indignities that Daddy had visited on her, the nuisance that Sophie and I had been, she might be reconsidering it all, putting it all back on the scale and getting a slightly different reading. She was able to tell me that she had been forced to place Nana in a rest home but I kept that news to myself for a while. She and Sophie wouldn't speak. Not that day. Not for a very long time.

Zelda insisted on leaving us after only ten days. She seemed vaguely uncomfortable in my Georgian Colonial, and particularly around Adam. He would nearly swoon when I told him how much money I had given Zelda to ensure her safe trip home in that battered old truck. Money was a little tight for us just then but what Zelda had done was well beyond price and I only wished it could have been more.

I'll have my revenge on Janet. I'll rub it in plenty. When Daddy and Grandmother arrive on Wednesday, I will present them with an immaculately clean house, a perfectly cooked meal, an adorable new baby, and the unbelievably happy bonus of Sophie and little Clare. The scene around my Thanksgiving table that year also goes in the annals of most perfect days. Four generations of us, sitting down all together for the first time, in my highly traditional dining room, partaking of a traditional family meal on a traditional American holiday. We are still a little awkward now and then, still treading lightly around certain subjects, avoiding others altogether, but we look for all the world—we *feel* that day— like a regular American family.

This, chickadees, is the things about happiness. You must take it where you find it. Don't question or second guess or wish for minor modifications. Laugh, eat, joke. Bounce the baby on your knee. Don't look forward or back. Keep your eyes focused on the faces around you. One of them may be missing come next year. Come next year everything may be entirely different. Memory may have to darken your perfect day with its tincture of melancholy and the happiness will never seem so clear and real again.   Should you find yourself happy, as happy as I was that Thanksgiving Day, don't even think. Just *be.* And if the dressing this time should turn out perfect, too—not too dry, not too moist, perfectly seasoned like Grandmother made it, eat a lot of it. Eat all you want.

CHAPTER XXIII

Sophie will spend almost four years with us in Emerald Hills. The four years, more or less, that I tell her she owes me for being the ultimate drop-out. She will be there for the Watergate scandal, for Richard Nixon's resignation and for the end, finally, of the war. It will have left deep wounds, an ideological rift in our nation that won't be bridged in our own lifetimes, maybe not even in our children's. It will have removed fifty to sixty thousand names from the national boomer death counter and another half-million, give or take, from the census of North and South Vietnam, Cambodia and Laos. But it won't take any more of our husbands or sons, our siblings, classmates or friends. Sophie will be there for the Arab oil embargo and gas rationing, for the last episode of *Gunsmoke* and the first one of *Happy Days.* And she will be there when we place Justin and Clare in the same pre-school program and consider the weirdness of signing our kids up for managed activities like "Suzuki Violin" and "Creative Movement."

Sophie had shown herself immediately to be a devoted and attentive mother and little Clare, from the beginning, to be both a well-mannered and happy child. She, like our Justin, is an interesting mix of physical characteristics and personality traits that are sort of Sophie, sort of me. Except for Clare's eyes, which are green like Sophie's, she could easily be my child and is frequently assumed so by strangers. Except for *his* eyes, which are brown like mine and Adam's, Justin is Sophie all over. Cut short his curly blonde hair puts only a downy gold suede on his little head but allowed to grow long it becomes the visual and tactile wonder that Sophie's was and people take liberties in touching it.

Sophie will never volunteer, and I will never ask, about Clare's father—about the foreshortened romance or the drug-clouded happenstance that had led to her daughter's birth. The two of us had spent nearly four years thinking, almost assuming, that Sophie's own father was a stranger we would never know. Both of us had revised our ideas on the connection between kinship and family. Still, I will wonder about this thing, the blood thicker than water, the opportunity points and show-stoppers on the double helix that may already be making or breaking us even as we stumble blindly on, believing that we can do, *be* anything. Of course we can't. Mine and Sophie's dullness at math was not, perhaps, an insurmountable obstacle, but it was nevertheless an inherited handicap and Einstein's reputation could not have been threatened by the Winters sisters. You might, hypothetically, become an NBA all-star if you stand at five foot four, but the odds are laughable. The astonishingly precocious musical aptitude that Clare was demonstrating at three years old may have had something to do with Sophie's rudimentary guitar-plunking skills, but I guessed not. Somewhere on the West Coast, I often thought, a talented musician was probably oblivious to the symphony he'd brought to life.

For Adam, Sophie's time with us would be somewhat problematic. As her stay extended from weeks to months, the slightly embarrassing unconventionality of our enlarged household seemed to make him a little uncomfortable. The

Lohans have Ed's divorced mother, living upstairs and using their place as a launching pad for her middle-aged liaisons. The Lee's have a shiftless brother-in-law camping out in their finished basement, just until he gets on his feet. The Markhams take in foreign exchange students like they're running a swinging door hostel. But none of that is quite like my sister and my niece, both of whom I think of as permanent additions to the family, even while Adam introduces Sophie as *moving back from California*, *with* us for a while, or *in transition*.

"When is she going?" he will ask me outright, one night after a difficult spell at the office and a week in which he's been both irritable and distant. He is sitting at the partner's desk, the big binder of the checkbook open before him and a stack of papers, bills I'm guessing, piled beside the calculator. I'm putting away my copy of *Jonathon Livingston Seagull*.

"Why does she have to go?" I ask, startled, a little panicky. We had lost so much time and I'm just getting to know this different, deeper, Sophie. "And where *should* she go?"

"I don't know!" he says angrily. "But look at this! Twenty nine bucks for children's shoes. The grocery bill's through the roof. And eighty dollars, for Christ's sake, for a *child's violin*?"

He had me. I had definitely spent money on clothes for Clare, a very few things for Sophie, but they had come to us practically threadbare. Inflation was driving food prices up like crazy and there were more of us now to feed. The violin? Clare's Suzuki teacher had not exactly used the word "prodigy," but she had made it very clear that Clare could benefit from an instrument she could take home, one smaller and better suited to her little hands.

"I'm sorry," I said. "I'll be more careful. I'll cut back."

But the truth was that I thought I had already done that. I had already cancelled all my magazine subscriptions, even *BH&G,* which hurt. I hadn't bought a single thing for the house in ages. I never went near a beauty shop and, whether Adam had noticed or not, we weren't grilling steaks anymore.

"She needs to get a job!" Adam said. And that stopped my heart. Sophie had been taking GED prep classes three nights a week at a nearby high school. My contribution, besides buying her textbooks, had been to bathe and bed the children in the evenings in exchange for which Sophie held the fort in the daytime while I got to take classes myself. I was currently taking Victorian Lit and my last science credit. I could actually see graduation almost in sight and had even started thinking about graduate school. Sophie herself had dreams of nursing school and I was encouraging her. The old Sophie would never have had the perseverance, but the new one did. We had a great system going for us and now Adam was threatening it.

"Adam! What kind of job do you think Sophie could get without a high school diploma?"

"Hell, I don't know. But something's got to give. What's your solution?"

"I don't know," I said. "But don't worry. We'll think of something." Adam just sighed as I made my escape from the study.

I was worried, sure. Selfishly, I was probably a lot more concerned about protecting the sweet little division of labor that Sophie and I had going on than I was about our stupid credit rating. But I knew Adam was right. Something would have to give.

It did. But not in the way I expected. Within three days Adam would be banging through the back screen door at mid day, wearing the face of an old man and carrying a cardboard box containing the contents of his office desk. Easton and Settler had needed to cut back, too. And Adam's rich salary had been just the place.

Nobody over-reacted. Nobody panicked. For a few days we all behaved normally. Normally for Zombies. We walked around expressionless, being overly polite and soft-spoken when we were forced to interact. Sophie and I mechanically prepared and served meals which generally we ate in preoccupied silence. Adam spent a few weeks sleeping until noon and then spending the rest of the day watching television in gym shorts. The children avoided him, even when he watched their cartoons. By the third month something had energized him enough that he began spending most of his day locked in the study on the telephone. There was no such thing as call waiting then. No one else could use the phone. When Adam emerged he was either ashen or choleric. Still the children avoided him.

My first thought, well, maybe not my *first* thought, but an early, unavoidable idea had been to sell the house. I checked the newspaper, the neighborhood re-sales, called a couple of agents to take the pulse. What I learned came as quite a shock. For the first time since World War II, the value of residential real estate was actually *declining*. Our house was probably worth considerably less than it had been even a year or two ago. There was a world of competition in new development in the suburbs and the builders were getting nervous, offering ridiculous incentives and avenues to "creative" financing. This, I thought, was an economic anomaly. A short-term fluke. Arthur Bateman had told us that "under all was the land." It was a finite, non-renewable resource. Real estate just wasn't supposed to depreciate.

If we sold we could surely come out in the black. And we had a little savings that wasn't in the house or, oh God, in furniture. But the depleted equity would be mostly eaten up by getting into another house and the expenses of the move. If we hung on, there would surely be a correction; the value would come back. This, anyway, was the reasoning I presented to Adam and, if he heard me at all, he seemed to agree. We had to hang on. But we had a household of six now and something had to give.

Clearly it was up to me. A very short, very humbling, exploration of other options led me to the inevitable conclusion that it would have to be real estate and so I get back in the saddle. Mr. Mitchner is immensely helpful in recommending me to a not quite close, but not too terribly distant broker, and I'm off and running. Running in circles for a good while because, beyond prestigious East Cobb, I still don't know my way around this confusing city very well. But I'm not treated as a green newbie by my new broker or his associates and they are helpful and supportive, very good with directions.

It's not what you'd call a perfect market. But it could be worse. The migration patterns from cities to suburbs still prevail and the South in general, Atlanta in particular, is holding up better than most parts of the country. In the beginning my selling clients are not so happy and my buying clients often have unrealistic expectations of bargains, but I get on. Little by little, bit by bit, month by month, my erratic commission checks become larger, more frequent, the hours I spend away from home longer, more grueling, but more lucrative.

Adam had acquired one short-term and disappointing position with another development firm but by the end of that year he has soured on working for others. He has found a partner in Ike Jacobson, who has mortgage banking experience as well. We borrow a little seed money, they rent some office space, and Adam's career—his quest for fame or fortune or power or whatever really he's seeking—is back on track. In a couple of months, he assures me, I can give up my work and we'll be fine. I am relieved for more than one reason. It has frightened me to learn how important his career is—how much Adam *is* his career. It hasn't been just the worry, the preoccupation with finances. That was to be expected. But Adam had spent months in a kind of weird suspension, floating mentally and physically in such murky self-absorption that he had not really been there at all. He hasn't helped with housework or the children and has resented every suggestion that he should. He has treated Sophie like a hired domestic and me not much better.

Sophie is the one during this shaky time who holds us together. She is the one who does most of the shit work, cleaning and cooking, wiping and diapering. It hadn't taken long at all for my little Lizzie, even Justin, to know where their bread was buttered. To know that Sophie can find the panties to the Cabbage Patch doll, the missing matchbox car, the preferred pacifier. Lizzie wants Sophie if she gets hurt. Justin knows that he can rely on Sophie to pack a lunch on the dreaded mystery meat day.

This, my chickadees, is the painful dilemma of the working mother. Children, especially the shallow young ones, are entirely too prone to wrap their sticky heartstrings around the one who is *there*. The one who feeds their little faces and wipes their little bottoms. The one in the warm afterschool kitchen who can *immediately* praise the crumpled crayon art, listen *now* to the triumphs and tribulations of their day, kiss the booboos *now*, when they hurt the most.

I think often these days about Thelma. About searching at the end of the school day for her gingerbread-colored face in the crowd in front of Maury Elementary. About the softness of her hands and the comfort of her starched lap. I think, too, about Maureen and see for the first time the obstacles she faced in learning to love two children whom she never dressed, bathed, fed, or scarcely touched. Impossible, I see it now. And not really her fault. Mothering is so terribly immediate. So vitally hands-on.

At the mailbox that October Alice Whitcomb slows her car to ask me if Sophie will be at bunko tomorrow night and I realize, again, that Janet is right. I am very conflicted.

Daddy had sent Sophie enough money to buy a battered used Volkswagen in which she manages to haul groceries and get the older children to pre-school and their other managed activities, but to make that year's two trips to Memphis and one to Nashville to see Janet graduate from Vanderbilt law, I have traded my sedan for a used van. It's an extended maxi-van with a custom high-top and re-configurable arrangements of tables and club chairs and benches that fold into beds. There is a built-in refrigerator, even room for a porta-potty when we need it, and believe me, we do. It comes, interestingly enough, with a CB radio and soon enough everyone has his or her "handle" and Justin (Big Foot) and Clare (Brio3), even little Lizzie (Cricket) are quickly speaking a crazy private language that Adam (Scrooge), Sophie (FlowerChild), and Mother Hen don't always completely follow. Four-year-old Justin has his "ears on" all the time and knows all the words to "Convoy," a cute but cryptic song about a trucker rebellion.

The very last time that we will all travel home together in

the van is for Grandmother's funeral. She had simply slumped over, fallen asleep, in one of the musty pews of her little church during a Wednesday night prayer meeting. Her little congregation, already shrunken at the time of my wedding to Jeremy, had now dwindled down to almost nothing, and the neighborhood that had been decaying even then has now become an ugly and dangerous place. There is a *For Sale* sign in front of the building when we arrive, all dressed up and leading a chickadee parade of Justin, resplendent in Navy blue suit and tie, Clare, dressed in mauve sateen and carrying her small violin, and Lizzie in white winter velvet, holding Adam's finger and pulling up the rear. Grandmother did not approve of dressing children in black and on this day, of all days, her wishes would be respected. I had brought a long shawl to protect our finery from the effects of O'Cedar but it wouldn't be necessary. Johnny Connor, I am told, is now polishing pews in heaven.

The arrangements for the service had been largely Daddy's responsibility and for the most part I approve of the job he's done, picking a tasteful gray casket, the hymns that we knew were Grandmother's favorites, the family floral tribute of gardenias that fills the little sanctuary with an almost unbearable sweet perfume. The little church is astonishingly full. There are people there that I have never known and scarcely heard about. There are the grown and unrecognizable second and third cousins—the progeny of her sisters from Eads, Tennessee, with whom I have only Christmas card relationships. There is a considerable representation from her days at Silverstein's, women and a few men who tell Sophie and me what she had meant to them in those years and how they had valued her advice. There are old neighbors, friends from the chain of midtown quadriplexes where I thought the affiliations had been slight and transitory.

Maureen is there, too, and I'm pleased that Daddy asks her to sit with us. They are still a handsome couple and I find myself wondering for the first time in my life if they had really loved each other. If they had ever felt for each other anything like what I now feel for Adam, what I had once felt for Jeremy. I remember Mr. Greer's advice and wonder if some people just can't help making it hard. If the difficulty isn't something in their natures, in the secrets of the double helix.

The minister, not Grandmother's favorite, but the son of a preacher I had heard her speak of, is well-prepared and seemingly sincere. I am a little surprised through his talk—half eulogy, half sermon—to learn how much my grandmother had really contributed to the life of this little church. She had kept the nursery once, later controlled the kindergarten and elementary classes that Sophie and I had attended. She had shepherded youth campground expeditions, led fund-raising efforts for teen missions, even apparently been a favorite teacher in the Young Married class. Roughly her contributions had paralleled the stages of our lives—mine and Sophie's—and I see for the first time that Grandmother, once Sophie and I had been taken away, had found some compensation in these other children. I wished now that we had spent more time with her. Been more appreciative and responsive to her after-school check-ups, the unrelenting inquiries into the details of our daily lives. I even wished I had never moved to Atlanta, putting all that distance between us. That's what you do at funerals. You wish you'd done things differently.

But I couldn't have wished for anything better than to see, just before the final prayer, Sophie's four-year-old Clare

298

stride confidently up the center aisle to play "Amazing Grace" on her small violin. Inappropriately I suppose for a funeral, Clare took a short, formal Japanese-style bow. Inappropriately I suppose for a funeral, the sniffling mourners applauded. Grandmother would have just loved that.

After the solemn gravesite service, in the same cemetery where Jeremy had been laid to rest, we make a late start back to Atlanta, changing the children into pajamas, ensconcing them comfortably with pillows and blankets in the commodious van. It is only Justin, the one with the most vivid, personal memories of Grandmother, who can't seem to settle down, who flops and flounces, popping up every thirty miles or so to ask us difficult questions. "Why do people have to die?" he wants to know. "Can Gram hear us where she is?" "Can we get her on the radio? "

Adam and I each stumble and hesitate, offer platitudes, tell him to settle down.

It is Sophie, finally, who answers all his questions at once, satisfying him enough that presently he can sleep, satisfying me too in a way that I will never forget.

"Dying isn't so bad," Sophie says. "It's like getting tuned in to a super special frequency. Where you can hear everybody. Everybody you love."

In the end, when our financial storm has been weathered, when Adam's partnership has pulled off its first big coup and we can afford to grill steaks again, it is Sophie, not Adam, who will be eager to change our household dynamics. Adam by then has emerged from his coma. He is energized and engaged by his business, more attentive to me and the children, even amiable and teasing with Sophie. He has become accustomed to the extra income of my job and the presence of Sophie and Clare suddenly seems less problematic. The house is big enough for all of us, he says. We're managing. We're doing pretty well.

But Grandmother has left us the proceeds of a small life insurance policy. It is enough for Sophie to rent a little house and she has found a roommate with whom she will have a new labor-sharing arrangement that will allow each of them to pursue their goals. I try to convince her to stay. Adam cajoles, practically begs. But she's made her plans and can't be dissuaded. Maybe my crazy sister Sophie is not as stupid as some people think she is.

CHAPTER XXIV

The Hippies have all but disappeared. Even the term itself has become derisive, almost comical, as the tardiest of my own drop-out generation, and the twenty-somethings just behind us, have dropped back in to get jobs, raise families, and begin a nice little romp with easy credit and rampant consumerism. If the established order had felt threatened by the revolutionary ideas of the last two decades, by the '80s it has re-asserted itself, comfortably in control again with Ronald Reagan manning the White House and Yuppies manning corporate America. Disco is old hat. There is metal in the music now, a logo sewn or stamped on everything we own. Madonna, the material girl, will sing the anthem for the decade.

The Hippie influence does still exert itself. From perhaps its most important contribution in showing us the value of organized protest, to alternative approaches to business through communes and cooperatives, from holistic medicine to health food, they have left their mark. From the concern they had focused on the environment to the consciousness they had raised on issues of war, civil rights, the causes of women and gays, the legacy lives on. Even if they've grown up and gone underground, cut their hair and turned their attention to less idealized endeavors like computer programming, hippie ideas have permeated the culture.

Sophie, for one, had been significantly altered by her years of hippie communalism and counterculture ethos. She has pursued a conventional career in nursing, a drug, even alcohol-free lifestyle, but her midtown household has seen an ongoing stream of wayfarers. For years it has been a bohemian stopover for people recovering from physical injuries, chemical addictions, or what Sophie describes simply as "runs of bad luck." Now it contains, besides herself, two graduate students, a married couple from Jakarta, and three children. They share housekeeping, childcare and meals, and collectively tend a massive back-yard garden. While her house is always chaotic, never tidy, not what you'd call "decorated," the arrangement, somehow, seems to work for all of them. Clare is thriving, doing well in school, has had a solo debut and performs with a youth chamber orchestra. When I return from visiting them I initially feel over-stimulated and appreciate the calm order of my Georgia Colonial. In another day or so I start to feel as though I have misplaced something but can't recall what it is.

Possibly it is because Adam is away all the time now. Each Sunday evening he packs his suitcase, neatly stacking the squares of laundered shirts, carefully matching the Countess Mara ties and pocket handkerchiefs for the well-dressed week ahead. On Saturdays I wash his underwear and t-shirts, socks and pajama bottoms to replenish the next cycle.

In the beginning I had attempted to keep up with the itineraries. Chicago on Monday for the Farnsworth meeting. Austin on the 24th, then two days in St. Louis before the 4:35 flight back to Atlanta. Gradually I have come to realize that this is an exercise in futility. For our purposes it's all the same. Monday through Friday, Daddy is GONE. If it's anything important, his office can always find him.

In the beginning we had spoken every night. I had shared the quotidian trivia, the spelling test scores, results of the dental check-up, news of the magnolia that our neighbors are planting too near the street. Gradually our pattern has changed to one call a week, usually on Wednesdays, and oddly we have little to say.

In the beginning I had felt panicky and helpless, abandoned with the responsibilities of two children, this big house. When a light bulb had blown out we had sat in the dark or moved to another location, awaiting Adam's return and the male competence that would find the supply, select the right wattage, put us all back in the light. Gradually I have learned to replace light bulbs myself, to get out the ladder, the toolbox, whatever I need to fix the things that need fixing. Gradually I have come to respect my abilities, to be impressed by, even to enjoy, my handywoman's skills. I touch up the paint, replace the dysfunctional thermostat, mix cement to repair a corner brick fallen off the patio steps. I mow the lawn and do the edging myself now so that Adam's precious weekend time with the children won't be taken up with maintenance.

Gradually I am even coming to resent Adam's interference in my household, his appropriation of and disruption of my children. I chafe when, after I have been the one to wash Justin's soccer uniform twice this week, to drive him twice to practice, to make and deliver the snacks and beverages for his team, to coordinate the endless phone calls for practices, pictures, rescheduling of rain-outs, it is *Adam* that everyone congratulates, *Adam's* back they pat, when Justin scores a goal. If I say anything, I sound shrewish and petty. Maybe it's because I'm becoming shrewish and petty. But, by God, half that goal was mine!

Somehow, without consciously sensing that it has happened, Adam and I have developed not just different rhythms, but different needs. I have been housebound all week, cooking endless rounds of meals in sweat suits, jeans and shorts. What I want to do on the weekends is to put on a little black cocktail dress, wear jewelry and perfume and go out to a fancy restaurant where someone will wait on *me* for a change. But Adam's days are filled with endless rounds of business luncheons and restaurant dinners, deals talked over in suits and ties in sterile hotels and conference rooms. He craves the quiet of home, the home-cooked meal, the luxury of falling asleep in beat-up Levis in front of the TV set.

We are all in our mid to late thirties now, still too young, I tell myself, for the classic mid-life crisis. But I worry sometimes if what proceeds it might not be a calm before the storm—a dead space in the doldrums of routine. I wonder about the old gang, if any of them have mastered the difficult balance between making a living and making a life.

After a two-year residency in Colorado, Sean had brought his New England education home to practice medicine in Memphis. He has a wife now, two young daughters, and, if my St. Jude bulletins are any indication, a host of other hopeful, smiling children to give his life direction and purpose. Maddie, still in St. Louis, is single again but Sophie tells me she is very "involved" and not likely to stay single much longer. Janet is married, but childless, and likely to stay that way. Her husband is nearly ten years older, an insurance mogul, and Janet is shooting for partnership in a mid-sized labor law firm. Even David has found someone to stick with. The problem had always been his stringent old-fashioned standards, and not, as our teasing used to suggest, the other way around. Terri is a broker now, juggling the management of two satellite offices with her second pregnancy. Except for Merrilee and Grady, the parents also of teen-age children, hardly anyone has been married as long as Adam and I have been, and few have children as old as ours.

Even Myra, the consummate idealist, has made a few adjustments. The Equal Rights Amendment had failed, falling three states short of ratification, but Myra is still fighting for women's rights as a full-time lobbyist in Washington, D.C. Near the middle of the decade the kids and I will make the overnight Amtrak trip to Washington. I will provide my children with their first experiences of train travel and a chance to see many of our nation's iconic monuments. Myra, in make-up, a designer pantsuit, Ferragamo shoes, will give us tours of the Hill, even getting for Lizzie a short chat with Shirley Chisholm and an autographed picture which I still treasure even if Lizzie doesn't. On the mall I will take rubbings from the memorial Wall of Jeremy, Connor, and Benny Belcher. There were others there, too, that I could have captured, but Justin and Lizzie want to press on, to see the Dinosaurs in the Museum of Natural History, the collection of early American dolls in another Smithsonian exhibit.

The reason for relating the details of the D.C. trip, and why any of this should show up here in the tale, is that we had needed suitcases. Quite a few suitcases actually, for four days and for three people, two of whom are children and must carry, along with two changes of clothes per day, other vital but space-consuming items like books and markers, the E.T. doll that Lizzie still sleeps with and the Walkman that is Justin's permanent appendage. We had even borrowed a small, rarely used little leather duffle bag that Adam took with him sometimes on longish trips. I had thrown most of the children's oddments into that bag and was looking that last night in our hotel room for Justin's Rubik's cube. What I found in rummaging the bag was an earring. One earring. A pearl and diamond earring. Nice size diamond. Real pearl. I know, because I tested it with my teeth, and obviously real gold. Nothing spectacular, but not junk jewelry either. And definitely not mine.

Think, can't you? Think of the explanation. Think of some time you might have used this bag. Think, maybe, of someone you might have lent it to. A neighbor. A friend.

No? Well, imagine a hotel maid, cleaning Adam's room somewhere in Boston or Chicago, oblivious to the fact that her pearl and diamond earring has fallen into his duffle bag.

OK, then someone else? Maybe at the airport. He's checking in and a well-dressed woman standing next to him at the ticket counter—perhaps wearing the matching necklace—happens to brush her hair back with her hand, accidentally dislodging this one earring which happens to fall exactly right into the tiny unzipped edge of his duffle bag.

On the train ride home I concoct dozens more of these ridiculous, implausible scenarios but in my gut I already know. When Adam picks us up at the Amtrak station, as he takes the affectionate blast of hurtling children and tries to attend to their excited jabber about everything they saw and did, I already know. This man—this attractive, well-dressed man, who travels five days a week and meets interesting, stimulating people, who stays in nice hotels and dines in fine restaurants, who might occasionally find himself needing a nightcap just before bed, and might wander down to the hotel bar—*this* man wouldn't have to drink alone.

I would like to report that Adam and I went home, settled our children, changed ourselves into comfortable but fashionable loungewear, collaboratively selected an appropriate cocktail, and proceeded to take it, and ourselves, onto the moonlit patio for a serious, rational adult discussion.

Ha! I wanted to kill the bastard! It was weeks before I could even confront him—weeks I would spend in a state of frenzied suspicion and paranoia, going through credit card bills and phone records, emptying the pockets of his suits, checking now frequently with his office, calling him in his rooms at night on the road for strained and trivial conversations that proved or disproved nothing.

Eventually I sought the advice of my peers. This had to be done cautiously because Adam and I back then were practically the Ozzie and Harriet of Emerald Hills. I consulted my best neighborhood friend, Laura Duncan, who shocked me by suggesting that I should get a lawyer and a tax accountant and start making notes of everything. She had even said—and this was a too much for me—that I should insist on using a condom when we did the dirty deed. It took me a while to realize that she was concerned about the newly identified AIDS virus but when I finally understood, I got scared. There was a whole world of misinformation about AIDS floating out there back then. There still is. But it worried me enough to make me realize that I couldn't go on this way. That I'd have to know, for better or worse, exactly where I stood.

I choose a Friday evening. Adam had gotten in early that afternoon from Houston. By accident or contrivance, both of our children are staying over at friends. Twelve-year-old Lizzie is *like* talking these days *like* a Valley Girl and it is *like* driving all of us crazy. Justin is obsessed with Pong, Asteroids and PacMan. But neither of them will be there when I approach the subject obliquely.

"Is she pretty?" I ask him. We are sitting in the family room, the room that holds my bonneted Queen Anne secretary

307

but also the TV and the ordinary, comfortable recliner, twice reupholstered since its acquisition, matching now the trim fabric in the boxed cornices on the windows. Adam has adored this recliner. It is *his* chair and he rests in it, almost supine. His hair is thinning a little, only on the very top, but he is handsome and still lean in jeans and a soft yellow sweater.

"Who?" he asks innocently, assuming perhaps I'm referring to one of the characters on *Falcon Crest*.

"The woman you're sleeping with."

He turns to face me. I have his full attention now and to his undying credit he will skip the fake indignation, the stalling and prevarications that might have extended the whole miserable process, buying us time, but adding to the pain and heartbreak.

"Lacey," he says. "It's over. It was nothing."

I am stunned. I had expected the stalling, the fake indignation.

"Who was she?" I want to know, using the past tense, giving him for the moment the benefit of the doubt.

"Nobody," he says. "Just a girl. It was nothing, Lacey. You have to believe me."

No. I don't.

Adam gets up, switches off the TV, comes to sit next to me on the couch, moving my magazine so that he can be close, closer that I want him just now.

"Believe me," he says again, taking my hand. "I'm sorry. It was stupid. I knew it right away."

We tried some of the usual things. I had my hair frosted,

bought sexy new underwear, and read, in only one week's worth of carpool lines, *The Joy of Sex* cover to cover. We went away for a weekend. That avenue yielded some interesting, albeit short-term, results. While Adam is both tender and passionate with me, while he may not be comparing my body to hers, finding me in contrast too passive, too unimaginative, too slow or too quick, this other woman, this nobody who meant nothing but has still known my husband in intimate ways I can only imagine, is right there with us. I invite her into our bed even if Adam doesn't.

There was a stint of couple's therapy. It started out well, I thought. The first few sessions have the characters in their proper roles. Adam is the cheating infidel, the woman a cheap, soulless home wrecker, and the children and I are the hapless victims. But then something goes wrong. Adams unburdens himself, sharing the stresses of his work, the loneliness of being on the road all the time, the feeling of being unappreciated, taken for granted, once he gets home. This affair, it seems, is only the fruit of a poison tree. One Adam and I had been cultivating, it seems, for years.

Apparently I have been too self-absorbed. Too narrow in my focus on home and children. I had neglected, possibly, to infuse into our relationship the stimulation of new interests, new ideas, even—the asshole of a therapist actually says this—the ideas I might have gleaned and shared from magazines and *books!* After our last session I come home so hostile that, like my Daddy, the only thing I really want to do is yell and throw something. Unlike my Daddy, I will be the one to have to clean up the mess. I refrain from throwing anything. Unlike my Daddy, I don't want to upset the children with a lot of screaming and yelling. I speak quietly to Adam through clenched teeth or I don't speak to him at all. But I enter a period where I will think a lot about Japanese houses. About how this ancient culture manages, with only rice-paper walls and translucent shoji screens to protect their privacy, to keep their children and the in-laws from learning their awful secrets.

Our own house, which has always seemed so vital to me, so alive and organic—so much a reflection of the happy, dynamic, cultured and artistic family that we are—this house, *our* house, now feels not just dead and static, but strangely alien. Everything in it mocks me, accuses me of house pride, the unhealthy obsession that may have cost me my marriage. There, the walnut drum table, carefully restored over the course of many days, stands sturdy and gleaming in the entrance hall. What should I have being doing *instead* in the days spent stripping and sanding, staining and varnishing? What neglect had I visited on my family, what opportunities had I missed, at the gym, at the beauty shop, even the library, to make myself more attractive, more stimulating to Adam? Adam had never really wanted me to go to school. He had discouraged me from working, except, of course, when we'd really needed the money. He had known that I had little interest in business—his or anybody else's—from the very beginning, and yet he'd married me anyway. Freud had wanted to know what women really want. I wanted to know, really, what men want in women.

Somewhere near the end, when Humpty Dumpty is well off the wall and all the king's soldiers are standing around shaking their heads at the sodden, fractured mess, I find myself in the playroom. That over-the-garage, kitchen-stair-accessed place, that, now that I think about it, really *should* have been memorialized in somebody's magazine spread. Not because it is all that glamorous but because it's a masterpiece of toy organization. In the early years I had made cute little animal curtains, installed shelves with color-coded plastic bins for holding alphabet blocks, wooden puzzles, and Lincoln Logs. I had painted, in primary colors, the small, originally white chest of drawers that had once held the meager preparations for Natalie's imagined arrival. In the last few years I had changed the curtain print to something less juvenile and cleverly and sensitively adapted the playroom to my children's growing interests, moving baby toys up or out, finding space for the growing collection of motorized Erector set pieces, the Star Wars figures and the Lite Brites that put my vacuum cleaner in the shop every few months.

Children don't play up here so much anymore and the room has been neglected. Our household idols by then have become the TV, the game console, the home computer that, even before the advent of the internet, is already a powerful magnet. Oh, chickadees, I sympathize. Spaghetti and meatballs, once upon a time, could still draw them to the boring family table. MySpace is unfair competition.

I began the tedious process of re-ordering the playroom, straightening shelves, robotically picking the Lite Brites out of the Lego bin, the dominoes out of the checkers. I crawl on my knees searching for the missing Princess Leia. I work puzzles for the sake of storing them whole and mate Barbie doll shoes for the sake, I suppose, of not causing her too much confusion when she has to make an early morning casting call at MGM or must gavel to order the director's meeting of General Motors. I find myself wondering about all of it. As I re-insert batteries, re-box games, I gradually deduce that my spoiled children, my family, has been wholly indifferent, if not always, at least for some considerable amount of time, to my carefully labeled, color-coded efforts to impose sanity, order, even beauty, on their self-indulgent lives. I experience, for the first, and I hope for the last, time, a complete psychic break.

Within five minutes I have swept the contents of every shelf onto the floor. Dumped every plastic bin of its contents of Legos or Lite Brites. I have desecrated my orderly alphabetical arrangement of children's books. I have tipped over, and stomped on, the three-foot vinyl model of Tyrannosaurus Rex and haven't given a happy damn where the innocent Pound Puppies have landed when I threw them.

After it's over I will sit at the bottom of the playroom stairs. My face will feel wet and fevered and my heart will still race from the excitement of the destruction I've caused. I will remember my Grandmother's story, about the day that she had caught my mother unawares and witnessed her seemingly unprovoked, seemingly irrational response to being discovered, singing her beautiful song to an imaginary audience.

CHAPTER XXV

So Adam and I are done. One of us, maybe, a bit more done than the other. His company, his partnership, is hard to value in terms of a divorce settlement. A small company, there are no stock options, pension funds, or a retirement plan to shore us up against a suddenly shaky future. I know, of course, that they've made a lot of money. But the federal corporate tax returns we subpoena to prove it will backfire on us. There are debts. Expenses. The expense, especially, of Rachel Washburn, the capable administrative assistant, in Atlanta of all places, on Friday afternoons, who had been the nameless nobody who had provided the meaningless nothingness that had given Adam such empty solace.

We would never prove that of course. Adam's confession to me had been recanted just in time for the divorce proceedings and the therapist, of course, was sworn to confidentiality. Adam, no dummy, had covered his tracks pretty well. One modest pearl and diamond earring, found in the bottom of a duffle bag, isn't exactly evidence. Besides, I have income potential! His lawyer argues that I have been a professional real estate agent for almost twenty years. My own attorney is too slow, and too ambushed, to offer up the argument that the twenty-year career has been thrice interrupted, and that the money-making part of it covers only about four years, not twenty. But I'm young and healthy. And unlike the defendant, I'm college-educated! The ink on my undergraduate degree, sixteen years in the making, is hardly dry, but we hadn't expected that one either. When everything is said and done, when I have lost twelve pounds and gone weeks keeping down only yogurt on my stomach, when my children have become frightened cowering rabbits—my father would be proud of the yelling I did—I am only awarded two years worth of alimony, an absurd monthly pittance as child support until Justin and Lizzie reach majority, and half the proceeds of the house. Adam, in the only stroke of luck I'm going to get in this whole ugly mess, asks for no furniture except an oak valet stand and his stupid TV recliner. Chickadees, I'm no financial advisor. But having it to do over, I'd still buy antiques.

But I'm back into real estate and I already have a fabulous new listing. A gorgeously furnished Georgian Colonial in Emerald Hills in prestigious East Cobb County. In the course of my on-again, off-again career as a real estate agent I will be called upon, and will volunteer, to do many strange and difficult things. I will have picked up clients' children from daycare, their husbands from the airport, their grandmothers from the nursing home, and their clothes from the drycleaners. I will have been asked, in the course of making arrangements to show homes—if I wouldn't mind awfully, and since I was going to *be there anyway*—to bring in the mail, meet the termite man, pre-heat the oven, walk the dog, talk some sense into the gardener, and once even to feed the snake. To grease and expedite closings I will serve as a harried courier of bank drafts, proofs of identification and other documents, but also of pastramis on rye, ice cream cones and Vodka martinis. I will produce French-English, Portuguese-English and Spanish-English dictionaries and also flesh-and-blood

314

translators of Japanese and Hindi. I will show houses at six in the morning and almost at midnight. I will spend days with a delusional millionaire buyer whose five hundred dollar earnest money check bounces, show 89 condos to a single client who changes her mind and decides to rent. I will spend hours sitting with sellers crying over selling their beloved home and see a two hundred thousand dollar sale fall through over rights to a fifty-dollar birdbath. But I will not do anything so hard, so painful and complicated, as selling this one particular house.

Like the doctor becoming a patient, I rankle at the well-intentioned suggestions from my peers that a room might be a little over-furnished. That maybe I should take down some family photographs. That the pyracanthea at the corner should be trimmed below the window. I find myself unpleasant to prospects I don't like, jealous of those I do. It's difficult to remember whose side I'm on. I need to sell this house. I just don't want to. The agents and their clients ask me where we're moving and are nonplussed to hear that I have no idea. The children are stressed by the constant pressures of keeping everything neat and clean, by the invasion of strange people parading through their rooms and opening their closets. It just isn't possible to leave the house for every showing. We've got to go on living, to use the shower and sleep in the beds and to do homework at the kitchen table. We do it all hurriedly, neatly, feeling guilty and nervous about the messes we have to make.

None of this may be terribly hard when you are moving up, moving on, excited by the next new stage in the family adventure. But it can be very hard indeed, especially to children, when their world has fallen apart and they have no idea at all what's going to happen next. Divorce, I conclude, is something that should only be undertaken in the first six months of marriage. Before you've accumulated so much stuff. Before you're encumbered by things like children, and sixteen year's worth of photograph albums and worthless but invaluable memorabilia like tiny gold boxes of baby teeth, third grade dance recital programs and T-ball trophies. These things can slow your packing. Increase your consumption of Kleenex.

Eventually, in spite of almost everything I can do to sabotage the process, we get an excellent offer on the house. At the closing Adam and I will sit across the table from each other, passing crosswise, not the best system, to sign and initial the dozens of papers that put an end to us more effectively even than the judge had.

To stay in the school district for Justin's junior and senior years we will rent a restored 1941 farmhouse which sits like a bygone artifact on 18 acres, with a duck pond, between two tony new subdivisions. Even if I could have afforded it, this house is not for sale yet. The heirs are waiting out the death of its stubborn owner, a Mrs. Beulah Nelson, who had once raised a family, and many cows and chickens, on this now valuable plot of earth. When she's gone, a developer will put twenty-five houses on this humble farm, but she's not gone yet and the kids and I get the benefit of her obstinacy.

In many ways the house on Farley Road is a strange place to be landing after the years of close neighbors and subdivision life, but there are some bright spots. There's room for a regulation-size soccer field in the back yard. Justin adores the riding lawnmower and becomes a conscientious groundskeeper. With Sophie's help I'll learn to grow vegetables here and much to Lizzie's delight, stray cats and dogs will proliferate without much resistance from me.

At first I'm more than a little bummed out by the idea of decorating. I'd put the better pieces of my furniture in storage and don't care anymore about coordinating colors or fabrics. But my traditional little whatnots and knickknacks, the odd and quaint pieces I've found and refurbished over the years, look comfortably at home in this rambling old place and this house, too, will get to all of us in ways we could never have expected. Justin will astonish me with his newfound maturity, his willingness to help with housework, his conscientious about locking doors and turning off lights and chastising us about waste and extravagance. Lizzie too will bloom here, making surprisingly practical choices in her clothes shopping, foregoing afterschool fun in favor of starting our dinner. She will study on the backyard picnic table with her first serious boyfriend here, bring her first junior prom date home to meet me, her eccentric Aunt Sophie, and the menagerie of animals that, by then, will include a goat—I swear I can't remember how *that* happened—a family of rabbits, and the current stable of dogs and cats.

It wasn't all great. We had some terrifically rough patches on Farley Road. Much of this newfound adolescent altruism was based on worry about me and the swings between mania and depression that I went through there. The divorce seemed to have called my whole life into question and sometimes I behaved very badly. While Adam, in his carefully orchestrated and fun-filled custodial weekends, never, as far as I know, ever shared a single criticism, even a disparaging innuendo about my failings as wife or mother, I didn't always take the high ground myself. To this day it shames me to think of things I said and did. But the work, for the most part, of rearing our children was already done by then and both of them would make us proud.

Justin's decision, made well before the Farley Road years, to pursue a career in architecture, I can take a little credit for. He had always been a willing, or captive, listener to my pompous talk of style and structure, form and function, in houses and other buildings. He had ridden with me, far too many times, to preview houses and share in the assessments of too much, or too little, decorative ornamentation, to consider the travesties of remodeling and refurbishment that violated the period and character, the very essence of what a home had been. He has also been the beneficiary of the considerable library with which I had educated myself about residential architecture and for years those books had rivaled science fiction and superhero comics in his recreational reading. That Justin should make architecture his career choice would seem perfectly natural to me.

But Lizzie's decision to go to Auburn, to struggle with the math weakness, but capitalize on her science interests, and shoot for enrollment in the veterinary school, I can only attribute to those years on Farley Road. To the complete accident of her discoveries there—in that unlikely natural oasis between new housing and shopping centers—where the last of the small threatened wild things had come to our comparatively uncivilized acres to rest, to heal, to reproduce, to find their last temporary refuge against the onslaught of development.

This house, surprisingly, will not only hold its own special memories but in our short years there it will stretch and extend us, sending us in directions we had not plotted on any map. You think, don't you, that you impose yourself, stamp your own individualism, on the places, the houses, you choose to live in. In fact the opposite is often true. Sometimes it works the other way around. Sometimes houses have their own ideas. They will haunt you with their histories, invade your dreams with their own demands, direct your attention to things always hungered for but previously unseen in the cunning chimney brickwork, the slope of the roof, the way the sun sets, just when you're ready, just when you need it, over the edge of the porch or the patio, the garden bench far at the back. You'd best be careful, chickadees, about choosing a house. Sometimes you own houses. Sometimes they own you.

By the last few months on Farley Road, both of my children have left me. Or at least it feels that way. Justin is beginning his third year at Georgia Tech in the College of Architecture and Lizzie is a freshman at Auburn. They are close, but not home, except for the occasional weekend. We have gone more than two years beyond our original lease, into the month-by-month, *let's see how it goes* arrangement that has depended completely on Mrs. Nelson continuing to draw breath. Alas, she draws her last one and my loose relationship with the heirs is superseded by pressured phone calls from quick-talking attorneys and the waiting-in-the-wings developer who will fill the pond, raze the trees, and send us, and all of Lizzie's creatures, on a search for new digs. I'm going, I tell them. But Rome wasn't built, and couldn't possibly be moved, in a day. There is a sudden flurry in finding homes for the animals, giving away the late bounty of the garden, putting these last remnants of furnishings also in storage, so that I will have time to think, to come up with another plan. They have already starting the grading when we say goodbye to the house on Farley Road.

This chapter, held by the rambling old farmhouse and full of the lessons that its rooms and green surroundings have taught us, is over. But the next chapter will have to wait a bit. We'll be in transition for a while. The kids will have to crash at their dad's place the rest of the winter and spring semester and Sophie will have to put up with me for a time. I think I have an idea now about how I want this next chapter to go. It's one this time that is really up to me to write. There is no marriage or husband or husband's career to consider. The chickadees are leaving the nest.

At midnight that last day of December, as New Year bells ring in the start of a new decade and Sophie, her friend Derek, and I sing Auld Lang Syne and lift glasses of champagne and apple cider to new beginnings, I've got some ideas percolating in my head. But first I've got to sell just a few more houses.

CHAPTER XXVI

Ah, the '90s. What a great time to be a real estate agent. New homes were getting bigger. And bigger. Buyers were demanding palatial kitchens, media rooms and home theaters, offices and gyms and big closets. *Huge* closets! Sometimes big enough to handle a dresser, nightstand, a small school desk and a set of ugly maple bunk beds. Where families with three or four children in the '50s and '60s had once shared a single bathroom, the new homes now had a bath off the kitchen, the nursery, the game room. Suburban buyers also expected "amenities" now—the swimming pool, the tennis courts, a playground and a clubhouse. A neighborhood golf course didn't really hurt.

Money was flowing and easy credit rained like manna from heaven. Everybody, it seemed, was moving up or out. The construction boom in the exurbs—a new word someone had coined to describe the suburbs of the suburbs—was reminiscent of the post-war housing boom. Paradoxically there was no baby boom to explain it. Families were getting smaller. It was not uncommon to show five bedroom homes to couples with one child, or none. Paradoxically, on the streets of most of our cities, there were as many homeless than ever.

The domestic servitude crisis had largely been solved by the tide of Latino immigrants and even though the public transportation problems for many of America's suburbs, like

Prestigious East Cobb County, had scarcely been addressed, there was now an ample pool of domestics to care for our children, clean our houses, and help us to plant, trim and douse chemicals on our landscaping. Affluent, college-educated mothers, having finally been successful at procreation with the help of fertility specialists, could now easily find a nanny or drop their offspring off at daycare in order to spend long days in the office. At the end of the day television would help them produce a thirty minute meal.

Paradoxically, with the disappearing stay-at-home mother there had also come a great resurgence in the "womanly arts." Cable channels brought us an endless line-up of shows on decorating, cooking, gardening, crafting and sewing. There was a new dignity in domesticity, possibly even a new obligation to embrace the arts your mother or grandmother might have taught you but that didn't interest you back then. It was OK. We could learn them from television. From specialty magazines and craft-store courses. While the grocery stores sold more frozen entrées and prepared meals than at any time in history, the cookbooks of our television chefs turned them into millionaires. Home and garden TV, the food networks, were not just educational and entertaining, they were big, they were HUGE business. I was unclear in all of this as to whether domestic values had actually increased in cultural currency or Wall Street had simply found a means to capitalize on our guilt. Either way there was glamour now in housewifery. Martha Stewart had the cultural status of a rock star.

The whole domestic renaissance thing had come a little late for me. There was no one to cook for anymore. Nothing to motivate me to sew or craft. Not even much incentive to clean. After Sophie and Derek married I had sublet a small furnished condominium and moved in with only clothes and a few boxes of books. The decor was very Zen, very minimalist, and in the beginning I had liked the sparseness, the absence of personal touches and unnecessary clutter. At first it had seemed a good place to reinvent myself—a barge of sorts that would carry me to the Next Great Thing. But a year later I was still in transition and felt most of the time like I was living in a motel. There were evenings that I would turn the lock, open the door, and feel suddenly crushed by the anonymity of the place. Beyond the framed picture of Justin in college cap and gown that I had placed next to the owner's stone Buddha, there was no indication that I even lived there. That anybody, actually, *lived* there. The place was not mine to redecorate I told myself. But I knew that wasn't really the problem. The problem was that the Next Great Thing had not presented itself. At the ripe old age of 45 I felt myself *over*. Completely and utterly *done*. Love and marriage. Childrearing and homemaking. The carpools, the game days, the school and neighborhood and community life—they were all behind me now.

I was still managing, by taking at least one class a quarter in the evenings or occasional afternoons, to stay in graduate school and those classes now became the central focus of my existence. I was older than most of my classmates but almost never the oldest. In every class in grad school the women had outnumbered the men and in every one there'd been a couple of us, forty-something ex soccer moms, who had returned to interrupted educations out of desire or necessity. Most of us were divorced and all of us were near-desperate overachievers. We always over-killed on the studying and treated every assignment as though it had life or death significance. I no longer resented the trial-by-fire that Dr.

Ketch had put me through so many years ago. My papers may not have been brilliant but they were mechanically and grammatically pristine. I had only a few more courses left now and found that where I once had been afraid of never finishing, I was now starting to worry about what would happen to me when I did. There wasn't anything else in my life now. Except, of course, for selling houses.

Fortunately, selling houses was pretty easy these days. Maybe too easy, I often thought, when buyers who I was sure were shopping over their heads, were easily, speedily, approved for mammoth loans and came to closing with down payments so meager that I wondered if they'd sacrificed anything more than a couple of pedicures and a better seat for a Falcon's game. Some of my peers were worried, too. But not much. It was easier than it had ever been to sell houses—a career gift horse whose mouth nobody really wanted to pry open. Some of my fellows had suffered for years through bad markets, hard credit, limited inventories. Many of them—I thought of Mr. Mitchner and of dear Nate Plunkett—had paid a lot of dues scrabbling out a living in a time when the ratio of commission dollars put in the bank to road miles put on the car would make even the most conservative economist laugh out loud. What could be so wrong with riding the wave? Besides, all of the financial intricacies were not really our concern. Those were problems for the mortgage banking folks—all of whom made more money and got more respect than we did. What were *we,* anyway, supposed to do about it? If a client bringing down seventy thousand a year wanted to look at half a million up, were we supposed to *refuse* them? I know what you're thinking, chickadees. There would be plenty of blame to go around.

On the one hand it was the same business I'd dropped in

and out of for years. Better, maybe, but the same business. On the other hand, it wasn't. By the mid '90s I am spending as much time on the internet and on the telephone as I am in the car. Increasingly it's on the telephone *and* in the car. Before long it will be on the internet, on the telephone, in the car.

And then there was the matter of the buyers. I was always happiest with the youngest clients. With the starry-eyed stupid. The ones who reminded me of Jeremy and me, trembling on the Schimler's doorstep. But I didn't get many clients like that anymore. My clientele now, largely the result of word-of-mouth referrals from successful suburban sales, was much older, more affluent, infinitely more sophisticated. Some of them were even single and some were simply investors, looking for a second, or third house—but not a home. I had a little trouble with these. I sat across from them at closings, refusing to examine my hypocrisy, but disliking them intensely as I pocketed their commissions. Sometimes it felt like I had sold them a womb. One they had no intention of using themselves but were going to "flip" for a profit. I was losing my objectivity. Burning out. It was time for a change but I didn't know what else to do. I had nothing to put on a resume but wife, mother, real estate agent. Even the local Dairy Queen wanted retail experience and I didn't have any. At the peak of my success—in a year that would have even made Adam jealous—I became pretty despondent. What I needed was a good therapist. And that's exactly what I got.

I met mine, quite by chance, in the customer waiting room of Carruther's Full Service Texaco. I was there for an oil change. He was getting a brake job. Not the ideal social setting, you think, but you'd be surprised how much you can learn about a person in the thirty-five minutes it takes to accomplish the advertised ten-minute oil change. Richard

Boyle was a clinical psychologist. Pretty impressive, I thought. And he let me know he was single, which definitely added another layer of interest. But he was also thinking about buying a house. He'd been living up on Lake Lanier and loved it there, he said. Loved the water, the tranquility, the natural setting. But the commute to his office was getting worse and since there were two more years to run on the lease for his office space, it made more sense to move his residence. At the very least to find a condo where he could crash on weeknights. Yes, I told him. That made sense to me, too. And it made sense that we would exchange business cards and get together to discuss his options. And from then on everything about Richard and me was going to make perfect, lovely sense.

He was not a handsome man by most standards. He was actually a little short. And a bit too barrel- chested. And there was that Brillo pad of steely gray hair. But I always thought his eyes—and oh, his hands!—were exquisitely beautiful.

Richard Boyle's most attractive feature, however, was that he was wonderfully easy to talk to. He was by nature a good listener and by profession a tactical questioner. Early on I found myself telling him all about Adam and me—a story frankly so typical of our generation that it wasn't even interesting. By then Rachel Washburn, who had lost, or planted, that incriminating earring had been replaced by the still younger Ginny Hicks, who had been dethroned by Cameron Williams, who was not *quite* young enough to be Adam's daughter, but was uncomfortably close. I had mostly gotten past the lean and angry years but sometimes, as I told Richard, it could still make me crazy. I remember telling him how I sometimes felt like I was being punished for having done what was expected of me. That I'd had to do penance for the fact that I had chosen to make a home and raise a family. Neither Cameron Williams nor Ginny Hicks, nor MY daughter, by God, would likely make that kind of mistake. The smart women would get their educations first, get their careers on track, make the necessary connections for the future, *before* they committed to marriage and children. They would have their own identities and their own bank accounts and find ways to hedge their bets. They would demand prenuptial agreements if necessary but at the very least get a clear understanding on divisions of labor and responsibility. I could get horribly carried away when I went off on one of those tangents. I don't know how Richard tolerated me, let alone why he encouraged me so, tilting his head in that way he had, asking me more questions to open more floodgates.

Certainly most of our first half-dozen dates and meetings were spent discussing my own little history. I told Richard about my childhood, supplying details I had almost forgotten. I tried to explain my relationship with my father—he asked me thoughtful questions, but hinted at nothing terribly Freudian. I told him Sophie's whole story—something I had really never told anyone but Janet—and was grateful to find someone who didn't think her years of hippie lifestyle, of drug experimentation or even her unwed motherhood were even slightly shocking.

Richard therapy was working pretty well for me and in a pretty short amount of time he'd come to know a great deal about my life. The details of Richard's own history, however, were not so readily forthcoming. Probably because he always returned the focus to me. And probably because I let him. The night that I learned about Richard's past would be memorable in more ways than one.

It was a Saturday. One it had taken some effort to clear of

client calls and showings so that I could accept Richard's invitation and drive up to the lake, to finally see this place that he was reluctantly thinking of giving up. The lake, named for Georgia poet Sidney Lanier, is a man-made marvel created by the Corps of Engineers through the construction of Buford Dam on the Chattahoochee River. The lake is enormous, encompassing some 38,000 acres of water bounded by nearly 700 miles of shoreline. It had become a recreational wonderland for fishing, boating, house boating and skiing and property values along its shores were going through the roof, particularly in a market where a vacation home seemed far less a luxury than a sound investment.

Richard's house resembled a Swiss chalet. It was built almost entirely of cedar and set on a wooded little knoll that enabled an amazing unbroken view of a vast expanse of the lake and its pine-studded islands. The lot fell away to a private dock where he kept both an inboard runabout and a small fishing boat, but that day we didn't go down to the water. I had arrived just before sunset and the place to watch it, he told me, was up here, on the deck outside the vaulted great room, with a wine glass in your hand and the strains of Coltrane playing in the background. We sipped our wine and nibbled on cheeses and watched silently for the better part of an hour while a molten gold sun sunk slowly into the lake against the pastel wash of pink and blue and purple sky. It was a spectacular sunset, I thought, and well worth the trip, but Richard had another treat in store. He was going to cook for me, he said. Chicken Marsala and pasta Bolognese. I was to do nothing, he said, but keep my own glass full and come promptly when he called me.

Richard headed off to the kitchen and I began wandering around, ostensibly to make a professional assessment of the house, but actually to absorb cues, essences of this man I was becoming quite smitten with. I thought it suited him, this place. The exposed wood beams, the massive stone chimney and hearth, the simple pine furniture, were all certainly masculine enough, but more than that, the house, like Richard himself, was unpretentious, easy and comfortable. There was a large master bedroom with its own doors to the deck and another tiny loft bedroom reached by narrow stairs and tucked into the peak of the roof. The other downstairs room was obviously used for a study. It was a little cluttered this one, and a little dusty, too. Two walls were lined with bookshelves which housed a fascinating collection, both in the range of subjects and the mysterious system he used for shelving them. I was about to pull out an interesting volume and had just set my wine glass down on the corner of his desk, on what amounted to the only few inches not covered with papers and files, when I noticed a family picture.

There was a beautiful brunette with bountiful shining hair and a sweet, but slightly teasing smile. There was Richard himself, perhaps in his mid thirties, with a bit more hair himself then, and between them a little girl, maybe five or six, squinting into the sunshine. The woman, I assumed, was his ex-wife. The child, it occurred to me with a shock, could be mid twenties or early thirties by now. Richard, eight years older than I, could certainly have grandchildren by now. But he'd never mentioned any. I realized how little I knew of his past life, of the woman in the picture or what had gone wrong in his marriage.

I returned to the kitchen where Richard was just now adding the marsala to his sizzling, fragrant skillet.

"She's lovely," I said, refilling my glass from the bottle of drinking wine.

"Who?" he asked.

"Your ex," I said. "I assume that's her picture on your desk?"

Richard froze, the cooking fork suspended in mid-air over the skillet.

"Don't call her that!" he snapped, whirling to face me, still holding the sharp-pronged fork. And now *I* froze. I had almost assumed Richard incapable of irritation, let alone anger. But he was certainly angry now. And I had caused it.

"I'm sorry," I said, taking a step backwards. It occurred to me that I didn't really know very much about this man at all. That Richard's lake house was quite isolated. That no one knew I was here.

For a long terrible minute we faced each other. I couldn't really read his strange new face but there was something there beyond anger. Eventually his shoulders dropped, he smiled and turned casually back to his skillet.

"No," he said softly. "*I'm* sorry. You couldn't know. I over-reacted."

"We weren't divorced," he went on. "Laura is dead. She died in a fire. Our daughter lived almost another month. If you could call that living."

I said the only thing I could.

"Oh, God, Richard, I'm so sorry."

I could not then, nor can I now, imagine such grief. I thought immediately of the hours and hours Richard had spent listening to me whine. I could recall every niggling little complaint about my misunderstood childhood. Good grief, how I'd wallowed in the luxury of his rapt attention! I remembered now vividly the night I had told him about Natalie. He had seemed so understanding. He had even offered me that night a quote from Anna Freud. "The horrors of war," she had said, "pale in comparison to the loss of a child."

But of course Richard would know that. I felt like a complete and utter fool. And yet oddly, unreasonably, betrayed.

"But you should have *told* me, Richard."

"Well, I've told you now," he said brightly, placing the filled plates on the kitchen table. "Shall we eat?"

And so we ate. And we talked. But this time it was Richard's turn to be confessional. Quietly, with a minimum of words and no drama, he told me the story of the ordinary household electrical problem that had taken his family and all but destroyed his own life. The fire had been caused by an overloaded extension cord. His voice broke only once when he told me that he had known the cord was inadequate. That he had bought a replacement for it four days before the fire but had been too busy to make the change. That cord had still been in his car, still in its package, when he had arrived home, late that night, to find his home engulfed in flames and the ambulances already gone.

"It was a bad time," he told me. "For a long time."

"Well, of *course*," I said, hurrying to assure him that I understood, that it was perfectly understandable that a loss, a personal anguish like he'd experienced, could cause someone to lose their bearings.

"No, Lacey," he said patiently, "You don't understand. I had colleagues in psychiatry, you know. Someone was always willing to write me a script. There were years, literally years, when I wasn't any good to anyone."

"Oh, Richard, I'm so sorry. But you came back! You made your way through."

Richard smiled. "I did," he said. "But it almost took

another tragedy. I had wrecked my practice. At the time I probably didn't have half a dozen patients left. But one of them was a young girl. Very troubled. A cutter. She showed up at my office late one night. In very bad shape. She really needed my help and I should have been able to give it to her. But I was stoned. Staggering. I mean I couldn't even remember her name, Lacey. I couldn't even dredge up her *name*!"

I remember waiting. Holding my breath. Terrified of what else he had to tell.

"The strange thing, Lacey, is that when she saw me, when she figured out the state I was in, she calmed down. She just looked at me like I was a dying dog or something. This incredible pity in her eyes. For me! She was about to go. To take her own pain back on out into the night. And I was going to let her. *I was going to let her go.* So I could pop another pill I guess. Get back to taking care of my own stuff. But she turned around. She was still giving me that look and she reached into the pocket of her jeans and brought out a package of razor blades. She put them down very gently. On the edge of my desk. *For me.*"

"That got through to me, Lacey," he said. "It clicked. Somehow I stopped her at the door and somehow I called an ambulance. For both of us. I got us both checked into the hospital. In a few days we found her a good residential treatment program. But I started climbing out that night, too. She told me a couple of years ago that I had saved her life. But it isn't true. She saved mine."

So that was his story. The dark nightmare of the soul that he had not only survived but somehow awakened from, stronger, clearer, better able to serve his patients. Not everyone is lucky enough to do it, Richard reminded me.

Almost no one does it without the help, usually of many, but of at least one other.

Knowing Richard didn't completely cure me of my own self-pity. It didn't instantly or automatically purge me of bitterness and fill my shallow heart with forgiveness for my father or Maureen, for Adam or Rachel Washburn, or even for myself. But it went a long way. And that night Richard became a part—not all, but a hugely important part—of my Next Great Thing.

I think it's important to say—he would not mind at all my saying it—that I didn't "fall" in love with Richard. Not like I'd fallen for Jeremy and Adam. It did not have the roller-coaster feeling, that wild exhilaration, the loss of control and of self-possession that I remembered from my youth. This was slower, more deliberate, and I was conscious of the process. It felt this time like I was *floating* into love, as though I were being swept, inexorably, but slowly and pleasantly, on a warm current of wind or tide to someplace I'd always wanted to go. This time it didn't feel like falling at all. It felt like homing in, like being carried to shore. This time I kept most of my wits about me. It was a good thing. I would need them.

The national real estate convention that year was going to be held in Las Vegas. It seemed the perfect location really, given that gambling on real estate was becoming a national obsession. I'd originally had no plans to go. With Richard's support and encouragement I was finally winding down my accidental career. I had only one remaining listing and a couple of clients that I was still working with. I wanted to go out tidily, professionally, but neither my head nor my heart was in it anymore. My Master's thesis had been turned in and I'd been offered a teaching assistant's position for fall quarter. I was both thrilled and terrified at the prospect of teaching and had no thoughts of further developing my real estate career through a trip to Vegas or anywhere else.

But for some reason Richard wanted to go. He really needed a break, he said. And I knew that this was the truth. He'd been unusually tired lately and plagued by insomnia. Our relationship had solved his commuting problems because most weeknights Richard stayed at my place and on the weekends we went to the lake. But his recent sleeplessness was taking a toll on both of us and needed to be addressed. We'd both been overworked and overscheduled for a long time, he said. It would be a nice little vacation for us, he said. We could even, he said, get married while we were there.

CHAPTER XXVII

In *Anna Karenina* Tolstoy observed that happy families are all alike. Had he been a real estate agent he might have said the same thing about houses.

Happy houses, whether cottage or castle, are alike in the signs they show of being cared for, in the simple evidences they reveal that someone is paying attention and, for now anyway, there is enough energy, enough help, enough money to keep the chaos at bay. A happy house may be very far from beautiful. It may well be filled with the crazy-quilt décor of hand-me-downs, thrift store finds, even new but jarring furnishings in the confused and unharmonious styles of bachelors, newlyweds, or occupants who have not yet discovered who they are, what they like, or how, at any rate, one arrives at "eclectic." The colors may be hideous or decades out of fashion. The homeowner's twenty-year collection of plastic Santa Clauses may parade across the mantel in the middle of August.

And a happy house is not always terribly tidy. You may easily ring the bell, prospective buyer in tow, only minutes after the children have lipsticked the carpet or dumped the Cheerios or just as the family dog has left a deposit in the foyer. The breakfast dishes or the day's third load of laundry may not yet have been scuttled into their respective machines. The refrigerator is papered with to-do lists, neighborhood

335

announcements, coupons and children's school art. There is clutter but not filth, dust but not dirt. Somewhere there is a place for everything, even if getting everything in its place is mostly a losing battle. But in happy homes someone is trying. Happy homes share the common, easily absorbed energy of lives moving forward—of growing children, growing gardens, plans being made, calendars marked with appointments with the future.

Unhappy houses, though, are unique in what makes them so and, as Tolstoy might have allowed, the nature of their unhappiness may be a reflection of their owner's. The external, cosmetic neglect born of some hidden, still invisible illness. The hairline cracks in the plaster or concrete or wallboard suggesting something has gone atilt. The slight sag of the porch, hinting of rot deep in the foundation. Crumbling footings, splintering wood, the smell of dampness and mildew in the basement. The owners have grown old, and there is too much to do. The pension and Social Security checks barely cover the costs of medicine. The young husband has run off with a topless dancer and there is no one to mow the lawn. The middle-aged wife has escaped into drugs or alcohol and there is no one to clean the toilets. Eyes are being averted, the money has run out, some crisis of health, or heart, or pocketbook has made it uniquely unhappy.

This was something like the case of Trina Anderson, and of her house, when Richard and I met the both of them on a cool but brilliantly sunny afternoon in September of 1993. The stop was en route, actually, to the airport for a five o'clock flight to Las Vegas where we were ostensibly going to attend a national real estate convention but actually where we were going to get married, lose $ 539 at the Blackjack tables, and have the silliest, funniest, most delightfully memorable week of our middle-aged lives.

This was not my listing or a house I planned to sell. There was the teaching assistantship for fall and the new direction my life was about to take with Richard. But I had been asked, rather mysteriously, as a favor to Sherry Ponds, to just "take a look" and our past association compelled me.

The Anderson house was in DeKalb County bordering on the Decatur historic section between Emory University and Agnes Scott College. Almost all of the streets there are quiet and restful, shaded by gigantic hardwoods. This home was a slightly Colonial Arts and Crafts bungalow, built probably early in the 20th century. My first impression was of pure delight—with the neighborhood, with the double-gabled eves and the wide front porch of the lovely little bungalow, and with the well-planned landscaping, the obvious investment of many years and much work. But even as we pulled into the drive I began to notice other things and so, he would tell me later, did Richard. There was more than one telltale sign that Trina Anderson's house was not faring so well in holding back the chaos. That it was unhappy in a unique but still mysterious way.

The roof was fine. It was clearly not original but it had been replaced in at least the last ten years and the shingle color and workmanship looked pretty good. It would take an inspector to verify this but I wasn't much worried about the roof. The gutters, however, sagged at several places and there were long streaks of dark mildew on the fascia boards to show that the gutter system wasn't working so well anymore. The front yard, while mown, was splotchy and weedy and the ivy, once controlled within the low circular brick confines of a planter surrounding a mammoth Chinese chestnut tree, was now spreading into the surrounding lawn. It didn't appear that anyone had edged the drive or walks in quite a while. A picket-fenced perennial garden, glimpsed just back from the side of the house, had gone to seed, only a few courageous irises sticking their heads above the tangle.

Trina answered the door herself, a slim, attractive woman in her early to mid sixties, I guessed, dressed in a dark, loosely-fitting silk pantsuit. She had soft silvery blonde hair and deeply intelligent brown eyes and I liked her instantly but I was taken aback when she pushed the knobby knuckles of a crippled hand against the glass-paned storm door.

I introduced myself, and Richard rather awkwardly as my fiancé, and she ushered us in warmly.

"I'm so glad to meet you!" she said, "Sherry tells me you're the best in the business. I wasn't so sure you'd have time for me."

"Heavens," I laughed, "of course I have time! And Sherry exaggerates." I was genuinely flattered but I wondered what Sherry was up to.

We followed Trina Anderson through a short but wide foyer floored with beautiful wide-plank heart pine into a warm and comfortable parlor, now the family room, where tall pine bookshelves lined the brick fireplace all the way to the ceiling and a beautiful impressionistic oil painting of a young couple picnicking under a grand magnolia hung above the mantel.

"Do you mind talking out here?" she asked us over her shoulder, "It's just so pleasant this time of year."

We filed through open French doors onto a screened-in porch furnished with antique wicker settee, lounge chairs, hanging plants, overflowing baskets of books and magazines. Through the blackened screening of the porch I could see what had once been a magnificent park-like back yard. There were brick walks and garden statuary and an ironwork bench placed for contemplation, or for admiring the assortment of beds and shrubbery, now unkempt and weed-choked.

Trina settled herself in a corner lounger with a matching cushioned ottoman, and hoisted up her legs. Her ankles were small and almost painfully delicate. On her feet she wore a pair of black satin Chinese slippers, brilliantly embroidered with gold dragons, shimmering lotus flowers and dragonflies. Richard sat down in the other wicker chair but I chose the end of the settee closest to Trina, dropping my handbag and my leather contract portfolio on the glass-topped wicker table. Richard and I exchanged glances. Everything about this woman was intriguing—her home, her clothes, her lyrical voice, but especially the gentle stoicism with which she seemed to be bearing her still-mysterious illness.

"Will you have a cup of tea with me?" she asked. "I almost always have one myself this time of day."

"Thank you," I said, "I'd like that," and Richard smiled broadly. There was something eerily familiar about that moment. About sitting in a stranger's house with a man I was in love with. About Trina Anderson's gracious manner. About the offer of tea. This, or something like this, had happened to me before.

From nowhere a young woman appeared on the porch. She wore the white uniform and spongy-soled shoes of a nurse, or nurse's aide, and carried a tea tray, three cups on it, and a small plate of assorted cookies.

"Carmen!" Trina said. "This is Lacey Harrison. The one I told you about. And her fiancé, Mr. Boyle. Lacey, I hope, is going to tell me what this albatross is worth."

"*Mi placer de encontrarle*," Carmen said. "I am pleased to know you."

"*Es el mío*," I said, because I knew enough Spanish to get that far at least.

Trina and Carmen exchanged a few more fluid sentences, mostly cryptic, but I caught a word here and there. Carmen had cautioned her charge about not letting herself get *demasiado cansado*, too tired, and then she cast us a quick, narrow-eyed warning glance before she smiled politely and disappeared.

We sipped at our tea and nibbled at the cookies. It was, really, *very* pleasant on her little porch. There was a light breeze wafting through the screen and it carried the faint floral perfume of something that still bloomed in the sadly overgrown garden.

"Let me show you something," Trina said, reaching with some difficulty into the basket beside her chair to hand me an old magazine-sized, clothbound brown book. The volume was titled *Southern Homes and Bungalows*, copyright 1914, and authored by a Leila Ross Wilburn. The pages of the old book were yellow and dry, nearly friable, and had to be handled very carefully. Inside there were sepia photographs of houses, similar to the ones in this area, each with several paragraphs of description and diagrams of floor plans.

"It's a pattern book," Trina told me. "There used to be a lot of them at the turn of the century."

Richard moved over to sit next to me and we gingerly turned the pages, noting the author's friendly, open tone in describing the features of the homes, the emphasis, again and again, on economy, and the quaintly touching little remarks in the footers: *Make sure the woman's workshop is complete. The cooking will be better for it.* Complete plans and specifications for the houses were available for $25.00, with extra sets available at $5.00 each.

"And this person?" I questioned. "This Leila Ross Wilburn. She was the architect?"

"Yes. One of the first female architects in the city. She designed many of the homes in this area. Turn to page 13."

We did, and found Plan no. 780. The original, unlandscaped version of Trina Anderson's house.

"Your house!" I cried.

"One of Wilburn's plans. The original owners found it in that very pattern book you're holding and built it in 1920. They lived here until the sixties when my husband Douglas and I bought it. Doug was a professor at Agnes Scott then."

I looked up, maybe around, not knowing how to pose my question.

"Doug died in '86," Trina answered. "A heart attack. My son, Kenneth, was only fifteen then, but Doug had left us a little insurance and we were able to stay. This was the only home Ken ever knew until he married. They're in California now. He teaches at Cal Tech."

"California," I sighed, thinking it a very long distance between an only son and a mother who needed a home nurse.

"California," she repeated wistfully as though she had read my mind. "And they've ten-year old twins, growing up without knowing their grandma."

"And you?" Richard questioned. "You're a teacher, too?"

"Oh, yes!" she laughed. "I was a teacher. But not like Doug and Kenneth. I taught in the public system. Thirty-three years. Fourth grade. Much more fun than being a stodgy old college professor!" Her eyes were twinkling and you knew she meant every word of it.

"I've retired now," she continued. "Almost four years ago when finally I had to give in."

This was the place to which we'd been headed since Trina

had first answered her door. I tried to steal myself against whatever she had to tell but I was a little annoyed at Sherry for not preparing me at all.

"RA," Richard said quietly. "Rheumatoid arthritis."

Trina smiled. "A gift from my father and granddad," she said. "I've had it since I was sixteen. But I've been pretty lucky. Only in the last few years has it gotten to my hands." She held them up before her. One was seriously clawed and crippled. The other not so bad. But the sight of them brought a quick sharp pain to the pit of my stomach.

"I'm sorry," I said and took a slow sip at my tea. "It must be difficult for you."

"Oh, I get along," she said energetically. "But I can't keep up this house anymore. I've been so stubborn about finally admitting it. I've exploited Carmen terribly, I'm afraid. She helps with the cleaning. Keeps me straight with my medicines. But even with her help I can't keep this house up. I need to sell. Obviously I'd like a little something for my son and his family. Mostly I want to get myself to California before those boys are grown. But I've taken too long to make up my mind. And now I need to sell quickly."

She had emphasized the "quickly" and I felt that I understood. For now anyway, she had explained enough.

"Your home is a treasure," I said, tapping the book on my lap, "Of course I'll help in whatever way I can."

"Look around!" she told us then. "Take your time. We'll talk more when you've taken your tour." I retrieved my pad for note-taking and Richard and I set off to explore the bungalow.

It was obvious that, at one time, this had been a happy house. There were indications everywhere that this scholarly middle-class family had once found the time and resources to travel. We saw Murano glass in the china cabinet, Indian brass tucked into the bookshelves, a soapstone polar bear perched on the edge of a table. There were pictures, too, of the smiling Andersons standing under a Roman arch, of them dancing together in an exotic bazaar or street festival, another of them with a toddler, scowling into the sun in front of what looked for all the world like an Egyptian pyramid. Life had once radiated from this house, apparently extending itself far across the globe before coming back home again, happily, to resume its domestic rhythms.

We lingered a bit in the parlor family room, both of us for a time gazing at the painting above the mantel. I don't know what there was about it but I'm sure Richard felt it too. He reached for my hand and we continued on that way for a while, making this the strangest home tour I'd surely ever taken.

Together we inspected the kitchen which was roomy and serviceable. The appliances, while not new, were in good condition and at some point in the kitchen's history, a cabinet had been sacrificed to add a dishwasher. The original plain craftsman-type cabinetry had held up well and now looked surprisingly modern. Still, the white cast iron sink and its fittings were in dire need of upgrading. There were some dark spots on the flooring here. The drain pipe under the sink dripped into a plastic bucket.

The master bedroom at one end and to the back of the house was surprisingly large with a second, smaller fireplace. The bathroom, an obvious addition, was well-designed and functional and the closet was ample and orderly. But there was the strong scent of rubbing alcohol here and nearly every square inch of the bedside table was covered with vials of prescription medication.

There was a good-sized guest room, slightly masculine in its striped wallpaper and heavy oak furniture. We concluded that it had once been the boy's, her Kenneth's, but except for one small photo on the bureau, of a child of about ten proudly holding up a stringer of fish, no boyish memorabilia or clutter remained.

A great deal of this home's character came from the millwork, the wide crown moldings, the solid six-paneled doors, the rare heart pine flooring and the abundance of handcrafted built-ins. There was, indeed, much in this house to be treasured. Unfortunately, it also had some conspicuous flaws. I had noticed the lines of dust sitting along the tops of the draperies and could see, almost exactly, how high Carmen had been able to clean. There was curling wallpaper, light fixtures filled with dead bugs, windows nearly opaque, baseboards that badly needed cleaning. And of course there was the yard and grounds and the very visible problems of the gutters. The flaws were cosmetic, most of them, or at least I hoped they were. But they weren't going to encourage the sale of the house or help to get Trina Anderson the best price.

I knew, believe me, that it was perfectly possible to sell a house in far worse shape than this one. I had sold structures that were practically carrion. There is always that perfect nexus where greed meets need. And come the big crash, not so many years away, even nearly perfect homes would readily descend to that state. But that black dawn was still over a distant horizon. I knew there would always be savvy buyers willing and able to exploit the suffering of their fellows. But I hated the idea of this happening to Tina Anderson.

The third bedroom had obviously been Douglas Anderson's study. It was book-lined also, with a lovely, gently faded Aubusson rug on the floor in front of a big mahogany desk below a coffered ceiling so beautiful that it made me bite my lip. I was scanning the bookshelves, about to tell Richard that it seemed that Douglas Anderson must have been a history professor when Richard suddenly clasped me from behind, pressing his face hard against mine, his scratchy beard prickly against my check.

"Lacey!" he whispered fiercely in my ear. "Let's buy it. Let's buy this house!"

CHAPTER XXVIII

This would be my last house, I thought. The one that would reflect my mature and finally serene self. In this house I would grow wise and calm and patient. I would let go of regret and bitterness here and learn to live simply. More slowly, too, I resolved. Less busy-ness. Time for introspection and reflection. For smelling those proverbial but illusive roses. I would decorate this house for comfort only, not for show. I would sink my deepest roots of all here, I thought. This would be the house my grandchildren came to, the home place that would stand as the constant in their memories someday when they thought of Thanksgiving dinners and Christmas Eve celebrations and the magical cookie jar that never ran out of their homemade favorites. Some of that happened, but not all.

The first couple of years were a flurry of repair and renovation. I recall it as a blur of ladders and scaffolding, painters and their buckets, workmen coming and going, their panel trucks jockeying for position in our driveway. It was crazy but it was lovely fun.

We had the gutters repaired and the exterior scraped and painted. We were dismayed to learn that all of the windows needed replacing but the banging and clatter and mess lasted only a few days and we hoped to get back some of that expense in smaller utility bills. The floor refinishing was the messiest but the wide pine planks restored to their original mellow luster made the whole house seem clean and new.

Of course we had the wiring inspected and installed new smoke alarms but I balked at a burglar alarm, at the technology that came with it, its constant reminders to be afraid. I'd take my chances, I said, and Richard agreed. We were taking our chances on a lot of things.

We put a little money into the kitchen, updating the appliances and getting Richard a center island where he could chop to his heart's content. A man who loved to cook was a delightful novelty and I didn't want him discouraged.

Over three springs we revived and expanded the Anderson's gardens, even finding a small patch near the back of the deep lot that was sunny enough for tomatoes and cucumbers and a few kitchen herbs. For the first time ever I had someone to garden with and Richard and I would spend whole Saturdays either working alongside each other or separately in our favored little plots, weeding and pruning, barely exchanging a word all day and yet sharing, I thought, an intimacy as profound as any there could be. The soil here was dark and rich, more like Delta earth than Georgia clay, and I loved the smell and feel of it, the cool loaminess that took me back to the days of playing as a child in The Woods.

Those first few years of Richard and I collaborating on our house were wonderful. Often, in the course of painting or scraping, teaming up to hang wallpaper or wrench the old screening from the sun porch, I would think back on Adam and me and wonder how we would have fared on such an endeavor. Adam and I had rarely, if ever, really worked alongside each other. We had almost never put ourselves to the same task, our shoulders to the same wheel. True, we'd been raising a family together but somehow even the work of that had served to separate us. Our hardworking pioneer fore-parents, I often thought, probably knew a little something about the bonding value of sweat.

We never, by mutual declaration, ever pronounced our house finished. Neither houses nor people ever get finished. There would always be work to do, I thought. Some little tweak or repair, rearrangement or redesign, to keep us busy, and happy. But in 1999, very early in the spring, when we would ordinarily be making the plans for this year's garden, Richard started to get burning pains in his stomach. Our GP suspected an ulcer and advised a CAT scan of his upper abdomen. The scan showed nothing conclusive but the doctor prescribed antibiotics and for a while they seemed to be working. We both got serious and careful about diet and for a while Richard's ulcer seemed to have healed. But then suddenly the pains returned, and with a vengeance. Almost every night he would rise and walk the floor. I would find him, standing white-faced and perspiring, in the kitchen or on the porch, sometimes in the yard in the moonlight staring at some spot in the garden that was not yet seeded or prepared, a little behind this year for its scheduled resurrection. I was never sure why the pains were worse at night. Why everything seems worse at night.

With Sophie's help I found us a gastroenterologist—the best in town, Sophie said, and Richard checked into the hospital overnight for a colonoscopy and a gastroscopy. That evening, while I sat with him in his hospital room we were diverted from thinking about test results by the television coverage of the Columbine tragedy. It was that place in the tragedy where the violence of the shooting and bombings was over but the whole school had been declared a crime scene and the authorities were letting the sun set, leaving the bodies of more than a dozen victims, as well as their two young killers, to lie all night on the cold floors of the dark school. Richard, whose own patients were adolescents, was deeply affected. I had my own bad feelings. Especially for the parents. But also for the future. For Richard, and for us.

But the next morning we were greeted with good news. The tests had shown nothing. We resumed our lives, grateful for the reprieve we'd been given. Grateful too, that his new medication, for a good while at least, kept the pain at bay. Of course it was a false reprieve. By the time a third ERCP revealed tumors in the head of the pancreas, more than eight months had passed and the cancer had become inoperable.

In 1995, in the rich sweet middle of the years that Richard and I would have together, when we were well along in restoring the house in Decatur to happiness and were still making plans for the future, I had attended my thirtieth high school reunion. I had begged Richard to go with me but Janet was going alone and he insisted that we should share it together. I would be glad that we did.

The reunion had been hilarious, outrageous, optimistic and life-affirming, and yet still sad and bittersweet. We had mourned our dead, of course. Not just our long gone war dead but the surprisingly small number of our enormously large class who had succumbed to accident or disease. We had also celebrated life and continuity—applauding the ones who had been longest married, the ones who had bred the most children, the grandparents, of whom there were many. We had made a big deal of the notable successes within our ranks. Our class had produced a US senator, two congress persons, an ample handful of state and local political figures, three dozen doctors and twice that many lawyers, a three-star general, a best-selling author and at least one bona fide movie star. But there were no recognitions for Peacemaker, Best Mother, Greatest Father, Best Craftsman or Organic Gardener, no Person Who Had Least Relied on Carbon-Petrol Chemicals. Our own generation, the ones who had tried to warn each other against becoming our parents, had resorted to our parents' value system to bestow recognition on our own.

On the last night there had been a big dance. Lots of the men were graying or balding, a few of them a little paunchy now at forty-eight years old. Very few of the women were graying—I was not prepared for the inordinate number of frosted blondes I'd see—but some of them, including me, had thickened a little too. On the whole I thought everyone looked wonderful and demonstrated, on the dance floor, that there were still some pretty good moves in that old gang of mine. At nearly midnight Janet and I had collapsed in our exorbitantly expensive hotel suite to review the evening, and, as it turned out, to examine the meaning of life.

Janet was on the couch, drinking directly from a bottle of white wine, and turning the pages of the little photo book that I had brought with me and had shown fifty times at least to old school chums and their spouses, even a few times to people I wasn't sure I knew. There was a picture in the book of Sophie and me with a giant, homegrown pumpkin. There was the picture of Clare, seated with her violin under her chin, which had been used to formally announce her ascension to second chair in the New England Philharmonic. There were pictures of Justin's boys, and the scrunched up face of Lizzie's brand new baby girl. There was even a candid sort of a family portrait of all of us, taken back at Lizzie's college

351

graduation that showed Adam and Daddy with their much younger wives—the stepmothers that all of us had finally adjusted to, concluding on the whole that it could have been much worse. There was even—and this picture, maybe, was the one to send Janet over the edge—a picture of Myra with her twins, adopted some nine or ten years ago from a Russian orphanage.

"You win," Janet said, kicking off her shoes and hoisting the wine bottle into the air. "You win the game."

"What game?" I said. "What are you talking about, drunken one?"

"The coin-toss game." Janet said. "You know. The coin with *family* on one side and *career* on the other. Don't pretend you don't know what I'm talking about." She had thrown my little photo book to send it sliding across the bed.

"Janet, that's silly. What about the riches and fame game? Who's won that?" Now I was being silly, but technically it was true. Janet *was* rich. Impressively rich. Her suburban home was practically a sheik's compound. Nine bedrooms. Pool and sauna. Stables and putting green. And maybe if Janet Winston, Esquire, wasn't a national household name, there were circles in which she was extremely well known. The world in which she and her husband moved was pretty powerful, and pretty darn glittery.

"Screw that!" she said. "Who cares about that?"

"Well," I said patiently, even though I could feel my pulse picking up and my throat flushing warm, "If you'd ever found yourself, at thirty-seven, without enough credit to buy a set of tires, you'd care. You'd care if you'd had to sell furniture to keep your kids in college! If it had taken you a whole lifetime to get a lousy liberal arts degree, you might feel differently!"

I don't remember what else we said, but we said a lot.

Janet made points that I hadn't thought of. Maybe I enlightened her a little. I had been largely unaware of Janet's own belated struggles to have a child with a man ten years her senior. She had never, for example, shared the trivial experience of an early miscarriage in the Dulles-Fort Worth airport on the way to a union arbitration. I had never bothered her with my own minor dramas, like the times I had run out of gas in the carpool line or had knowingly written a bad check for veterinary goat care.

The sun was rising when we finally closed the balcony curtains, switched off the light and dropped into bed, red-eyed, exhausted, but purged somehow of decades worth of resentment that we had not even known we harbored.

"Lacey?" Janet asked in the darkness. "Have you ever thought about what you'd do different? What you would you change if you could?"

I thought.

I thought of Jeremy and of Natalie. Of my part in their lives, and their deaths. I thought of the compounded failures of love and understanding that had sent Sophie away for so long. Memories of Adam and me spun through my mind, the whirl of them taking the shape, finally, of a dark downward spiral, and that place where we might have stopped our descent, missed or ignored, lost to us in the speed, the rush, of living.

"*Everything*," I said. And for a second anyway I meant it.

But that lasted only a second. Another answer, equally true, came at me immediately as I saw the faces of Justin and Lizzy, and of lovely, talented Clare. As I thought of the life that Sophie and Derek had made for themselves. And the one Richard and I had made. As I got a sudden image of him, chopping vegetables with those beautiful hands of his in the

353

kitchen of our warm, happy-again house back in Decatur.

"Nothing," I corrected. "Nothing at all."

I would have reason to reflect a good bit on that conversation. Richard and I would have our own version of it. Almost everyone does, I suppose, sooner or later. For Richard and me it had to be sooner.

"It's a little like a house of cards," Richard observed, on one of his good days in early December, when he'd been able to come into the family room, to enjoy the fire and see the blinking tree I'd decorated, and to admire our favorite painting, a gift from Trina Anderson, now bedecked with a garland of greenery, the young picnicking couple within it enhanced by the firelight, the depths of the woods beyond their little clearing coming mysteriously alive with the flicker of the candles on the mantel.

"It stands or falls," Richard was saying. "And there's not much we can do."

I was the one, supposedly, who was literary. The one who knew about metaphor and figure. But years ago I had learned to listen up when Richard thought out loud. Years ago I had learned that he was the real poet in our pairing.

"Try to pluck them out," Richard went on. "Our sins, our crimes, our most shameful and humiliating hours. All of it then will come tumbling down. Bringing the good with it."

"I can see that," I said, tucking around him that old cream and gold afghan, the one I had made years and years ago, when Adam was gone all the time and I had endless evenings to teach myself to knit.

"You're saying that we build on our mistakes," I went on.

354

"I can see that."

"Yes," Richard said. "But I think it's more than that. I'm not sure we'd even know where to put our hand in. Which of those cards *was* the mistake. Or which sin, if we chanced to remove it, would be worth bringing down another blessing."

I had nothing to say to that. I would never know whose sin, which sin, he was thinking of. There were too many options. It was getting late.

What Richard wanted, his last fervent hope, was to still be here when the new century, the new millennium, was rung in, and to experience it in our own little house. He got most of what he wanted. Our hospice professional, a lovely young woman from Nigeria whose accent from time to time caused me a few problems but who had never failed to communicate with Richard, persuaded the both of us, the day before New Year's Eve, that it was time. That Richard would be more comfortable, his pain medication better monitored, if we went ahead with the move. For most of New Year's Eve day he was somnolent, not comatose because he moaned and grimaced in his pain and when I called on Amaka she sometimes pushed the morphine button for us, and sometimes just shook her head and patted Richard's hand.

A couple of times that day when he seemed to be at ease I had crawled up into the bed next to him, aligning myself as closely as possible alongside his still, but wonderfully warm, body. I'm not sure he knew that I had ever been there, but I took comfort from those visits and very late that evening he surprised us, rousing himself, drinking a little water, asking lucidly for the head of the bed to be lifted so he could better see the television.

We watched the footage, much of it recorded hours and hours ago, as TV tracked the imaginary line of midnight traveling around the globe. We heard the countdown begin in Sydney and saw the fireworks there and the Aussies dancing in the streets. We heard the ancient bell toll in the New Year for the Japanese and saw spectacular pyrotechnics over the Kremlin. We heard Big Ben strike twelve in London and watched the river of fire run down the Thames. They showed us the Pope bestowing his blessing in Rome and Richard lifted a hand, pointed, and grinned, when the Eiffel Tower become a golden fountain of fireworks.

Eventually the coverage of the imaginary line began to move across the ocean to converge with our own clocks. The local network showed the sea of people in Times Square waiting for the famous crystal ball to drop but moved just in time to downtown Atlanta where our own symbolic peach descended to the joyous roar of the crowd and our own night sky exploded in burst after burst of showering sparks.

When I looked over to gage Richard's response to our own hometown celebration I could see that sometime in the last few minutes or seconds he had closed his eyes for good.

I like to think that he made it. I really hope he did.

.

CHAPTER XXIX

Wood, I think, and the examples of trees, can provide a lovely metaphor for human experience. In our first seedling stages we are weak and vulnerable, dependent on luck, protection from the elements, the nutrients in good soil for giving us a start. We can go almost any way then. Whatever is asked of us, we'll try to accommodate. Train or trim or stake us unnaturally, we'll grow to your aberrant design. Deprive us of sun, a little water, the barest of natural necessities, our growth will disappoint. But usually, even with the slightest, the most unenthusiastic encouragement, we become sapling youths, flexible and fast-growing, capable of reaching ridiculous heights without even half trying. In the beginning we are all softwoods—pines, spruces, larches or firs—and like these, terribly impressionable. You can dig your fingernail and leave a mark. A careless word will leave permanent scars. But in time most of us become hardwoods, and like the broadleaved oaks, are harder to damage, harder to bend, more resistant to change and the vicissitudes of storm. We begin to develop what we call "character"—that same quality that reveals itself in the growth rings of trees, in the variation of light and dark that bespeaks seasonal change and varied experience. Wet, quickening springs. Long dry summers. Brilliant but melancholy falls. Bitter cold winters. They all start to show. In our mirrors. In our cores. In our souls.

I am most definitely a hardwood now. Considerably less flexible, significantly marked and altered by the seasons I've passed through. My own growth rings are there, even if you can't see all of them. And try as I might I cannot help but thinking of them as having been formed in houses, in the places that held the growth and the change, the seasons of my life.

It amuses me now that here, in this little hillside cottage, I seem to have oddly come round again to my first infatuation, at the very beginning of my long romance with houses and of my short romance with Jeremy. My own little house stirs memories of the Schimler's English Tudor, and indeed that style is its influence, the architectural progenitor of the American Cotswald cottage, the humble farmhouse version of English manor homes. My own cottage is stucco and stone— not English fieldstone, but native Georgia rock, quarried not twenty miles from here. My house has the steep cross gables, the small-paned casement windows, the asymmetrical design that always promises surprise inside. My sloping roof cries to be thatched but its hand cut cedar shake shingles approximate that rustic look, and obviously they are far more practical. The Schimler's had three, but I have one prominent stone chimney, set just at the arched front door, and the wide fireplace it ventilates inside makes my one, and only, common room useful and beautiful too. To my way of thinking, I live in a storybook cottage—the Hansel and Gretel house in the woods that you, my chickadees, seem to adore as much as I do, even if a few of the local children are certain that I'm the witch.

The man who built my cottage, a scholar and farmer and homesick native of Kent in rural England, would be pleased, I think, to see the solar panel in the sloping attic roof upstairs. He would be happy, I think, about the compost heap, the newly unstopped spring and the rain barrels set around to catch the precious extra. I have taken more than my fair share. It's past time to conserve. Coward that I am I dread the prospect of standing before my grandchildren, my great grandchildren, to answer to the judgment of my selfishness. My only defense would be that it was us, the unmanageable mass of my own generation, who first sounded the alarm. I wish more of us had heeded it ourselves. There is not much I can do in the time that I have left, but I am learning, from the extension service, from the school, from people like my crazy sister Sophie, how, at least, to begin.

I've pared down considerably but I still have too much stuff. Too much to organize. Too much to store. The signs of my former, and even my current, house pride are everywhere. Especially in the bonneted secretary that grazes my low ceiling and looks too large, too sophisticated, for this simple little house. But I found I couldn't part with it. Its writing shelf is laden with chickadee pictures and in its little cubby holes and behind the tiny marquetry doors that can be opened only with skeleton keys I keep the most cherished of my treasures. Little gifts made with small hands just for me. A tiny gold box of baby teeth. A gum-wrapper crown from a long-ago chess win. Three wedding bands.

And of course I'm still conflicted. Even if the conflict for me is once removed. No one suffers but the sociable cat when I must go off to teach a class or attend a faculty meeting or indulge myself for a whole luxurious day in any way I please. But my concerns now are for our daughters, and for theirs, and with the role that law and policy, circumstance and economics, but especially their own biology will play in their choices. The time for making strides up the professional career ladder still coincides with the childbearing years and for too many women that dilemma feels like Janet's two-sided coin. Heads or tails, they're going to lose something, and heads or tails, they'll be subject to the criticism of others and their own second-guessing.

My Victorian Literature students are unanimously perplexed and angered by the censorship that Thomas Hardy experienced in challenging patriarchal authority and sexual hypocrisy. But they argue spiritedly and cannot come to agreement on the real roots of the tragedy in *Jude the Obscure*. The conservatives among us—and they are many here in this rural red-state enclave—argue that Jude and Sue's infidelity, their unconventional relationship, the children born out of wedlock, have an important role to play. You can't just flaunt the laws of God and man without expecting to pay a price. Others groan and point to a tyrannical class system, the draconian divorce laws, even the problem of Sue's own restless intellect which has no hope of worthy outlet. Great fun, all of it. And my students are capable of some excellent thinking. But even lifted out of the Victorian context, gender issues remain. Myra could tell them that Sue would still have some conflicts today. That the women's movement still is so fraught with five decades' worth of female advance and retreat that almost any decision Sue made would still be condemned.

Maybe I'm naïve, but I'm hopeful that our daughters and granddaughters will find it easier. The internet and telecommuting now offer the promise, not just of a greener way of working, but of an avenue, for both men and women, to productive and fulfilling work that doesn't require abandoning the home, especially the children, whose needs don't always correspond to nine to five scheduling. We have the Family Leave Act now and the notion of daycare in the workplace seems less radical. The stay-at-home dad is not such a joke.

In the meantime we have to be tolerant of those who are learning by going where they have to go. Every family in some ways has to re-invent itself. The meaning of home has to be re-created over and over again, in broad strokes by each generation, in finer detail by every unique combination of married couples, caring partners, the mixes of family and friends who choose to live together in the same house to rear a family and make a home.

Janet was always right. Everyone *does* deserve the chance to strive for self-fulfillment. And women *do* need to assert themselves if we're to have their perspective in the workplace and in the halls of power. But I still think I was right too. When we choose to become parents the equation gets complicated. Someone else's self-fulfillment must become equal to, even take precedence over, our own. And I still think that in a perfect world the low-paying professions that women so naturally gravitate to—teaching, caretaking, nursing, nourishing and pacifying—would not be just respected, but exalted.

For me, the culture wars, the political and social debates, are all still important. I do my best to participate, to stay informed and to stay relevant, but more and more I find myself less apologetic for my domesticity, not conflicted at all when I pick up *Better Homes* before reading *Newsweek*.

I don't really miss the real estate business but I do miss the houses and I get wistful sometimes thinking that I may have decorated and furnished my very last one. Lately I've been thinking about constructing a playhouse down by the spring. Justin could design it and do the specs. It could be any style I suppose but I'm envisioning something fanciful and romantic. Maybe a Queen Anne with all the gingerbread details. Sophie could help me plant a diminutive garden where the children can learn about growing things. I can see a wooden table and little chairs. I imagine a small authentic pie safe or a cupboard to hold dishes and tea things. Lace curtains would be absolutely perfect.

The End

Made in the USA
Charleston, SC
15 March 2010